Y0-BVY-416

TREATMENT OF THE CHILD
IN EMOTIONAL CONFLICT

Treatment of the Child In Emotional Conflict

HYMAN S. LIPPMAN, M.D.

Director, Amherst H. Wilder Child Guidance Clinic, St. Paul,
Minnesota; Clinical Professor, Department of Psychiatry and
Department of Pediatrics, University of Minnesota Medical
School, Minneapolis; Clinical Professor of Social Work, School
of Social Work, University of Minnesota, Minneapolis

SECOND EDITION

The Blakiston Division
McGraw-Hill Book Company, Inc.
New York   Toronto   London

TREATMENT OF THE CHILD IN EMOTIONAL CONFLICT

Library of Congress Catalog Card Number: 62-14356

II

37979

Preface to the Second Edition

Several new subjects have been added to this, the second, edition. The chapter on reading disabilities treats of a problem with which workers in education, psychology, and child psychiatry have labored for more than thirty years, without finding procedures for helping most retarded readers and learners. This subject has not received the recognition it deserves in the literature on child psychiatry, for a solution to this problem would offer a rich opportunity for prevention, since the ability to read well at an early age is important in determining the child's subsequent learning.

A chapter on group therapy was added because of the important contribution group work has made to the understanding of children in our clinic. The use of dream material, in working with children, was referred to only briefly in the first edition; however, because it is a subject very important to me, I am pleased at the opportunity to include it as one of the new chapters.

This edition has also given me the opportunity to follow up most of the cases discussed in the first edition and to include several additional cases, particularly those of children with obsessional neurosis, because so little has been published on this subject. In most instances the follow-up studies were possible because parents, of their own accord, came to the clinic for further consultation. In other instances the therapist or caseworker called the parents or wrote to those who had moved away. These follow-up reports are brief summaries of what has happened to the children and of their current status. All the parents were grateful for our continued interest and sensed our readiness to offer further advice if it were indicated, and in some instances, it was. Although the decision to include the follow-ups came too late for complete re-studies, which would have had greater values, I feel that these summaries do have merit.

The child-guidance movement is growing, as individual units in the family of social agencies or as a part of all-purpose clinics in smaller communities; matching contributions of money from the state have made this possible. This is good because it offers the families of the children with emotional problems an opportunity to work with experts who are trained in their professions and dedicated to their work.

HYMAN S. LIPPMAN

Preface to the First Edition

To evaluate the different methods used in treating emotionally disturbed children in a clinic is always difficult. So many things happen to a child during the course of clinic treatment, through the several disciplines involved in his therapy, that it is impossible to determine which clinical procedures have been most productive. Different clinics use different technics, based on their own experience and the orientations of their staffs, and any clinic staff will introduce methods of its own in which its members have become proficient.

Technics which work with one child may be useless with another; methods which are effective in one clinic may be unsatisfactory when tried elsewhere. I feel, however, that every clinic engaged in intensive therapeutic work with emotionally disturbed children can supply workers in the field with valuable information about methods of treatment. It is a responsibility of every clinician to describe the technics which he has found most helpful as an aid to our greater understanding of emotional disturbances in children.

The methods of therapy described in this book are those in use at the Amherst H. Wilder Child Guidance Clinic, St. Paul, Minnesota. They are based largely on the principles of therapy I received during my psychoanalytic training in the seminar in child analysis conducted by Anna Freud in Vienna and the seminars and demonstration clinics of August Aichhorn. This opportunity to study at first hand the technics of child analysis and to observe the thoroughness, the warmth, and the understanding of these two teachers in their work has been invaluable to me as a clinic therapist.

Since joining the staff of the Wilder Child Guidance Clinic in 1931 I have tried, together with fellow team members, to discover methods of applying some of the features of child analysis to the treatment of large numbers of children seen once a week. The concepts of analysis which have been most helpful to me in my work have been the methods of evaluating ego strengths and weaknesses; the use of dream analysis to grasp quickly the child's conscious and unconscious fantasies, fears, and conflicts; the significance of anxiety, and the methods of locating its source; the recognition of unconscious resistance to therapy; and the significance of the unconscious role of the parents in their child's emotional adjustment.

Children in emotional conflict suffer from varying degrees of anxiety, but they all suffer anxiety in some form. The more accurately the nature of the anxiety can be determined, the more specific will be its treatment. The most carefully established diagnostic evaluation, however, will be of little value if the treatment cannot be carried on in a relationship which is acceptable to the child.

In this book I have repeatedly emphasized the importance in therapy of the relationship between the child and the therapist. Children in emotional conflict have been traumatized by their parents and by other adults whom the children have grown to distrust. They come to the therapist from homes filled with tension, hostility, misunderstanding, and confusion; from parents filled with guilt and self-blame for having failed in spite of great efforts to be good parents. The children come to the therapist tense, confused, and frightened and can submit to a therapeutic relationship only when the therapist can put them at ease and make them feel safe.

The child-guidance clinic can provide many different methods of treatment. In working together with children and their parents, the members of a clinic team quickly lose any preconceived idea that the principles upon which a particular therapy is based are the best. Faced with the suffering of the children and the anxiety of the parents, the members of the staff unite to develop methods of lessening unhappiness as quickly as possible. Together they bend their efforts toward helping the child to help himself. The best features of each discipline come into practice in the interests of those they serve.

My choice of cases and subjects for consideration in this book was based on my own interests and areas of special concern. I have not tried to illustrate all the conditions studied in a child-guidance clinic, since what I wanted was to describe a point of view toward therapy rather than to present a comprehensive picture of child-guidance services.

The clinician working in a child-guidance clinic must devote all his time to serving disturbed children. Much as he might enjoy doing research—and he is the ideal person for it—he must step aside in favor of the full-time research staff and limit himself to describing his own attempts to vary and to improve clinical practice. Aware of the need for his services, the clinician is always searching for methods that are effective; he will not abandon them for other procedures unless he is certain that these are effective in reducing emotional conflict.

I am deeply grateful to Dr. Herman Nunberg, now of New York, for his many kindnesses and helpful suggestions over the years, and to my teachers in child behavior at the Institute for Child Guidance in New York. I am grateful to my fellow workers in the clinic, whose contributions as members of the psychiatric team have made possible the therapy of the cases described. I owe a great debt of gratitude to the tireless efforts of my secretary, Junia Malm, and to Jane Sherman, without whose editing work I could not have written this book. Betty Leake has made several valuable recommendations for which I am grateful. And I give thanks to Addie, my wife, to my daughter Arlene, and to my son Henry for their boundless patience with me during my long period of isolation while at work and for their confidence that the book would be written.

I am deeply indebted to Dr. Edgar J. Huenekens of Minneapolis, who during my period of training in Pediatrics initiated my interest in working with behavior problems of children.

Dr. Robert Waelder's profound knowledge of psychoanalytic theory made him an invaluable source of help, and I am deeply grateful to him for his careful reading of my manuscript. I am indebted, too, to Dr. Gregory Zilboorg for many valuable suggestions that helped to make my book more readable.

Finally, I owe a great deal to the staff and board of directors of the Amherst H. Wilder Foundation for their cooperation in maintaining the child-guidance clinic at a high level of performance.

HYMAN S. LIPPMAN

Contents

xi

Section I

APPROACH
TO THERAPY

CHAPTER I

Treatment of the Child in Emotional Conflict

A child suffers emotional conflict whenever anything interferes with the satisfaction of his instinctual drives and his frustration produces a state of tension. The interference may come from the outer world; from internal demands for instinctual gratification which most environments do not tolerate; or from forces within the child which oppose his gratifying instinctual drives.

External circumstances which frustrate or fail to satisfy the child's basic needs often produce pathogenic disturbances. Every child needs to feel loved and wanted, to feel secure, to be recognized as a person, to express some of his sexual and aggressive drives, to have a degree of independence, to be helped to accept reality with a minimum of conflict.

The external factors are closely related to the internal ones, and usually, excessive demands from one side produce a counterreaction from the other. The external disturbing factor may be constant, as when a parent makes excessive demands on a child or when the environment gives him few outlets for affection or pleasure. Frequently, however, the external factor appears suddenly and precipitates a frustrating situation. If the parents recognize the child's suffering and can change the situation, the child's emotional conflict disappears. Few cases of this kind come to a child-guidance clinic.

All children are subject to anxiety and irrational fears. They are part of experience during the period of immaturity and insecurity. No one can entirely protect the child from anxiety, though his parents' love can greatly ease his apprehension; nor can anyone protect the child from the early fear of being abandoned, which he must have each time his mother leaves. Not until he has learned that her leaving the home is followed consistently by her return will this kind of anxiety disappear.

The child cannot be spared the anxiety he suffers when another child is born to the family. Sibling rivalry is a normal accompaniment of life and remains until the child can sense from the behavior of his parents toward him and toward the rival that he is deeply loved and always will be. A child's hostility and his wish to harm the rival sibling make him afraid of losing the affection of his mother, who appears to love this new child. The fear of punishment which naturally follows these hostile wishes is responsible for many of the fears and anxiety dreams so common in early childhood.

Internalized conflicts, like conflicts produced from outside the child, may produce emotional disturbances of a transient nature, some of which may clear up without any therapy. Such transient conflicts may produce nightmares, difficulty in falling asleep, and sudden periods of withdrawal from play or activity. These behavior manifestations express repressed conflicts and may suddenly disappear if a state of psychic equilibrium develops spontaneously. Sometimes the child's behavior improves because the parents, alarmed by the symptoms, decrease their demands on the child.

A child in emotional conflict behaves in ways which produce disturbances in him or in those around him. Feelings of being disliked, of being unloved by his parents, of losing the ability to control his own behavior, of being overcome by fears, of being different from other children, unsettle him and rob him of energy that should be used in work and in play. Most of the emotional conflicts responsible for a child's referral to a child-guidance clinic are recognized by his parents or school teachers, who are dissatisfied with the kind of adjustment he is making. Formerly most complaints involved difficult, aggressive, unruly behavior in a child. Now parents and teachers are coming to recognize that the child who is withdrawn and unhappy often needs help even more.

The line between the so-called "normal child" who is emotionally healthy and the child who has emotional problems is often very fine. A tolerant parent or teacher may overlook problems which would disturb an anxious parent or teacher. The fact that adults who work closely with a child are concerned about him is sufficient cause at least for an investigation of their complaints or requests for help. In some instances a problem which on the surface appears to be unworthy of consideration may turn out to be pathogenic for a given child.

Most children are eager to act out their sexual wishes and aggression when they feel free to do so. They learn very early how the outer world responds to their drives for gratification, largely through the reactions of their parents and other adults in the home. A child learns that some things he says and does are permitted, others are not. When his demands are rejected or frustrated he grows angry, but he is too insecure and weak to fight back and resorts to the only method available—having hostile thoughts and wishes about the parents who are depriving him. Since he loves them and is dependent on them, however, he becomes frightened and insecure. Most of the early fears of young children can be explained in this way.

During the first two or three years of life, when a child attacks a younger child, for example, he will feel remorse but he will not feel guilty about it. By degrees he learns to control his inner drives, having discovered that in this way he avoids punishment, is more warmly accepted by his parents, and generally feels more comfortable. His ego, which has been growing stronger, has learned to master more situations and to postpone gratifications. Some time between four and six years of age the child becomes more highly socialized and identifies with the standards of his parents. During this period he develops a conscience or superego to help him control his inner drives. He has changed from living on the pleasure principle to accepting the demands of reality. Now if he acts in a dissocial manner, or even if he feels angry, he will suffer from feelings of guilt. This process of socialization occurs when the child's parents are emotionally mature, have accepted social standards, and wish to raise a healthy family.

A child in emotional conflict rarely comes from such a setting. His conflict is derived from pathologic circumstances in his early relationship with his parents. The basic needs of a child whose parents have not accepted social standards and have rejected him from birth cannot possibly be satisfied. His reality will be painful from the outset; he will be subjected to repeated traumatic situations and denied the opportunity to be socialized. Much of his emotional conflict will grow out of his search for satisfactions he cannot find at home. His poorly modified drives will force him into dissocial behavior for which he will be punished.

Conflicts of a different nature will appear in the child of neurotic parents. Their own conflicts and rigid standards will force them to oversocialize him. They will prevent the healthy expression of his instinctual drives and deprive him of experiences that nurture his ego. He will become insecure and emotionally dependent upon his parents. Such a child, unable to express drives, reacts within himself. He develops neurotic symptoms and suffers from the anxiety and insecurity of neurotic conflict.

It is hard to understand why some children are able to act out their aggression in spite of opposing forces while others react by withdrawing and directing their aggression against themselves. Freud was convinced that differences in the constitutional make-up of the ego helped to determine this difference in behavior.

Although the normal child is rarely free from some qualities of a dissocial or neurotic nature, he has sufficient outlet for his drives and is sufficiently controlled to be in a state of emotional equilibrium. He has found it possible to accept social standards without becoming oversocialized. By referring to a child as normal we imply that he has attained a state of emotional maturity commensurate with his ego development and the forces to which he must respond. The normal child, then, has a degree of independence, has a capacity to give and receive affection, can work effectively and enjoy work as well as play, is in harmony with his conscience, and can satisfy his drives acceptably. He feels little hostility toward himself or others. He has a good grasp on reality and suffers little anxiety. He has a strong ego, a healthy superego, and a controlled instinctual life.[1]

Most children cannot meet all these requirements for normalcy, but they are able to make satisfactory adjustments to their circumstances. They meet problems that arise without suffering conflict. They experience fewer traumatic situations than neurotic children because their egos are strong enough to cope even with difficult situations.

The causes of emotional conflict in children are much better understood today because of the great contributions of psychoanalytic research. Our knowledge of unconscious psychology has helped explain why the child behaves as he does. The influence of constitutional factors on emotional pathology is still largely unknown. Observations of normal and pathologic behavior in children provide a fund of clinical data which strongly suggest that inherited constitutional factors significantly influence behavior, but most references to constitutional factors must be provisional.

Constitutional factors include only those traits which originate in the chromosomes. The child at birth has already been subjected to many influences unrelated to hereditary factors. He has spent nine months within the uterus and has been subjected to physiologic and pathologic influences from the blood circulation of his mother. He has suffered from the trauma of delivery through the birth canal. During the first few days of life he is conditioned by a

[1] Saul, Leon, "Emotional Maturity," Philadelphia, J. B. Lippincott Company, 1947.

great number of new and strange experiences which vary considerably under different conditions.

These influences may have varying effects upon the child because
of his constitutional make-up, but they must be considered separately. These and the many emotional experiences of the child
during the first few weeks of life make a diagnosis on constitutional
factors alone very difficult.

The treatment of a child with emotional problems is directed toward eliminating the problems by discovering their causes and removing them. To help a conflicted child, a therapist must work
directly with him and with all the important influences on his life.
Treatment of the child has as its main goal the strengthening of his
ego. Efforts are made to direct the emotionally conflicted child
toward emotional health and maturity, so that his development,
which has been retarded by conflict, can proceed along its normal
course. Treatment is directed toward helping the child to live as
comfortably as he can in society. The child must be able to forgo
seeking his own primitive pleasures in favor of accepting society's
demands.

The aims of therapy are materially affected by the program
which the individual therapist, the outpatient department, or the
child-guidance clinic can provide for children and parents. The aim
will depend on the intensity of the direct and indirect therapy and
the training experience of the individual therapist or clinic team.

Allen [2] describes the aim of therapy to be aiding the child to help
himself so that he can find his own capacities. Treatment should
enable him to leave the therapist and make his adjustment through
his own strengths. He must be helped to see himself as an individual different from all other individuals and yet related to them
(particularly his father and mother). Therapy should give the
child his chance to grow.

Many children who need treatment for emotional conflict do
not receive it. Most communities in the United States do not have

[2] Allen, Frederick H., "Psychotherapy with Children," New York, W. W.
Norton & Company, 1942.

enough psychiatric clinic services for children to meet the need. Most communities are still not sufficiently aware of the importance of dealing with emotional conflicts in children to provide for adequate treatment.

Who are the children so disturbed that their future adjustment will be jeopardized unless they can obtain therapy?

1. Acting-out or delinquent children whose dissocial behavior cannot be controlled by their parents, teachers, or others in authority. If they are left to their own devices, society as well as the children will suffer.

2. Neurotic children whose anxiety is great enough to produce serious suffering and create suffering in others: children who are so neurotically inhibited that they cannot enjoy work or play; children who have trouble making friends and who seem always to be in some kind of difficulty; children who are chronically afraid and insecure; and children who persist in bed-wetting and soiling and exhibit psychosomatic symptoms.

3. Children with normal ability who have learning problems. Many such children are suffering from emotional conflict. Teachers and school authorities are giving increasing attention to this problem, but they lack facilities to deal with their more severe cases and need the services of a psychiatric team.

4. Very unstable and immature children who cannot deal with reality without help from others. A large number of children are dependent and unable to assume responsibility for the tasks most children handle well. They need a helping hand to get to school, do their school work, bring home assignments, go on errands. Their need for supervision is much greater than that of most children.

What happens to these children when they do not receive therapy?

Most of the dissocial group continue to get into trouble until the law catches up with them. Some of the more fortunate ones find adults to love them and give them the attention they need, and they come to accept social standards. Many are removed from their own homes to emotionally healthier settings through the social agencies. Many of their families are helped through good family-agency casework to become more integrated, and the children lose some of their need to act out.

The neurotic children, if untreated, continue to suffer. Either the symptoms persist, other symptoms take their place, or the pathologic symptoms become established as character traits. Untreated neurotic children become neurotic adults. Under more fortunate conditions the emotional tension within their homes may decrease enough to allow these children to develop and strengthen their egos, making regression to neurotic illness less necessary. If the neurotic conflicts of the parents lessen, for example, they will decrease their rigid demands and neurotic anxiety.

Some neurotic children improve without therapy through associations with adults other than their parents. Sometimes neurotic children improve for no apparent reason. Maturational changes may affect such improvements.

The immature child rarely improves unless the factors that encourage his remaining dependent are recognized and removed. These factors are usually the immaturity and instability of one or both parents, who rarely appreciate the need for therapy, especially when it demands consistent efforts from them.

The child with serious learning problems will continue to fail if he does not get help. If he is fortunate enough to find teachers who have the time and are willing to give him special attention and help in his schoolwork, his learning difficulty may disappear. His emotional tie to the teacher motivates him to want to learn. Without this help he will feel inferior and inadequate about schoolwork. He may become truant and delinquent, or he may resign himself to crippling failure. A child's special talents in working with his hands or in athletic activities may counteract the traumatic effect of chronic school failure.

All these children will have a much better chance for happiness and emotional well-being if they receive therapy. A child with moderate diabetes may live for many years without medical treatment; he will be healthier, develop faster, and live longer if he gets the medical treatment he needs. A young child will give up temper tantrums if his parents ignore them, but they will never learn what their child needed and what internal mechanism he was forced to develop to meet the ungratified need.

Considerable controversy still exists over the question of who should be permitted to perform psychotherapy. Increasing numbers of nonmedical people are doing direct treatment work with emotionally disturbed adults and children. The problem is complex, since the demarcation line between serious mental conflict and lesser emotional problems not requiring treatment by a physician is not easy to locate. Little question remains regarding the extremes of emotional illness. Diagnosis and treatment of psychosis, epilepsy, and organic disease of the nervous system are the province of the physician. Discipline, child training, and problems created by reality situations do not require treatment by a medically trained person.

The problem becomes more complex in cases of children suffering from deep emotional conflict which theoretically a physician should treat. Such illness, however, requires treatment by psychoanalysis, which is not taught to medical students and not even required for the physician receiving graduate training in psychiatry. The physician, therefore, or the psychiatrist who has been neither analyzed nor specially trained to treat children with serious unconscious conflicts is unable to help them.

Abundant evidence, on the other hand, demonstrates that a nonmedical person thoroughly trained to psychoanalyze children can help a child who suffers from crippling neurotic illness. The author was a member of Anna Freud's seminar in Vienna from 1929 to 1931. The seminar was composed of nonmedical therapists and child psychiatrists who were in training to become child analysts. All the members of the seminar had been psychoanalyzed and had received previous psychoanalytic training. Several severely neurotic children were in analysis with a few of the nonmedical therapists. These therapists were supervised by Anna Freud, and the group discussed the case material as it was presented. The high quality of

the treatment, the judgment of the therapists, and the results obtained were convincing evidence that a well-trained, intelligent,
nonmedical person is qualified to treat neurotically conflicted children. Other evidence during the past twenty years has corroborated
this impression.

Medical practitioners view with alarm any encroachment upon
what they consider their field of work. Their concern is justified,
since many nonmedical people make false claims of curing organic
medical conditions, and the consequences are often tragic. The
physician, conditioned by his rigorous training in differential diagnosis to see the need for specific medication and the importance of
recognizing minute changes which may mean life or death to his
patient, suspects any group not similarly trained that attempts to
treat any medical condition. The well-trained lay analyst, however,
cannot be put in the same category with those who make false
claims. The lay analyst has no interest in replacing the physician.
He insists on a complete medical history and examination of the
child before he begins therapy. He calls in the physician whenever
he suspects that an organic condition is operating.

The present controversy about lay analysis in this country is similar in many respects to that which took place in Austria at the
time Freud wrote "The Problems of Lay-Analysis." [3] Here Freud
defends the right of lay analysts to practice psychoanalysis, if they
subject themselves to the same training required of the medical
analyst. This book is remarkable for its lucidity in discussing the
complexities of psychoanalytic theory as well as for its arguments
encouraging the acceptance by the physician of the trained layman
as a psychoanalyst.

Nonanalytic therapy of emotionally conflicted children and
adults by nonmedically trained therapists, particularly clinical psychologists, is also a subject of controversy. These therapists have
devoted considerable time and energy to developing a training program that will prepare them to perform therapy acceptable to the

[3] Freud, Sigmund, "The Problems of Lay-Analysis," New York, Brentano's,
1927.

medical profession. A few years ago, a committee of the Group for the Advancement of Psychiatry met with representatives from the field of clinical psychology to prepare a program of training for clinical psychologists acceptable to the psychologists of the committee and to the membership of the Group for the Advancement of Psychiatry.[4] The factors they stressed were the extensive training of the clinical psychologists and the supervision of their therapy by dynamically trained psychiatrists. This supervision would ensure adequate recognition of organic factors not only at the beginning of therapy but during its entire course. Once such standards are accepted by the profession of medicine and clinical psychology, much of the friction now existing should disappear.

In the meantime, many clinical psychologists have established private practices in therapy of emotionally conflicted patients. Since neither the medical profession nor the general public is informed about the standards of the clinical psychologist's work or the nature of the problems or illnesses he accepts for therapy, the field is wide open for speculation and attack. Undoubtedly this group contains some unethical practitioners, just as the medical profession includes some unethical physicians, and to eliminate the abuses will require a good deal of time.

More recently, social caseworkers have become interested in entering the field of direct therapy of individuals who are emotionally conflicted. The caseworker who has been adequately trained to be a therapist and who devotes her time largely to the direct treatment of emotionally disturbed children is no longer acting as a caseworker; she is now a therapist. The same prerequisites which apply to the clinical psychologist apply to the caseworker doing therapy. Both groups need to be well trained in psychodynamics and in all the details of therapy. Both require considerable knowledge of psychopathology. Both need to give their client assurance that his physical condition will be diagnosed and treated by physicians. Both should have their therapy, whenever intensive, super-

[4] "The Relation of Clinical Psychology to Psychiatry," Group for the Advancement of Psychiatry, Report no. 10, July, 1949.

vised by an analytically trained psychiatrist. When the therapy is
supervised by an experienced lay analyst, the medical aspects of
therapy must be supervised by a physician.

The psychiatrist doing therapy with emotionally disturbed children can benefit from the experience of social caseworkers and
clinical psychologists. Eventually such material will be an integral
part of the training of the psychiatrist who will perform therapy
with children.

Committees of representatives from all professional schools training child therapists could help establish basic requirements in
training, experience, and personality make-up for future therapists.
Deliberations in committees, when they are based on mutual respect for the sincerity and integrity of each profession, will help to
solve current problems in therapy. The bitterness characterizing
some of the recent controversies widens the gap between the professions, confuses the public which has become aware of the great
need for child therapists, and denies large numbers of needy, conflicted children the help they must have.

Well-trained child therapists are needed in all social agencies,
schools, juvenile courts, hospitals, and institutions concerned with
the emotional welfare of children. The lack of trained therapists in
institutions for delinquent youngsters alone is appalling, especially
since most children in these institutions would benefit from sound
therapy. They remain in these institutions from one to three years,
an excellent opportunity for long-time treatment that could enable
them to return to their community as better socialized youngsters.

The personality of the therapist is an important factor in determining his suitability for treating disturbed children. Certain qualities are beneficial in developing a quick, positive relationship to a
child. The therapist must enjoy working with children and want to
help them. He should be able to love children and accept their
love, but he must not depend on the love of the children he serves.
His affectionate tie to a child should be strong but impersonal
enough to allow the child to relate to others. The goal of their

relationship is to make the child eventually independent of the therapist. During therapy the child at times may be particularly dependent and his tie to the therapist correspondingly strong, but such a situation will not last except in an unusual instance when a child with great dependency needs cannot give up the relationship.

The therapist should be free from neurotic illness or serious emotional conflict since he must be able to react objectively to all kinds of symptoms and behavior in children and their parents. He must be secure enough to accept the emotional attacks which neurotic children direct against him, recognizing that they are displacing aggression from others they dare not attack. He should feel strong enough to be firm when severity is necessary. A therapist who is too passive to deny a child anything or who allows him to control treatment is of little help to the child.

The therapist must know how children behave; he must understand their interests, tricks, and defenses. Experience in camping, scouting, and recreational work with groups of children is valuable preparation for treating children. Knowing how most children usually behave will help the therapist recognize unusual behavior. Most adults who choose to work with conflicted children have found that they get along well with them and readily win their confidence. They can identify with children with different personality characteristics, and by placing themselves in the child's position and feeling as he does, they quickly learn to speak the child's language.

While identifying with the child, the therapist should avoid over-identification to the point of failing to be objective with the child's parents. The therapist who works well with children but cannot tolerate rejecting parents is unprepared to treat disturbed children. Parents, especially those who have rejected a child, are quick to sense hostility in the caseworker or therapist and to withdraw their child from treatment.

The child therapist must have great patience and perseverance and be content with small gains. He must accept the child who

continues with dissocial behavior, recognizing that the child is behaving in the only way possible for him and that it remains for the
therapist and the other members of the team to discover why the
child continues with dissocial behavior.

The therapist's thinking about the child must be independent of
the team, even though he works cooperatively with them. Important as is the information he receives from others about the child,
he must come to his own conclusions through his interviews with
the child. He may discover that the child's behavior or attitude
makes sense in the light of an early incident, long forgotten by
the family, or a misunderstanding that has not been recognized.
The most sincere, honest parents may distort an incident because
of unconscious conflicts which affect their objectivity.

The experiences of the therapist help determine his decision to
work with children. Often traumatic emotional experiences in his
own life influence a therapist in wanting to help children who have
suffered emotionally. Unfortunately, many bright and talented
young people are unable to overcome the effects of their early
traumatic experiences and fail at therapy in spite of excellent training. Such people need a personal analysis before they can do constructive work in child psychiatry.

Many analysts insist that all persons planning to do child therapy
need personal analysis. Sufficient evidence demonstrates that analysis is not an absolute requirement, since many highly capable therapists with intuitive skill and keen insight have not been analyzed.
Such therapists, however, have a vast knowledge of dynamic psychology and a "feel" for unconscious emotional conflict which an
analytically trained therapist may lack. In view of the important
role unconscious conflict plays in producing emotional disturbances
in children, a personal analysis and analytic training provide valuable knowledge and technic in therapy.

The successful child therapist must understand the dynamics of
family life, the common problems that arise within a family, the
influences which strengthen or disunite the family. He must be in
constant touch with the family through his interviews with the

child and the caseworker's interviews and home visits. He will then realize how the treatment he is giving one member of the family is affecting the others.

The child therapist must know the community. He needs to know its resources for recreation, athletics, the arts, and education. He should understand the destructive influences which promote delinquent behavior and the weaknesses which precipitate problems. He must be ready and willing to fight for changes which will provide social advantages and eliminate sore spots.

CHAPTER 2

Methods of Therapy

The Child-guidance Clinic

Child-guidance clinics were first established shortly after World War I as a means of learning about the emotional life of children and instituting a treatment program to eliminate emotional conflict. Psychiatrists, profoundly impressed by the research findings of psychoanalysis, had come to recognize that emotional conflicts in the early years caused the serious emotional conflicts and illnesses of adult life.

The use of a psychiatric team was introduced by child-guidance clinics. A psychiatric social worker, a clinical psychologist, and a psychiatrist working together can obtain a comprehensive picture of all the important factors in a child's emotional life. A brief description of the way a clinical team operates will help the reader visualize the methods in use in the Amherst H. Wilder Child Guidance Clinic in St. Paul, Minnesota, the source of most of the case material in this book.

The caseworker, specially trained in the psychiatric aspects of social work, assumes the responsibility for investigating the social, physical, and educational life of the child. She interviews his parents and discusses their emotional experience and attitudes, their feelings about each other, this child, their other children, and other matters relevant to the child's problems. She visits the school, the home, and the neighborhood and contacts all social agencies acquainted with the child's family. She obtains a history of the child's development, his illnesses, accidents, and operations, including his and the parents' emotional reactions to these experiences, many of which may have been traumatic. The caseworker pays special attention to the emotional tone of the child's experiences and relationships. All the facts which the caseworker gathers constitute the social case history which is available to the other members of the team.

The clinical psychologist evaluates the child's intellectual capacity, his achievements in school subjects, his special abilities and, particularly, the special disabilities about which he may be profoundly disturbed. He makes personality studies with standardized projection tests. He observes the child's work habits and his reactions to failure. The child usually spends about two hours with the psychologist on his first visit to the clinic, and he often asks questions about the rest of the study. The psychologist's replies and assurance are a step in lessening the child's anxiety about the study. He may want to explain why he has come to the clinic, but the psychologist does not encourage this since the psychiatrist will be discussing such material in his interview. Should the child develop a strong, warm relationship to the psychologist, however, and need to tell him significant material, he is allowed to do so. In some cases the psychologist continues the child's therapy, with his treatment supervised by the psychiatrist.

The psychiatrist attempts to learn how the child feels about his experiences and how he reacts to them. He is especially interested in the child's emotional relationships to his parents, siblings, and friends; his interests and hobbies, likes and dislikes. He discusses the child's attitude toward problems and his plans for the future. Through these interviews, the psychiatrist attempts to evaluate the child's current emotional adjustment as it is related to his past experiences. He makes a preliminary psychiatric study of the child, consisting of three to six interviews, depending on the time required to accumulate sufficient data for a diagnostic formulation. This formulation is tentative, as are the reports of all of the members of the clinic team.

The staff of the Wilder Child Guidance Clinic includes a group therapist as a member of the team. Groups of six to eight children of approximately the same age meet with the group therapist once a week for an hour and a half. These activity groups offer the staff a valuable opportunity to observe how the child relates himself to other children and to the leader. Usually, the child has taken part in three to five group sessions by the time the clinic team meets in conference. The group therapist has a fairly reliable picture of the methods the child uses to obtain attention and recognition. The child's methods of defense come to the surface in the group, where he has to relate himself quickly to children about whom he knows little. The permissive atmosphere in the group and the large number of play and work opportunities offer him a chance to participate with others or withdraw by himself. Opportunities are provided for supervised active aggression which he may use or not as he wishes. By observation the group therapist can learn much about the child; few parents or teachers have as good a chance to watch small numbers of children working and playing together for long periods of time. The group therapist, moreover, is trained to notice the many methods children use to relate themselves to other children and adults. See Section 2 for further material on group therapy.

Reports of the physical findings of the child are obtained from the child's physician whenever the history records recent or frequent illness. The psychiatrist makes his own brief neurologic examination, and he arranges for more complete neurologic and other physical studies when these are indicated.

The members of the team meet in an initial conference to report their individual findings. Agencies who know the child and work with his family are invited to send representatives to this conference. The group agrees to a plan of future work with the child, his parents, and others who will participate in helping him. The staff decides in some instances that the work already accomplished is sufficient to help the child and that the clinic need give no further service. In most instances the child and parents continue in treatment at the clinic, and at the conference the team decides on the treatment measures to be taken.

The psychiatrist at the Wilder Child Guidance Clinic dictates the interpretive discussion to a secretary at the conference. The discussion includes the essential problems revealed by the study and an explanation of the precipitating as well as the underlying factors that appear to be significant. When time permits, this material is used as a base for theoretical discussion of the dynamic forces operating in the case. The staff tries to embody the contributions of all the members of the team into the interpretive discussion. The caseworker usually dictates the identifying data which begin the report and the treatment plans which close it.

After acquainting the parents with the plans made in conference and obtaining their acceptance of them, the caseworker continues her work with the parents. She deals with all the important situations which develop in the child's environment during his therapy at the clinic. She maintains contact with the social agencies interested in the child. From time to time she arranges for brief treatment conferences to discuss progress in treatment by the members of the clinic team. She occasionally assumes the responsibility for direct therapy of the child, and her therapy is supervised by the psychiatrist. In such cases another caseworker usually deals with the parents.

The clinical psychologist handles the child's school progress and arranges for tutoring in subjects for which the child needs special help, often doing the tutoring himself. Usually his tutoring draws him closer to the child, and he may take over the therapy for the emotional problems. At the Wilder Child Guidance Clinic, the psychiatrist generally performs the psychotherapy of the child or supervises the child's therapy when it is performed by another

member of the team. The secretarial staff tries to keep the dicta-
tion current so that each member of the team is aware of the work
being done by the others.

Most children in treatment remain in a therapy group while they
are in individual treatment. Sometimes the child receives direct
therapy only in the group and sometimes only by the individual
therapist. As one might expect, a child usually feels more at ease
in a group with other children, especially when the danger of being
attacked is minimized by the presence of the group therapist. He
learns more quickly to enjoy the work in a group than to enjoy
talking or even playing with an adult in a closed room.

Treatment conferences, when the members of the team meet
to discuss the progress of therapy, are held about every three
months. Earlier impressions are substantiated, or new formulations
are made. The team decides to continue with the same treatment or
recommends changes in therapy. Treatment may have begun with
the caseworker seeing both parents, the individual therapist treating the child, and the group therapist working with the child. Occasionally the clinic team decides that prolonged treatment, considered necessary at the time of the initial conference, is not
needed, and the case is closed. When this is the decision, the team
evaluates the case at the time of closing and prepares a closing sum-
mary.

In 1957 we instituted a new procedure to improve our working
together as a clinical team. The diagnostic phase of the study has
not changed, and the findings of all the team members are still
dictated, but prior to the new plan, team communication in treatment cases depended primarily on written records. In spite of a
large contingent of secretaries, it was difficult to keep material up
to date, and there was no opportunity for discussion with other
members of the staff except during a lunch hour or a chance meeting.

The present plan provides one-and-one-half hours per week for
each team, which includes the child therapist (usually the psy-

chiatrist or the clinical psychologist), the caseworker, and group worker. We meet in different combinations each day so that all cases carried in common can be discussed. This procedure permits us to have face-to-face, verbal communication, and decisions can be reached earlier on whether to close certain cases, to work more intensively with others, to arrange for joint interviews, to limit therapy to a group or to an individual therapist, to get further school data, to change therapists, etc., and they are based on the combined thinking of the group. There is no need to dictate the decisions of these team meetings, since each member takes his own notes. Periodically, beginning three months after the diagnostic conference, each team member summarizes his findings in preparation for a treatment conference. These summaries are dictated and included in the clinic's case record. The result is that much time formerly used in writing up reports is available for other work.

Details of this plan may be found in a report from the Amherst H. Wilder Foundation.[1] Miss Ethel G. Harrison, Program Director for Children's Services, directed the clinic staff in a time study, in 1956, which resulted in this change of team operation. The staff is very pleased with the new system.

Occasionally a follow-up study of children who have received treatment is possible. Graduate students in social work and clinical psychology receiving their inservice training at the clinic occasionally make such studies as part of their graduate work.

The child-guidance clinic prefers to limit its intake to emotionally conflicted, neurotic children requiring treatment unavailable from the other social agencies in the community. The patients accepted for study include children with neurotic fears and phobias, crippling anxieties, neurotic inhibition of learning, neurotic acting out of aggression and delinquency, and psychosomatic illness.

[1] Harrison, Ethel G., and Isaac Hoffman, Management of the Team Approach in a Child Guidance Clinic, St. Paul, Minn., Amherst H. Wilder Foundation, 1956.

Cases which illustrate these categories and details of the treatment employed by the psychiatric team are described in the chapters on treatment.

Although the major portion of available clinic time could be devoted to the therapy of seriously neurotic children, a child-guidance clinic is a community agency closely related to the social agencies in the community—schools, courts, and physicians—and must be prepared to meet their demands for diagnosis and treatment of less serious problems.

Other Resources for Treatment

Most children who suffer from emotional conflict do not receive treatment by a psychiatric team in a child-guidance clinic. Many other resources in the community provide treatment for the lesser emotional problems. The social agencies which provide social services to children or to families, the probation offices, the schools, and the children's institutions, select as members of their staff social workers who have had some training and experience in dealing with disturbed children. The more experienced workers assume the role of supervising the work of the less experienced staff members who work directly with the children.

These social workers in the social agencies do not consider themselves child therapists. Their function is to take care of all the welfare needs of children and their families. When children are removed from their own homes, or when parents for some reason cannot supervise their children, the caseworkers act as parent substitutes. Children will bring their worries and fears to a caseworker when they know she is genuinely interested in them. Since she is familiar with the community's resources, the caseworker can provide for most of a child's important needs; and since he trusts her, she can help him with some of his emotional problems as well. The caseworker helps the child work through the emotionally traumatic situations to which he is subjected. Illness or death of the parents, removal from home, school failure, parental neglect or lack of interest, all can create considerable anxiety and worry. The caseworker may help an adolescent girl accept her illegitimate child, or work through with her the plans for placing the child in adoption. She helps the girl deal with her hostile feelings toward her own mother or other members of the family. These conscious emotional conflicts produce unhappiness and must be dealt with. The caseworker learns to differentiate the less severe emotional problems from those which are more serious and require the services of the psychiatric team.

Many caseworkers in social agencies have a special talent for working with children who have emotional problems. They are able to win the confidence of a child quickly and seem to intuitively sense his emotional needs. Such caseworkers, when trained to work with emotionally conflicted children, are extremely valuable to child-placement or family-service agencies.

Direct treatment of the youngsters under his care is an important part of a probation officer's responsibilities. He must be able to form quick emotional ties to adolescents who act out in a dissocial manner. This task is usually difficult, and probation officers develop considerable skill in working with their probationers. Most of the recent additions to probation-office staffs are trained social workers, many of whom have had graduate courses or advanced degrees in social work. Emotional problems that may arise in the probation officer's direct work with youngsters are described in an article by the author.[2]

Social workers and clinical psychologists who have been trained to do direct therapy and casework treatment with children are a great asset to the treatment program in institutions for children. Institutions which provide supervision of direct treatment of children can give valuable inservice training to workers interested in giving such treatment. The tremendous need for trained staffs in large institutions for children will be considered in Section 6, The Child Who Acts Out.

[2] Lippman, Hyman S., The Role of the Probation Officer in the Treatment of Juvenile Delinquency in Children, in "The Juvenile Offender," Clyde V. Vedder (editor), New York, Doubleday & Company, Inc., 1954, pp. 360–365.

Residential treatment centers for emotionally disturbed children are staffed with trained psychiatrists, caseworkers, and clinical psychologists experienced in working directly with serious emotional problems in children. The number of residential treatment centers is growing rapidly to provide therapy for the more seriously disturbed children who cannot respond to treatment while living in their own homes or in foster homes. The methods of therapy possible in such centers are described by Bruno Bettelheim and his staff [3] and Fritz Redl and his coworkers.[4]

The child psychiatrist in private practice should have the assistance of other members of a psychiatric team in order to treat emotionally conflicted children. Otherwise he must be prepared to perform therapy with both parents, and visit the schools and other significant persons or agencies who work with the child. To do less deprives him of the data necessary to establish a diagnosis and perform therapy. The same procedure is necessary for the clinical psychologist and social worker who plan to do intensive therapy with emotionally conflicted children.

The child analyst sees a child in analytic therapy three to five times a week. The technic of child analysis has been described by Anna Freud [5] and Melanie Klein,[6] both pioneers in analysis of children. As in adult analysis, the aim of child analysis is to uncover the deep unconscious conflicts responsible for the neurosis. One feature of child analysis which distinguishes it from adult analysis is the closing period of therapy in which an education procedure relates the material gained from the analysis to the child's everyday life situation. The child analyst may work with the mother, seeing her once a week, or he may engage the services of a caseworker to see the mother regularly for interviews. The

[3] Bettelheim, Bruno, "Love Is Not Enough," Glencoe, Ill., Free Press, 1950.

[4] Redl, Fritz, and David Wineman, "Children Who Hate," Glencoe, Ill., Free Press, 1951.

[5] Freud, Anna, "Introduction to the Technic of Child Analysis," Washington, D.C., Nervous and Mental Disease Publishing Co., 1928.

[6] Klein, Melanie, "The Psychoanalysis of Children," London, Hogarth Press, Ltd., 1949.

caseworker arranges also for a psychological examination and a complete physical examination, if the child has not had one recently.

Child analysis represents the ideal form of therapy for the deeply conflicted child, but unfortunately the amount of time required and the cost involved limit the number of children who can receive such treatment.

During recent years pediatricians have become interested in dealing with children's emotional problems. Many of them have read widely on the subject and some have taken special courses to learn more about functional illness of children. A pediatrician who has known a child and his parents for many years can usually gain the child's confidence quickly. Many pediatricians are skillful in using suggestion and emotional support to lessen suffering from disturbing neurotic symptoms.

Most pediatricians have not had special training for treating an emotionally disturbed child, nor have they time in their busy schedule to devote to therapy; but their appreciation of the role of emotional conflict increases their contribution to the child's welfare. Many pediatricians have developed skillful methods for dealing with disturbing symptoms which the parents are unable to handle without help, and so long as the pediatrician recognizes that he is dealing only with symptoms, the measures he uses are generally safe. He must realize, however, that disturbing behavior symptoms reflect something in the child's life which demands attention; by eliminating the symptoms he may have lost a valuable opportunity for discovering pathologic conditions which, if untreated, may cause later emotional illness.

When a pediatrician's or general practitioner's treatment has failed to clear up the symptom, or when the symptom has disappeared only to be replaced by another, he must be prepared to refer the child to someone trained to treat emotional problems of children.

The community provides many other resources for dealing with the lesser emotional problems of children. The teacher in her

everyday work with the child, the recreation worker, camp and
school counselors, the worker in a character-building agency,
public health nurses, religious leaders, juvenile police, and many
others can make real contributions to the emotional welfare of
children. The more any individual in direct contact with children
knows about the mental hygiene of child life, the more helpful
he can be in dealing with problems and in recognizing those
which require the kinds of therapy he cannot provide.

CHAPTER 3

The Use of Dreams in Therapy

Most children, in my experience, dream and enjoy relating their dreams. They often tell them to others in the family in the morning, and they will tell their dreams to their therapists, too, once their initial restraint in talking to strangers is overcome. They may need some help to get them started telling their dreams, but anyone accustomed to working with children will have little difficulty. If the therapist enjoys working with dreams and recognizes their importance in studying emotional conflicts of children, the child will absorb his enthusiasm, thus making the process a pleasanter one. The therapist must understand the mechanism of dream formation and must have a knowledge of dream interpretation, though he will seldom interpret unconscious, latent dream thoughts in his therapy interviews. He will have learned about working with dream material from his supervised treatment work with children, from his own analysis, and from his analytic training. He will have learned even more if he dreamed extensively during his own analysis. The therapist will find working with dream material more rewarding if he enjoys working with fantasies, has a capacity for fantasy, and is able to "tune in" readily with the fantasies children present in their play, stories, and dreams. The child will recognize that the therapist understands his fantasy creations and considers them significant.

The qualities just mentioned will help a child therapist to feel more secure in many aspects of his work with children, especially in his work with children's dreams. The therapist's feeling of security will in turn help the child to relax as he tells his dreams. Beginning child therapists tend to shy away from using dreams, especially if they have not been analyzed, because they fear stirring up more than they will be able to understand and thereby interfering with their relationship to the child. However, their fears will lessen as they learn that dreams furnish valuable material, even when only the manifest dream is discussed, and that even this content is not discussed until it is safe to do so. It is wise for the beginning therapist to be supervised in his work with children's dreams until he is quite familiar with such material.

In 1945 I reported on the use of children's dreams in our clinic work.[1] Most of the report dealt with the usefulness of manifest dreams in the understanding of current emotional conflicts and in recognizing the significant tensions in the environment that produced these conflicts. The material in the report demonstrates how frequently children's manifest dreams reflected underlying conflicts, the uncovering of which is useful in therapy as well as in diagnosis.

According to E. H. Erikson,[2] any item of human behavior shows a continuum of dynamic meaning, reaching from the surface down to the core. He noted that, clinically, we often interpret dreams entirely or in part on the basis of their manifest appearance or content. We then search for what seems to be the more worthwhile, underlying content, as though the manifest dream itself contained much less that was significant. "It takes practice," he explains, "to realize that the manifest dream contains a wealth

[1] Lippman, Hyman S., The Use of Dreams in Psychiatric Work with Children, in "The Psychoanalytic Study of the Child," vol. I, 1945, edited by Anna Freud, Heinz Hartmann, and Ernst Kris, New York, International Universities Press, Inc., p. 233.

[2] Erikson, Eric Hamburger, The Dream Specimen of Psychoanalysis, Journ. Amer. Psychoanalyt. Assoc., vol. II, no. 1, 1954, p. 16.

of indicators not restricted to what the listener happens to be receptive for."

Proctor and Briggs [3] recently studied the manifest dreams reported in diagnostic interviews. Of the one hundred children interviewed, forty-three reported dreams. Several therapists studied the same dreams in an attempt to determine how much of the dynamic picture could be reconstructed from them. The authors conducted the study because they were impressed with the amount of emotional material provided by the first dreams reported. They concluded, however, that, while much information about the nature and quality of the forces in a conflict was obtained from these dreams, too little about the final, relative strength and distribution of the forces was revealed to warrant extensive conclusions. Nevertheless, their estimate of the value of manifest dreams did not change.

Our early study of children's dreams revealed that 46 per cent of all children who were asked about dreams reported they dreamed frequently, 20 per cent dreamed occasionally, and only 2 per cent insisted they never dreamed. Ten per cent were aware of dreaming, but said they were unable to recall what they dreamed. In a group of forty-seven children who said that they dreamed, thirty, or 63 per cent, told their dreams willingly; fifteen, or 32 per cent, required urging, and two required a great deal of urging. These figures are quoted because several therapists have reported that children resist telling their dreams. It is my impression that such resistance is due either to the use of wrong technics or to the therapist's anxiety in dealing with dreams.

It is my practice to ask about dreams in the first few interviews—often in the very first diagnostic interview. While talking about sleeping conditions, I ask the child how he sleeps, how long it takes him to fall asleep, and whether he usually dreams.

[3] Proctor, James T., and Andrew G. Briggs, The Utility of Dreams Reported by Children in the Diagnostic Interview, read at annual meeting of the American Orthopsychiatric Association, 1960.

If he says that he does dream, I ask him what kind of dreams he usually has. Are they pleasant and fun, or are they scary? This may be enough to start him giving an illustration of a recent dream or two. I am more likely to ask for dream material when the study appears to be for diagnostic rather than for therapeutic reasons, since I am looking for as much material as I can obtain in a short period. When, under such conditions, the child says he does not dream, I show surprise and tell him that most children we see do dream. I may help him to recall dreams by asking if he ever dreams, at times, about his family or friends or school, if he ever dreams of falling or of being chased or of animals? Sometimes I say, "Tell me the scariest dream you ever had in your whole life," and I assume an air of relaxed inquiry, while still indicating a great interest in the child's dream creation. But I try to avoid giving him the impression that he has failed me if he cannot report any dreams.

Under certain conditions I do not ask about dreams, for a child who shows resistance to the study or who is afraid that he will reveal secret material is likely to become more resistant and suspicious when asked to tell his dreams. Such an attitude is found particularly in delinquent youngsters.

Often a child may feel that dreams are expected of him and will concoct one, or he will relate a movie incident as being a dream. These are readily recognized by anyone experienced in working with dream material. Ordinarily the incidents in concocted dreams will follow each other in logical order, as in a story, and there will be little vagueness or distortion. At times a child will modify a real dream so as to make sense of it. It is not easy nor is it important to distinguish between a dream and a fantasy, since both are creations of the child's thinking, and they picture the thoughts which the child is attempting to work through.

Ruth Griffiths[4] made a profound study of children's dreams,

[4] Griffiths, Ruth, "Imagination in Early Childhood," London, Routledge & Kegan Paul, Ltd., 1935.

fantasies, and imagery, and many of her conclusions have been verified by later research. She believes that an emotional experience takes place in the child's day life, a memory is stirred, and an unsolved problem is reanimated. The result is a dream which is remembered by the child. It is as though the dream remembers something to be undertaken—a problem that cannot be tackled directly because of its essentially unconscious nature, and so the dream thoughts are taken up by the daydreams, or the fantasies, and brought nearer to the conscious level. The dream thought, being dynamic, remains in the awareness of the dreamer and finds a way of being acted on in the many kinds of thinking activity that the child has, such as fantasy, playing, storytelling, drawing, and symbolic behavior. I am very much impressed by Ruth Griffiths' concept of the dream as a vehicle for forcing the psyche to find a solution in reality for a problem previously unsolved, and although this concept has been shared by others, nowhere else is the process described so clearly and thoroughly.

This mechanism is similar to what we see when a fantasy vividly persists during a period of current conflict, until the conflict is resolved and the fantasy is no longer needed. We also see this mechanism in the recurrent dream which is stirred up by a particular conflict and in the neurotic symptom which persists until the underlying meaning is understood. Ruth Griffiths recognized a sameness in the material which the young children she studied presented in their dreams and in their play fantasies. She felt that the symbolism in the play fantasies was derived from the dreams.

In my work I occasionally discover some children who seem totally to lack the capacity for fantasy. This lack first comes to my attention when I try to get them to associate to an element of a dream. They do not seem to know what I mean, in spite of repeated illustrations. I have noted also that such children tend to dream seldom and that they have difficulty in creating an image. When asked to close their eyes and to picture a blank screen upon which a figure will appear, they say that they see nothing, whereas most children have no trouble in visualizing objects.

We hope to carry out a study on the capacity of children to dream, daydream, associate ideas, develop imagery, use fantasy in play, and make up stories, in order to determine to what extent these qualities are interrelated. It should be noted that Dr. Louise Despert [5] found that anxious children, whose records contained little or no evidence of dream material, were also inhibited in their fantasy expression as well as in their play expression.

One of the functions attributed to a child's play is that of providing a safe outlet for his hostile feelings toward parents and siblings, without fear of retribution. These are feelings he can control, and he is aware that there is something unreal about them. If the pressure becomes too great, he can manipulate the play so that those who are harmed become well and those who are killed come back to life. It would be interesting to determine whether children who show considerable hostility to persons in their fantasy play have had this stirred up in dreams during the same period. Our contemplated study may answer this question.

Children have an uncanny awareness of the significance of dreams and their relation to waking thoughts. They trace their dreams to events of the day, to movies or television programs they watched, or to thoughts they had before retiring. A few report that, before falling asleep, they conjure up dreams of violence to avoid having dreams of "dirty stuff," since dreams of sex make them feel guilty. Some children who dream excessively insist that they can control their dreaming when the dreams produce too much anxiety and that they have different ways of waking themselves up. They have learned from previous dreams of the same kind to recognize their bizarre and unreal experiences as dreams. Occasionally, children say that they can continue a good dream by falling asleep again, and some claim that they can

[5] Despert, J. Louise, Dreams of Children of Pre-School Age, in "The Psychoanalytic Study of the Child," vols. III and IV, 1950, p. 141.

even return to where they left off dreaming. More often, children report that they try to return to a dream but fail.

Children are often aware that their dreams are related to intentions. One child dreamed that a teacher she dearly loved was shot by a man who walked into the classroom. After telling the dream she said, "Gee, I hope Miss Jones never finds out I dreamed this about her. I would hate her to know I killed her in my dream."

I have long been puzzled by children who say (but are unable to explain the connection) that they failed to dream because they were too tired or because they slept too soundly. One child recently remarked, "I know I didn't have a scary dream, because if I did, I would have awakened." He was implying that if he awakened he would have recalled his dream and could have related it to me.

One boy, who was an enuretic, said he never dreamed because he was such a sound sleeper. Since he was eager to control his bed-wetting, he set the alarm clock, but slept through the alarm which awakened others in the house. He had a newspaper route and was late for his work three times in a short period, because he failed to hear the alarm clock. His failure to awaken for the newspaper route and for going to the toilet reflects mixed feelings about both enterprises. An adolescent, who was an enuretic, was placed in an institution for delinquent youngsters, during the course of therapy. Shortly after this change of residence his bed-wetting ceased. When asked how he accounted for his better control, he replied, "One of the counselors wakes the bed-wetters up at two o'clock, and I wake up before he comes to my bed; I hear his heavy footsteps coming toward me." He added that, when his father used to come to his bed to awaken him, he never awakened. Apparently, he was able to control the depth of his sleep.

During the past few years scientists at the University of Chicago have been conducting experiments with manifest dreams,

by means of electroencephalographic tracings which have been
shown to record dreams. Wolpert and Trossman [6] found that,
when the subjects were awakened by the examiner during or at
the end of a dream period, they were usually able to give detailed reports of their dreams. However, if even a few minutes
were allowed to elapse before the subject was awakened after
dreaming, the contents of the dream were forgotten. This does
not establish the fact that only those dreams are recalled when
the dreamer awakens during a dream or immediately after it
ends. It may be that, when a child is very tired or is in a very
deep sleep, he may not awaken during his dreaming, and later
he is unable to recall his dream.

Children often have severe anxiety dreams, during which they
awaken their parents who attempt to comfort them and to assure
them that they have no need to fear. The child who does not
awaken during the dream may be terrified by the parent and try
to avoid him. In the morning the child cannot recall the incident
nor remember what he dreamed; unfortunately, therefore, we
are denied an opportunity to capture clues that could explain the
panic caused by the dream. The fact that the child had not awakened may be the reason the incident and dream were forgotten.

The dreams of a child may occasionally help to decide whether
or not to continue therapy. A series of dreams that reflects distrust of the doctor or of the group activity may suggest that the
child feels threatened by the study or is unprepared for it. When
a friendly discussion fails to lessen such anxiety, it may be better
to put off working with the child and to confine the work to the
parents. In contrast, we recently concluded that a child had made
sufficient progress at home and in school to warrant bringing
treatment to a close. The child, who had previously offered little
in his interviews, suddenly began reporting dreams that reflected

[6] Wolpert, E. A., and H. Trossman, Studies in Psychophysiology of Dreams
—Experimental Evocation of Sequential Dreams, *Arch. of Neurol. and
Psychiat.*, no. 79, 1958, p. 603.

deep anxiety and preoccupation with castration fears and death, and it was obvious that therapy had to be continued.

Many dreams are so revealing that little discussion is necessary. The therapist may discuss the material revealed or may make a mental note to use the information at a more opportune time. The latter course may be particularly indicated if the child is still distrustful. Later on the dream can be discussed out of context, and the child may speak freely about the subject.

The following are a few dreams that tell a particularly revealing story:

"I dreamed you weren't going to be here today. My brother told me, 'That guy who's going to examine your head went on a trip.'" The wish here is obvious.

An eight-year-old Negro girl told this dream: "A man with a white face and a hood pulled me into a hole and wanted to make me white like he was." This child felt rejected because she was a Negro. She discussed this feeling freely after telling the dream, without referring to the other elements in it.

"I was looking at a TV picture. My stepmother was one of the actors. She pointed a gun at me and shot me while I was looking at the picture." This eleven-year-old boy, who lived away from home, had always sensed his stepmother's rejection of him. He reported this dream in his first interview; it characterized his feeling toward his stepmother, whom he feared, throughout his therapy.

"I fell out of a boat. I began to drown. Then I saw my father swimming. I swam just like he did." This ten-year-old boy's father had died several years before, when he was just learning to swim. The dream wish and the feeling of need for his father are clear, and they could then be discussed.

"I dreamed I was back home. My stepfather was living. He laughed at me and said, 'I wasn't killed. They just told you I died to fool you.'" This twelve-year-old boy had killed his alcoholic stepfather who, in a drunken rage, was chasing the boy's

mother to beat her up. The boy shot his stepfather with a shot-
gun. Before this dream he had insisted that he was not at all
concerned about shooting "the old drunken bum." After telling
the dream he said that he had awakened "so happy" and then
suddenly realized it was only a dream. He discussed his anxiety
at length.

Of sixty children interviewed consecutively in our study, more
than half reported that they frequently had anxiety dreams, and
approximately two-thirds of them reported that they had dreams
involving great danger to themselves. Dr. Despert,[7] finding anxiety
dreams of children of preschool age so numerous, concluded that
the expression of anxiety was one of the functions of the child's
dream. At the same time, these anxiety dreams served as an outlet
for hostile, aggressive impulses.

Many of the anxiety dreams of children are as clear as that of
the boy who killed his stepfather. A child may not wish to discuss his anxieties in the early part of his study, but once he has
told a dream that reveals anxiety, he may find it easy to continue
with the subject. Having just dreamed about the subject, he usually
will have numerous memories about threatening experiences, since
his psyche is already preoccupied with anxiety and danger.

Some dreams contain anxieties that are not easily recognized,
unless the therapist suspects the possibility of ominous contents. An adolescent boy dreamed of "two, very high walls going
up as far as I could see. I was on a carpet, and the carpet was
very deep and came up to my shoulders." When asked to tell
more about the walls, he said, "The two walls joined at one point,
so that it was impossible to go any further"—and he was doomed.
This dream was reported early in the study, and before the boy
was prepared to say more than that he had many fears of accidents
involving himself and others.

A twelve-year-old girl dreamed she was being ridiculed by her
sister. Her mother, who was standing nearby, was also critical.
The dreamer touched an electric clock and felt she was being

[7] Despert, *op. cit.*

electrocuted. She told her mother what was happening and her mother laughed at her.

This, too, was a dream reported early in the study and was not discussed. As the study progressed, it became clear that the dream contained her most significant problems. She felt hostile and competitive toward her sister and feared that her mother preferred the sister to her. Her feelings for her mother were markedly ambivalent.

An adolescent boy, with severe school phobia, dreamed he was in a hospital. The rooms were like cells, and there were bars on the window. "I told my Ma there was nothing the matter with me. She told this to the doctor, but he said I had to stay on in the hospital."

His symptoms were intensified after this dream, and he remained at home and away from school for some time. The boy had been in the hospital for study before coming to the clinic and panicked when he had to stay on for two extra days. About a year before this dream, his father had been hospitalized for severe depression and remained in the hospital for many weeks. The bars on the windows in the dream reflected the boy's fear that his school phobia was similar to his father's depression, which meant that he, too, was "crazy." The dream offered an opportunity to discuss his fear of becoming psychotic.

A twelve-year-old girl, with a severe neurotic illness that kept her out of school, told, as one of her first dreams, that she was running home and saw a neighbor looking at pretty girls in a swimming pool. When he saw a very pretty one, he cut her up into small pieces.

The bizarre quality of this dream reflects the severity of this girl's neurotic involvement. She failed to respond to weekly interviews and later required hospitalization, where therapy could be more intensive. Bizarre dreams, like bizarre drawings of children, suggest severe regression.

I have omitted illustrations of typical Oedipus dreams, pregnancy dreams, dreams expressing castration anxiety, and other dreams of severe regression to oral and anal stages. Such material is seldom dealt with in the therapy of children in a child-guidance clinic or in child psychiatry, unless the therapy is intensive and prolonged.

Enough illustrations have been presented in this discussion to indicate the significance of dreams in revealing readily recognizable emotional conflicts or conflicts that can easily be uncovered. The more experienced therapist will utilize dreams more extensively in treatment as well as in diagnosis, and he will discover clues not obtainable in other ways. It is well to close this discussion with a warning to avoid the use of dreams whenever a child indicates that he is disturbed or becomes uncomfortable by discussing them. When the child is threatened by any technic the therapist uses, there is danger of weakening the therapeutic relationship, with the result that more will be lost than gained.

CHAPTER 4

Involving the Parents in the Child's Therapy

To help the child with emotional problems, the therapist must understand clearly the emotional relationship between the child and his parents. Parents who bring a child to the clinic for treatment usually are ready to participate in any plan the staff may formulate. The caseworker explains the clinic procedure to the parent, describing the several examinations required to establish a diagnosis. In the intake interview with the mother, the worker learns about the problem as the parents see it and about any experiences which may have led to the child's disturbing behavior. She needs a limited amount of information to identify the child: his age, school placement, the other children in the family, the places where the family has lived. After receiving this information, the worker attempts to help the mother to speak spontaneously about matters of concern to the family. The caseworker will accomplish her purpose rapidly if she can overcome the resistance most parents have at the beginning of the study.

These resistances stem from the parents' feeling that they are responsible for the disturbed behavior of their child, and that their seeking help is evidence of failure. The caseworker tries to assure them that they are acting wisely in attempting to solve problems which, if untreated, would probably later produce suffering and perhaps tragedy.

The caseworker encourages the parents to discuss their current emotional concerns about their child, their other children, and themselves. She does not use a formal list of penetrating questions, since she knows that most of these questions will be answered in subsequent interviews as the historical data logically unfold. In this way the parents feel less pushed, and the interviews have a more friendly character.

Parents usually want to know how serious the problem is and how long it will take to help the child or to determine whether the clinic can help him. The caseworker tries to help them see that effective results will be obtained only if they permit the staff to use as much time as is needed. The amount of time required will depend on the seriousness of the child's disturbances, his capacity to respond to therapy, and the parents' willingness and ability to participate. Since these are all unknown at the first interview, the staff prefers to delay dealing with the question of time until the initial diagnostic phase of the study is completed. Frequently the caseworker can determine that certain children's problems are so serious or so long-standing that considerable time will be needed to help them. In such instances the caseworker tells the parents to plan on several months of treatment by the clinic staff for them and the child.

When parents do not accept the worker's judgment on the need for long therapy, she may discuss the matter with other members of the staff. If the staff agrees that the caseworker's evaluation is wise, the worker recommends that the parents either accept the clinic plan or withdraw their application. Studies show that if parents' objections do not decrease early, they tend to grow more numerous as the study demands more of the parents' involvement.

Parents are informed that the staff prefers not to give advice or answer direct questions about methods of discipline, punishment, or planning for the child. Advice on these matters requires considerable knowledge of the parents and the child, and they can be understood only after several interviews with the family. In dealing with the parents' questions, the worker helps them to see that the goal of a child-guidance-clinic study is to help parents use their own judgment and methods to deal with any emotional problems they may later face in relation to their child.

Parents sometimes reveal in the first interview that they feel entirely responsible for their child's emotional problems. The caseworker explains that this is rarely true and briefly presents her reasons. She wants to prevent the parents from trying to place the entire responsibility for treatment on the staff. In essence, such parents are saying, "We have failed miserably with this child and are at a loss to know what to do with him. You take over and teach us how to deal with him." In the early interviews with such parents, the caseworker will search for positive constructive measures which they have used, pointing them out to the parents and even enlarging on them. The parents must stop condemning themselves if they are to understand the other factors contributing to their child's emotional disturbances.

Parents are less likely to emphasize their mistakes and deficiencies if the caseworker can help them to see that their child, as every child, is individual and different from all others. He is attempting to adjust to life in his own particular way. They may not like the way that he has chosen, and he will not be likely to appreciate their efforts to change him, but together the parents and the clinic staff will try to find some common ground acceptable to him and to them.

In her early interviews with the parents, the caseworker discusses some of the methods used by the clinic psychologist, the psychiatrist, and the group therapist. She explains the positive emotional tie the child will develop with these staff members and the need for its being strong in order to overcome the child's resistance to the study. She advises the parents to ask the child a minimum of questions about his experiences with the clinicians and above all to refrain from making derogatory statements which may be stimulated by the child's remarks about the study. The worker tells the parents that like them the child may have mixed feelings about the study or even oppose it and may do what he can to discontinue treatment. The child will accept a plan for study or therapy more readily when he has a chance to know the staff better through several contacts with them. These words of caution to the parents apply particularly to the child's early interviews with the psychiatrist, who, despite his attempts to get the child to like him, may stir up negative feelings in the child because of the nature of the information he is trying to obtain.

Whenever possible, the caseworker sees both parents together early in the study. From observing their behavior together she can see many factors in their relationship more clearly than is possible through separate interviews. She can see which parent is the more dependent, the more dominating, or the more convincing in relation to the other. She gets a picture of the way the child is likely to see them, since he sees them as they react to each other. Occasionally the mother will come alone, explaining that the father is too busy or uninterested to participate in treatment. Accepting this explanation without question will cut off the caseworker from a valuable source of information about the child. Usually when he understands the need for it, the father is eager to help. The worker may need to help the mother see the need for the father's participation and to lessen her fear that the father will distort the picture or point out her weaknesses.

The father's role in treatment is more limited in the case of the young child, though in recent years fathers have played an active part in the care of young children, beginning with early infancy. The father is generally more interested in the older child who presents problems, and considers this to be his responsibility.

Following the joint interview with both parents, the caseworker sees them separately and often obtains information which each wants kept from the other. Later on, when treatment is well under way and the parents feel more secure and more sure of their roles as parents, their need to keep material from each other lessens.

Fathers are usually grateful to the worker for having encouraged them to participate and frequently admit feeling closer to the child than they had before treatment.

Many caseworkers prefer to assume treatment with both parents. They feel that they know the total family situation better through their direct contact with each parent and can deal with any differences of opinion, competitiveness, or mutual distrust more effectively in this way. Other caseworkers prefer to work with only one parent, especially when there is great friction between the two parents. They fear that the struggle of each parent to be the favored one and the need each has to be assured that the other has not distorted the picture will interfere with therapy.

Rarely does the same therapist work with a parent and child. The child needs an adult for himself; he is not ready to share his new friend with his parent. The therapist, however, may meet the parents for a few words of greeting, usually in the presence of the child who has already agreed to the meeting. This brief greeting often gives the therapist a clearer picture of the parents than he can get from any description of them.

The parents usually appreciate an opportunity to meet the child's therapist; they feel less left out. They may even ask to talk to the therapist, and this request is granted. If they raise questions which the caseworker usually discusses with parents, the therapist refers them back to the caseworker who can give the questions the consideration they need. If the child's therapist is the psychiatrist, parents frequently ask his opinion as a physician of the possibility that organic brain damage may account for the child's disturbed behavior. They may want also to discuss the effect of past illnesses on the child's present condition. The psychiatrist always attempts to answer these questions.

The caseworker presents at the initial conference the data obtained from her early interviews with the parents, along with the reports of the other staff members. She continues her casework with the parents in all cases in which the staff has decided that the child will need therapy. By this time the worker has had several interviews with the parents and usually has developed a strong enough tie with them to discuss factors which may hinder progress in treating the child. Aware of the marked sensitivity of most parents who need help for a disturbed child, the caseworker discusses negative factors in a way that arouses a minimum of irritation or embarrassment.

One such factor is the parents' interest in what the child discusses with his therapist. The worker acknowledges their wish to help the child and to be sure that what the child says is accurate. The parents can be most helpful in their child's treatment if they encourage him to talk freely to the therapist about the way he feels in all matters and to overcome his reticence about discussing personal or family matters with others.

The caseworker points out discrepancies in the parents' statements whenever they affect important decisions. As treatment progresses, the parents become aware that the solution of their child's problems depends upon accurate information. They come to realize that they are in good hands and feel free to express their negative as well as positive feelings about the therapy.

The caseworker usually interviews the parents weekly. She obtains regular reports of the child's behavior in and outside the home. She observes the emotional reactions of the parents to changes in the child's behavior resulting from therapy and helps them to accept periods of aggressive acting out when conflicts are stirred up. When the child's aggression becomes excessive, the worker reports it to the therapist, assuring the parents that the therapist will attempt to control the situation unless it interferes too seriously with treatment goals. The caseworker's contribution to the welfare of the child and the parents will be greatest if she includes in her thinking and planning the emotional needs of every member of the family. The work with the child being studied at the clinic will be of little use if it causes serious problems to develop in others in the family.

The caseworker deals with problems which arise whenever the child has made disparaging remarks about his therapy, or has reported to his parents that the therapist has made negative statements about them. The child may have misunderstood the therapist's remarks, or he may consciously be trying to bring the treatment to an end.

The worker avoids intellectual discussions with the parents. She discourages them from using generalizations as a defense against focusing attention on the problems for which they seek help. The worker who has a tendency to theorize has little to give in a treatment program with parents.

Casework therapy with the parents has several important functions in addition to those mentioned in connection with the treatment of the child. In talking about their child, parents describe situations which lead them back to their relationships to their own parents and conflicts arising from them. They may describe their suffering from feelings of being unwanted and unloved, of favoritism shown to others in the family, or of their shame and humiliation at a parent's desertion or imprisonment. They may admit cases of anxiety or mental illness in members of their family and confess a fear that they too may develop mental illness.

The caseworker allows the parents ample opportunity to tell about these experiences in detail, offering them the comfort and ease from tension which comes from confiding to a sympathetic listener. She points out whenever possible the part these experiences and the attitudes resulting from them have played in their relationship to the child. Usually, as their story unfolds, intelligent parents recognize of their own accord why certain problems developed in their child.

Many parents identify with their own parents and carry out patterns of behavior they condemned in their parents. Since identification with another person often creates an unconscious need to react similarly, unfortunate behavior may persist for several generations.

A mother of an adolescent girl grew up in a home where her own mother had been critical of the young men with whom her daughter associated. Her mother warned her many times that she would become pregnant and end up a prostitute. She had been so embittered and developed such hostile feelings toward her mother that she resolved never to expose a daughter of hers to such humiliation. Fifteen years later, however, she disclosed to the caseworker that to her amazement she was making the same remarks to her daughter. The caseworker helped the mother to see that her condemning and accusing attitude might even be responsible for her daughter's defiant, rebellious behavior. Apparently this explanation was sufficient to change the mother's attitude toward her child's behavior, for within a short period of time she reported that her relationship to her daughter had improved considerably.

Another mother, anxious about her son's poor achievement in his studies, forced him to give up pleasures enjoyed by his friends, so that he could complete his homework. The caseworker remarked to the mother that she seemed unduly concerned about her son's achievement, and asked about the mother's own experiences in school. The mother recalled that she had not been a good student and that her parents had compared her unfavorably with an older sister who was brighter than she. The mother was able to see that she was attempting to prove that her son was brighter than the children of the sister with whom she had competed and was still competing. As soon as the mother was able to lessen her pressure on her son's schoolwork, he responded with greater effort and achievement.

Both these mothers were unaware of the part their own experiences played in producing their children's problems. In both instances, however, the caseworker, with little effort, succeeded in helping them to discover how they had been influenced. Neither mother had repressed these experiences into the unconscious recesses of her mind; otherwise the caseworker would have required considerably more time and a special technic to bring the memories of the events back to consciousness. The thoughts connected with the experiences were lodged in the preconscious or foreconscious part of the mind, ready by associations supplied by the caseworker to enter the conscious mind.

The process of bringing to conscious awareness the many experiences, wishes, fantasies, and thoughts which lie in the preconscious mind and are responsible for much confusion and conflict is one of the major duties of the caseworker who treats the parents. By a process of clarification, the caseworker is able to help parents discover distortions in their thinking about themselves and their child and to recognize the many forms these distortions take. The parent who has learned to clarify her thinking in this manner becomes less self-condemning and less critical of others.

Many parents who bring their children to the child-guidance clinic suffer from serious neurotic conflict and illness; and often, the parents' illness is responsible for the emotional problems of their children. Since neurotic illness is largely due to deeply repressed emotion, the caseworker's usual methods will bring about little change in the basic symptoms. Much suffering and discomfort accompanying neurotic illness, however, is due to stresses and misunderstandings in the environment created by the neurotic parent. Casework therapy may alter these to such an extent that the emotional problems in the family members lessen considerably. Caseworkers frequently hesitate to treat clients who are severely neurotic, assuming that they can be helped only by a psychiatrist or a psychoanalyst. Most psychiatrists realize the value of casework therapy, however, and refer many of their most seriously disturbed neurotic and psychotic patients to a family agency for additional help.

Casework with parents may reveal no factor within the home or in the parents which usually produces problems in children. The caseworker will then redouble her efforts to learn about the school, the neighborhood, and the recreation life of the child in an attempt to discover the source of the conflict. Casework with parents is performed as an aid in helping the child make a better adjustment, not as a means of providing therapy for the parents themselves. Therapy for parents is a function of psychiatrists or other professionally trained therapists in private practice. Parents who are unable to pay the cost for such services can receive treatment from outpatient psychiatric clinics or from family agencies whose staffs include experienced caseworkers trained to treat emotional conflicts. Most family agencies employ psychiatrists as consultants to help caseworkers and other members of the staff in the diagnosis of clients, in planning for therapy, and in determining whether or not the agency is equipped to deal adequately with their more seriously disturbed children.

The caseworker in the child-guidance clinic responsible for intake usually recognizes families in which the chief problem lies in the emotional conflict of the parents, even though the child for whom they wish help presents problems. When the parents accept the suggestion of referral to a family agency, the clinic worker usually manages the transfer for the parents.

One form of intensive and extensive treatment of the seriously disturbed child, collaborative therapy, is still in the research stage. Collaborative therapy is psychoanalytic treatment of the child while the parent or parents are receiving psychoanalytic treatment. Such therapy is indicated when a child acts out or behaves in a neurotic, aggressive manner in order to satisfy the unconscious needs of a neurotic parent and will be discussed in the chapter on acting-out behavior.

As the problems of the child and the parents diminish through therapy, the parents often become strongly attached to the clinic caseworker and try to prolong the relationship. Feelings of emotional dependency develop to some degree whenever a person in need of help receives it. The more insecure, anxious, and alone a parent has felt, the more important will be the warm understanding of a therapist.

Some caseworkers attempt to prevent parents from developing a dependency relationship to them. They believe that dependency is a sign of weakness which must be discouraged. Most parents who refer a child to a child-guidance clinic enjoy being independent. They cling to the caseworker in many instances because they feel defeated and in need of help. While seeking help they feel inadequate and do not trust their own judgment. Their feelings of dependency will lessen as their egos are strengthened by casework therapy. Dependency in these parents represents an emotional need which the caseworker must recognize and meet as an important part of therapy.

Frequently parents become dependent upon the caseworker as their child develops a strong tie to his therapist. Working through the dependency relationship between the parent and the caseworker may help to lessen the dependency tie between the parent and the child.

The worker must be sure that she herself does not encourage the parent to continue being dependent on her. After working with a needful parent for many months and helping her become resourceful and adequate, the caseworker may enjoy the relationship and unconsciously attempt to prolong it. Usually the other members of the team will recognize this situation and break the tie.

Occasionally in child-guidance-clinic studies, the child's problems have lessened enough to warrant ending therapy, while the problems of the parents persist and require further treatment. To transfer the parents to another agency at this stage is unpractical and unwise. The clinic caseworker, having established a positive relationship to the parents, is in a much more favorable position to help these parents than is a caseworker in another agency. The clinic caseworker, therefore, continues to work with the parents until they no longer need her.

Many parents bring their children to a child-guidance clinic because someone has suggested it. The suggestion may come from the police department, the probation office, or the judge of the juvenile court. Since it comes from persons in positions of authority, parents frequently take the suggestion as an order and fear that the court will remove the child from the home unless the clinic can change his behavior.

Parents may be angry or offended at suggestions from the schoolteacher or principal to refer their child to a child-guidance clinic, unless they themselves have felt that the child needs help. They are more likely to be disturbed if they dislike the school or have had difficulties in their own school experience. The school social worker often helps the parents accept study at the child-guidance clinic, since she considers the needs of the family as well as the needs of the school. She usually continues her work with the family until she is fairly certain that the parents are ready to involve themselves in a clinic study.

Parents who resist a clinic study may attempt to sabotage treatment by coaching the child in what to say and threatening him with punishment if he discloses certain facts. Usually this state of affairs is not difficult to recognize after one or two interviews between the therapist and the child, and the caseworker and the parents. The caseworker can speak frankly to the parents about their need for help and explain the impossibility of helping them unless they feel ready to cooperate in a treatment plan.

The process of helping resistive parents to accept clinic service is a part of the treatment itself. When the caseworker is unable to change the negative attitude of parents toward the clinic study, she advises them to withdraw their application and assures them that the clinic will be pleased to assist them whenever they want to return.

Some of the clinic's most serious problems occur in children who come from disorganized families where the parents' own unhappiness, confusion, and conflict make it difficult for them to invest time and energy in the problems of one of their children while the entire family structure seems to be falling apart.

Caseworkers in the clinic are accustomed to this picture and are aware of the multiple needs of these families. Often the court sends the parents of disorganized families to the clinic for help with a delinquent youngster. These parents come to the clinic distraught, angry, and disillusioned. They are fed up with social agencies and distrust them. Spending time with such parents at the right psychologic moment may help them to see the wisdom of allowing the clinic to work with the child and with the many problems in the home. Although a child-guidance clinic cannot deal with the total situation of a disorganized family, the caseworker's interest may be the parents' first evidence that someone is willing to give their problems the consideration they merit. Previously, understaffed social agencies may have been unable to do more than consider the parents' recurring emergency needs. After the clinic caseworker has succeeded in awakening interest in a thorough study of the family problems, she helps the parents to accept a referral to a family caseworking agency, assuring them that all the family problems will receive the help needed.

Parents who are in conflict with each other may disagree with any plan for their child which the other parent suggests, including the study of the child in the child-guidance clinic. Under these conditions the caseworker begins her work with one parent, hoping to modify the parent's attitude toward the other parent long enough to enable them to agree on the particular problem in the child which demands attention. Such agreement may lead the parents to a discussion of their differences about other matters and to a greater acceptance of each other.

When the parents are divorced and remarried, the caseworker attempts to see the parent who lives apart from the child. The parent who has custody of the child (usually the mother) may resist such a plan, particularly if she fears that contact with the other parent will stir up previous complaints of her unfitness to care adequately for the child. The caseworker may allay such concern by assuring her that she will defend the mother's reputation as a good parent and inform the father that she is seeking information from him to obtain a more complete picture of their child.

Many parents cannot respond to casework therapy, and it would be helpful if the intake worker could recognize at an early stage in the study those parents who will be unable to benefit from what the psychiatric team has to offer them and their child. Experienced workers are more skillful in this regard, but it is so difficult to be sure of early evaluations that in most instances the intake worker accepts a questionable case for a diagnostic study, leaving the decision regarding future therapy to the staff conference.

Parents who cannot give themselves to others, who are strongly competitive and feel threatened by any demands made upon them, will rarely benefit from therapy in child-guidance-clinic work. With sufficient time and effort many of them would respond better, but such help is not possible in a community child-guidance clinic. Parents whose behavior suggests a deep need to suffer seldom respond to casework therapy, since the continued problems in their child may be a necessary part of their conflict. These are tragic situations, since many of these parents are deeply anxious for help but cannot respond to therapy.

So much has been written regarding the part played by parents in the development of emotional conflicts in children that one may overlook the fact that many problems which occur in children are unrelated to the behavior or the attitudes of their parents. The child's behavior may be responsible for the emotional conflicts and unhappiness in the parents, who are unable to accept the unusual behavior patterns of the child. The parents' reaction may intensify the child's disturbance, but it is not basically responsible for the unusual behavior. Children suffer from intrapsychic conflicts which result from many early situations. Physical illness, constitutional defects, accidents, the trauma of long periods of separation from a sick mother, exposure to sadistic, mentally sick, or markedly indulgent relatives, early sexual seduction, and a host of other factors are often responsible for the development of serious emotional conflict in a child. When in addition to these factors one considers the great variations in the instinctual make-up and drives which are present at birth and which make problems of training extremely difficult, it is apparent that numberless situations produce disturbed behavior and conflict in a child. These situations are not sufficiently stressed in popular literature, nor even in the technical contributions devoted to problems in children. Much of this literature refers to the ambivalent attitudes of conflicted parents but disregards the fact that ambivalence includes both positive and negative emotions. When the negative aspects are overemphasized the parents feel attacked and the caseworker fails to give sufficient consideration to the positive contribution of the parents.

The increasing number of parents who open the interview with remarks like, "Tell me what I have done wrong," "I know it's my fault," or "I suppose I'm the one who should be examined," reflects the reaction of the parents to the literature they have read and the conversations they have heard. Anxiety is often needlessly aroused in parents who have made real contributions to the welfare of their children, and they lose confidence in themselves and their ability to be competent parents.

This discussion has dealt with some aspects of the problem of involving parents in the treatment of the conflicted child. Other aspects of this problem will be described in the case material in the chapters on treatment.

CHAPTER 5

Introducing the Child to Therapy

Most children who come to a child-guidance clinic are there through no wish of their own. Someone—a school teacher, a physician, a judge, or the parents themselves—has recognized a need for treatment. Popular literature on emotional problems of children has helped parents to see the wisdom of obtaining treatment for an emotionally disturbed child, but it has not done away with their mixed feelings at the thought of referring their child to a psychiatric clinic. Their concern is likely to be greater when they learn that they must reveal their own emotional experiences as a step toward understanding their child. If, as is so often true, the parents are unhappy, tense, and neurotic themselves, they may experience acute anxiety at the prospect of a study.

Parents who are anxious about the study or who have mixed feelings about it cannot prepare their child to enjoy or accept this new experience. The caseworker, who is the first staff person to see the mother, discusses with her various ways of helping the child to be more at ease about coming to the clinic for study. She explains how the clinic staff works with the child; the psychologic tests he will take; the group of children he will meet in the group-therapy part of the study; and the interviews he will have with the psychiatrist. The mother's tension diminishes in the warm and friendly atmosphere of the casework interviews, and she soon finds herself ready to prepare her child for his first visit and to explain the reasons why she wants treatment for him.

In spite of attempts to make it appear pleasant, however, children do not usually enjoy their first visit to the clinic. It remains for the staff members to make a child feel at ease and enjoy his visits. Children referred because of disobedience, defiance, or delinquency usually object strongly to clinic study and submit only when clinic treatment is demanded of them. They go to the clinic as they go to the dentist, and from their point of view with about the same unpleasant prospects.

At the Wilder Child Guidance Clinic, a child admitted for study usually sees the clinical psychologist first, since the child will be less frightened by an examination similar to his everyday schoolwork. During the examination the psychologist and the child discuss informally the other staff members the child will see. Members of the staff do not work with the child in any formal order, and the psychologist may interrupt her examination at any point if the child seems disturbed by the procedure.

Usually the psychiatrist's interview with the child follows the psychologic study. He may be the first to see the child, however, especially if the child's chief problem involves school and the staff fears that psychologic testing will upset him and color the rest of the study. A child with severe anxiety symptoms may be eager to see the psychiatrist first, and his study will begin with a psychiatric interview. On the other hand, a child who is upset at the prospect of seeing a psychiatrist will not see him until he feels ready. In some instances, the psychiatrist never sees a child whose strong objections persist; another therapist works with the child, and the psychiatrist supervises the therapy.

The child's initial contact with the therapist is more pleasant for him if the therapist's room is furnished with toys, airplanes, soldiers, a blackboard, drawing paper, pencils, and crayons. If the objects are scattered around rather than neatly arranged, the child will see that they are to use. An anxious child may look quickly at the toys without examining them closely or venturing to play with them. A child who wants to avoid an interview may engross himself with the play objects and spend the hour talking about them. The therapist may not interfere with him for several periods, waiting until the child no longer needs to hide behind the play objects.

Many therapists go to the waiting room to greet a child when he first comes to the clinic. Others prefer to have the receptionist or the mother's caseworker accompany the child to the interviewing room and introduce him to the therapist. This method gives the child the advantage of seeing the therapist before the parent does, since the parent is usually in the waiting room with the child. The presence of other parents and children in the waiting room, moreover, creates a less propitious setting for the first meeting.

As the door opens and the child enters the room, the therapist's opening salutation is a valuable first step in making him feel welcome. A warm "Hi," calling him by name, and a friendly smile can lessen tension in a child, and the change may be noticed at once. His tension may return as he approaches the chair to sit down, but that does not matter; his first impression is that the therapist is a friendly person.

In order to make a child comfortable, the therapist himself must be relaxed and at ease. The beginning therapist needs preparation and support from his supervisor before he begins interviewing conflicted children. Most young psychiatrists in training at child-guidance clinics have had previous interviewing experience with adults, and unless they have worked with children in camps or in recreation work, they may feel ill at ease and anxious with children. Once he begins to interview the child, the beginning therapist must be able to feel that his supervisor will accept whatever goes on during the interview. Unless he has this assurance, he will lack the sense of quiet relaxation which is so necessary in helping a disturbed child feel at ease.

Therapists' methods in interviewing children vary, and no one method has any real advantage over others. The therapist must like children and enjoy them. He must not expect an enthusiastic response from them, and he must be prepared for rejection at the outset.

Children in turn may expect the therapist to distrust and reject them, if this is the way most adults have reacted to them, and anything else may surprise them. The more resistant children may distrust a friendly attitude, and they may respond best to casualness mixed with enough warmth to imply acceptance rather than rejection. Whatever attitude the therapist uses as he greets and talks with a child, he must feel the way he acts. Shrewd, sensitive youngsters will spot a false attitude quickly, and their suspicion and distrust will increase.

The therapist working with a child must use methods with which he is familiar and comfortable and which give him the best results. August Aichhorn once described an incident which occurred at an institution for delinquent boys outside of Vienna. A gifted young therapist whom Aichhorn had newly added to his staff was reputed to be very skillful with difficult boys. Within a few weeks, however, the therapist reported to Aichhorn that he was getting nowhere with the boys assigned to him; they were getting out of hand. Aichhorn asked him what he thought the basis for his failure might be, and the counselor explained that he had been trying to use Aichhorn's methods when disciplining was necessary. When Aichhorn asked him, "In what way do my technics differ from those you were used to?" the counselor answered with embarrassment, "When the boys in my group became unruly or defiant, I boxed their ears." Aichhorn replied, "Box their ears here, too." Knowing that the young man was mature and deeply fond of youngsters, Aichhorn could be sure that he would use punishment in a constructive manner.

An anxious child may be quite frightened when he first talks with the therapist. His parents have instructed him to "tell the therapist everything," but he fears telling everything because his thoughts are "bad" and mean and stupid, and he is ashamed of them. Recognizing the child's concern, the therapist tells him that his reaction is expected and that his fear will lessen as he learns to know the therapist better. He will learn, too, that the thoughts he rejects in himself are common to most children with emotional problems. The therapist may help him by telling him what some of these thoughts are, so that the child will understand that he is not so different as he imagines.

To overcome anxiety and distrust, the therapist must help the child to feel safe with him as soon as possible. A child generally feels safe when he is convinced that what he says to the therapist is confidential. He comes to recognize that the therapist accepts the negative aspects of his behavior as a logical outcome of the experiences to which he has been subjected. Through the absence of criticism and the therapist's objectivity and continued friendliness, the child becomes aware that he is dealing with an adult different from any he has known.

A child whose parents have been overemotional, condemning, and judgmental may, early in his interviews with the therapist, describe this behavior of his parents. The therapist should avoid identifying with the child's negative attitude toward his parents and his condemnation of them. This will not help him develop a quick, positive relationship with the child; he may only indicate to the child that he, too, is judgmental and quick to come to conclusions without sufficient facts. From the child's standpoint an adult who is so quick to attack his parents may someday similarly turn against him.

A child feels safe when he realizes that the therapist respects his opinions during the interview. He senses that his thinking and feelings are important to whatever plans may be made. His fears of being forced to discuss sensitive subjects, to tell about the unhappiness and misery in his home, or to talk about his sexual misconduct, disappear when he finds that he is talking to an adult who understands what it is like to be in an uncomfortable situation. Most problem children do not take long to recognize an adult who is on their side.

Many children who come for psychotherapy, however, have

grown to be so distrustful of adults that they need several interviews to restore even a little confidence. One of the best indications of this change in a child is his spontaneous talking about something which has emotional content and which he might otherwise not want to discuss. Once a child begins to talk freely, interviewing becomes more productive, if the therapist continues to go slowly and waits for the child to introduce new subjects.

If a child can feel in the first interviews that the therapist is not only safe but understanding, he may soon conclude in spite of his resistance that the therapist can be useful to him. In part this conclusion may be due to the welcome contrast between what he finds and what he expected. Largely it is due to his ego's awareness that the therapist has made it possible for him to think differently about himself.

The therapist must be prepared to meet children who are defiant and hostile and who are determined to have nothing to do with the study. Such a child may enter the room without returning a greeting, answer in monosyllables, or mutter a few unintelligible words. Usually, though not always, the therapist knows about such attitudes in advance. In any case he must show no anger or condemnation, nor should he give any sign of anxiety. He will find talking to a child of this kind easier if he keeps in mind that the child's unpleasant behavior is a result of defensive psychic forces which help to keep him intact. The child's defiance is evidence of his anxiety and distrust. He probably has been threatened with being sent away and considers the clinic study as a step in this direction. The therapist tells such youngsters at the outset that he recognizes that they do not want to be helped and that they are angry and hurt at being forced to come to the clinic. He explains that he has no intention of adding to their discomfort and that the study can be dropped whenever they wish it. The hostile child with little anxiety may accept the suggestion of quitting and decide that he will not return for further treatment. If the child decides to stop coming, the therapist must be sure that he leaves feeling that he can return for treatment whenever he thinks he may gain something from it.

The early breaking off of treatment with a child rarely occurs in a child-guidance clinic. From previously gathered information the clinic staff is sure in almost every case that a child will accept treatment for a while at least. Before suggesting to a child that he can discontinue treatment, the clinic therapist must realize that he is a member of a team and that the other members of the staff are investing time and energy with the parents and with the many other problems which face the family. The other members of the team may want the child to continue in treatment. Frequently parents refuse to go on with the study if the child is not in treatment, even though the staff may feel that much can be gained from continuing with them. So long as the child is coming to the clinic the parents are able to point out to others as well as to themselves that it is primarily the child who needs treatment. One cannot overlook this need in parents.

Children who are tense and anxious in their early interviews appreciate a light touch in the discussion to help lessen the seriousness of their problems. Pointing out some humor in their situation may help them if it is not overdone. The therapist's manner must make clear that he has no intention of turning the interview into a comedy act, since the problems to be discussed are serious and require serious consideration. Occasionally a child may resent the introduction of humor into the interview, feeling that the therapist does not appreciate the degree of his suffering. Too unhappy to laugh or want to laugh, he feels that the light touch is out of place.

Problems of children are solved more easily when neither the child nor the therapist feels rushed and the therapist can devote as much time as he needs to understanding a child and making plans for treatment. At times, however, the therapist must be prepared to act quickly and make decisions in the first interview. He may find, for example, that he is dealing with a much sicker or more disturbed child than he had anticipated from the history and that he must take radical steps in order to avoid a tragedy. He may have to make plans without benefit of further information and without assistance from other members of the staff. Such a situation may occur when the school, the court, or the police are unwilling or unable to tolerate further acting-out behavior in a child.

The therapist must be prepared to deal with manifestations of aggression when they first appear in his interviews with a child. When these are dealt with at the outset, so that the child knows what is and what is not acceptable, the therapist can avoid a good deal of later annoyance. Destructive behavior and aggression is less of a problem when the clinic has a room set aside for this purpose, but since few clinics can make such provisions the therapist usually must come to a quick understanding with a child about breaking objects which belong to the clinic, cutting into desks and walls, or striking the therapist. In general, a child gains more from an interview in which he can accept the therapist as an authoritative figure toward whom he must behave in a socially acceptable manner. He must feel that the therapist is strong enough to deter him from acting unwisely or dangerously. The child who acts out in an uninhibited manner during the course of the interview usually invests most of his energy in acting out rather than learning about himself. If he does not recognize this, the therapist must point it out to him. So delicate a situation requires considerable tact and objectivity, and the therapist will solve it with a minimum of annoyance if he is sure of himself and of the position he is assuming toward the child's aggression. When the therapist is unable to control the uninhibited behavior of a child, interviewing is not the method of choice for dealing with him.

Many children who suffer from emotional conflict have great difficulty in expressing themselves in an interview, even when they know how much depends upon their ability to talk about their experiences and feelings. While the interview is devoted to ordinary subjects they are comparatively at ease, but they become almost mute when faced with emotionally charged material related to their personal conflicts. The therapist must allow such children as much time as they need to reveal their feelings. Their problem is not distrust of the therapist, since they are eager for help, but they fear having to face certain material. The therapist must overcome the temptation to use devices which encourage such children to talk before they are emotionally ready to do so; they should not feel that they have been tricked into revealing material. Given sufficient time, these inhibited and disturbed children may find it possible first to touch on sensitive subjects and later to discuss them more freely.

A child who is mute in all situations which require speech, however, is a different matter. Few conditions are more frustrating to a beginning therapist than a child who is too timid to talk, and the therapist usually charges this failure to his own inadequacy. He will be happier about himself if he reads the protocols of experienced child therapists who have been unable to get such children to talk. Other forms of communication are needed, such as play material, drawings, and working with clay. These methods should be introduced in the first interview to avoid the child's embarrassment at causing the therapist anxiety through his failure to talk. Assuring mute children that they will be able to overcome this problem as treatment continues is a useful early step in their therapy.

The use of play material in treatment is not limited to the child who is unable to speak spontaneously. Many therapists include play material in their treatment contacts with all children below ten to twelve years of age, and occasionally with those in their teens if they enjoy this play. Since the therapist has read the child's case history before seeing him and is familiar with his most disturbing problems, he can prepare a setting with toys that will help to stimulate a discussion of some of the troubling situations. When the child encounters the setting, the therapist explains that the play material is for him to use in any way he wants. The toys which most interest children are house furniture set up in separate rooms —kitchen, bedroom, bathroom. There are characters to represent father, mother, grandparents, brothers and sisters, including a baby. Other play objects and vehicles in use are conveniently scattered about.

The therapist usually asks general questions about the child's interests in some of the play objects or rooms to help him overcome reticence. As the child becomes more familiar with the play, the therapist asks questions about his home, the other children in the family, his father's employment, and so forth. He looks for emotional reactions displayed toward certain play characters in the home. Hostility may appear early toward a sibling, a parent, other children whom the child brings into the play. Fear of animals, of the dark, of the use of the toilet may appear. Often the child ascribes these fears to another child who obviously represents himself, though many times children state frankly that they have these fears in the play and in real life.

Through helping the child elaborate on behavior or attitudes which the characters portray, the therapist learns how the child feels and reacts emotionally in many situations. The amount of explanation the therapist will give about the child's play depends on the child's ability to respond to play technics, his sensitivity to certain activities, and the strength of his tie to the therapist. It depends, too, on the personality of the therapist. Some therapists remain relatively quiet and offer few explanations unless certain that the remarks will stimulate significant discussion. Others are more active in the play, include themselves as characters in the production, and create scenes which they hope will stimulate reactions in the child.

By explaining what takes place in the play the therapist helps the child to understand the experiences and conflicts which he has revealed. Most of the explanations deal with conscious and preconscious conflicts. The situations which the child enacts in play are familiar to him, but often he cannot see how they have created problems. The therapist can clear up misunderstandings and confusions which have kept the child unhappy and hostile.

Occasionally a child's unconscious thoughts and wishes come through in the play. The therapist does not interpret them, even when he is certain of their meaning. He may be strongly tempted to make such interpretations, thinking that they will resolve the child's conflicts more quickly, but this rarely happens. Instead, the child, unprepared to face his unconscious wishes or fantasies, becomes disturbed and he may find the therapy too painful for him. Interpretation of unconscious material belongs to psychonanalytic treatment, when the therapist can interview the child several times a week and can be sure of the child's capacity to face his unconscious thoughts. Seeing the child once a week does not permit the slow, painstaking effort required to uncover deeply buried conflict. The therapist, however, does not ignore any unconscious material which appears in the child's play. He may gain from it valuable insight into important aspects of the parent-child relationship.

Many therapists prefer to limit their contacts with the child primarily to verbal communication with the occasional inclusion of play material, especially if the child demands it. Children enjoy talking when the therapist is skillful in selecting subjects, and once they are accustomed to talking in the interview, they enjoy it more and more. Even children six to eight years old may like the experience of sitting quietly and talking to an adult who shows keen interest in what they say. Older children prefer to talk, though occasionally an adolescent may feel more relaxed if allowed to work with his hands as he talks. Clay modeling is a pleasant way of helping a child enjoy the interview, and it is less distracting than constructing a train or plane which requires concentrated attention. Playing with clay also gives the child a convenient means of acting out hostility against people in his life whom he represents in clay figures.

Little girls enjoy sewing or knitting as they talk and are delighted when the therapist joins them in this activity. The therapist also may feel more relaxed in working with the child as she sews. These methods help the child feel that the therapist enjoys seeing him relaxed and at ease and may represent a marked contrast to the attitude of the adults in the child's home.

Some therapists feel that it is important to visit personally the home of every child who will have prolonged treatment. A therapist can do this only with the parents' and the child's permission, but he often gains information which cannot be obtained in any other way. A therapist may find it easier to inject himself into the emotional tone of a situation the child describes in his home or neighborhood if he has been there and has emotionally absorbed the setting. The child may feel closer to the therapist who has taken the time and has felt him important enough to visit him.

A child's drawings may help materially to develop a friendly tie with the therapist and to give him significant information. Children generally enjoy drawing, especially when they learn that the therapist does not expect artistic creations. The therapist may make a few rough sketches to encourage the child. Often a child is delighted to draw a picture of something he has recently dreamed, and the therapist may suggest this as a way of including his dreams in the interviews. In his first interviews with the child, the therapist may tell him that his dreams will help the therapist understand him. Children enjoy telling their dreams to their parents and to other children, and they rarely object when the therapist asks them to relate or draw dreams. There is no better or quicker way of gaining information about a child's current attitudes and emotional feelings, especially his fears and anxieties.

These remarks about the early phases of treatment demonstrate the need for flexibility in the therapist to enable him to use many different methods of introducing a child to a program of therapy. The methods vary greatly from one therapist to another and from one child to another treated by the same therapist. Since much of the success of subsequent interviews depends on the child's conditioning in the early interviews, the extra time and effort required to put the child at ease and to make him feel safe is well spent. The importance of helping the child enjoy the therapist and the interviews becomes more apparent as the treatment progresses, when the child must be able to face some of the destructive and hostile thoughts and wishes which are responsible for his conflict. He might find this unbearable without a strong relationship early established between the therapist and himself.

In saying goodbye at the close of the first interview, the therapist may add, "I'll be seeing you again before long." He does not ask "Would you like to come in again?" since he wants the child to take his return for granted. The study is begun on the assumption that the child will be seen several times to give the therapist sufficient information to make a diagnostic evaluation and contribute toward a treatment plan.

Section 2 |

GROUP THERAPY
WITH CHILDREN

Group Therapy with Children

In 1948, with the help of Professor Gisela Konopka, of the School of Social Work at the University of Minnesota, the Clinic began to organize diagnostic and treatment groups under the supervision of group social workers. The children, after being introduced to the plans for the group activity and after discussing some of the reasons for their coming to the Clinic, can involve themselves in one of the interesting work or play activities at their disposal. Even the child who is shy and withdrawn can, by observing what takes place, sense the pleasure and enthusiasm of the other children. By contrast, the child who meets the individual therapist alone, no matter how pleasant and inviting the room or friendly and warm the therapist, finds himself in an unfamiliar and uncomfortable situation. There are exceptions to this response, which I shall discuss later on, but in the main, a child is ill at ease when asked to make himself at home with an adult he has never seen before. As a result, many interviews are often required for a child to feel as relaxed and communicative as he does in a group setting. These facts are not surprising, since it is natural for the child of latency years to communicate more easily with his peers and through the medium of play.

The activity therapy groups meet once a week for one-and-one-half hours. The children range in age from four to thirteen years, with the majority being from seven to eleven years old. They are usually grouped within a two-year age span, with from five to seven children in each group. We have separate diagnostic groups, in which we observe children as a part of the diagnostic study; frequently these children later move into treatment groups. The length of group treatment varies, with the average being from seven months to a year. However, a child often will remain in a treatment group for more than a year and, in some instances, for as long as two years. At times children will start together in a group and terminate treatment as a group. More often, some children complete their group treatment earlier than others, and new children are added to the group. With few exceptions the children are of the same sex, although we have had groups of younger children of both sexes.

For the past few years, children usually have their first contact with the clinic in a diagnostic group. We found this to be the quickest way to counteract their frightening fantasies of a child-guidance clinic. When the child has been in a group once or twice before he sees the other members of the staff, he generally speaks with great enthusiasm about the fun he has had in the group, and if he knows he is in a diagnostic group that will meet only four times, he may already have plans for demanding that he be allowed to continue in a group.

Evaluations of some children are completed with the diagnostic-group study; others may have to remain in treatment either with the individual therapist alone or in a treatment group. Frequently a child receives both forms of therapy, with the parents continuing in casework treatment.

One of the most valuable aids for establishing a diagnostic evaluation of a child is by the observation of his behavior in a diagnostic group, by a group worker trained to recognize subtle differences in normal behavior and behavior that characterizes serious emotional conflict and illness. A few illustrations will reveal ways in which such observations help to establish an evaluation.

An eight-year-old child, referred to the clinic because of withdrawn behavior in the home and at school, remained withdrawn during most of his group-activity sessions. When a younger, weaker child was added to the group, however, the withdrawn child suddenly came to life. The younger child was attracted to him and looked to him for help, and during the process of their working together, he helped the younger child to accomplish a difficult task he would otherwise not have been able to perform. This could only have been accomplished in a group which exposes children to many different kinds of emotional situations and is supervised by a therapist trained to recognize and deal with emotional problems in such groups. In the case of the withdrawn boy, a method had been found to approach him in a meaningful way.

Another boy, eleven years old, described by his teacher as noisy, fidgety, and antisocial, won himself a reputation in the group as a likable, versatile boy who had leadership qualities. He reacted well to the group worker and followed directions and suggestions well. He was able to do effective work when he was happy, and he was happy in the group where the group worker quickly recognized his virtues and allowed them to flourish. Such a development was impossible in his crowded schoolroom even though his teacher wanted to help him, and it could not be achieved in his home situation, where he was badly handled by an emotionally sick mother. What the group study demonstrated, by way of diagnostic evaluation, was that this boy could respond in a setting that allowed for his specific needs for recognition.

A fourteen-and-one-half-year-old boy was referred to the clinic as a reading problem. He was described as being apprehensive and a perfectionist, and he avoided aggressive encounters. In the first and second diagnostic-group sessions, the boy behaved as he did elsewhere, like an inhibited, isolated adolescent. In the third diagnostic-group session, the group worker, in an effort to extend her diagnostic picture of the group, exposed the children to the room designed for preschool children. Within a minute of entering this room, the boy became intensely involved in the preschool equipment, selecting the more infantile materials and playing with them enthusiastically. In this brief episode, the youngster gave the first clue to the intensity of his need to regress. Having been allowed to express his real interests without censure, the youngster began to respond directly to the other group members and to the group worker.

Although in the majority of cases the group observations tend to corroborate the facts in the history and in the studies of the psychologist and psychiatrist, a diagnostic group often provides data not obtainable from the history or from the other members of the psychiatric team. We rarely fail to discover significant bits of behavior from the group study, that help in formulating a more accurate picture of the child's strengths, weaknesses, and potentialities for responding to treatment. In this connection, it is well to point out that diagnostic evaluation does not end with the diagnostic-group study, since new material from several other sources may change the diagnosis. Behavior changes in response to particular therapeutic efforts may mean that a previous diagnosis should be changed. A child diagnosed as narcissistic may find, after many attempts to relate to several different children, one to whom he can attach himself very warmly, revealing that he is able to relate emotionally to others under the right conditions. Such additional hints may come from the group, the caseworker, or the individual therapist at any time during study or treatment.

In our clinic, a team consists of the child's individual therapist, who may be the psychiatrist, the psychologist, or the social worker (in order of frequency), the caseworker, and the group worker. As stated before, the team meets once a week to review progress of treatment and to plan for the child and parents. At these meetings the group worker presents her observations, which often reveal factors previously not stressed. This new information, which may be useful to the other members of the team, is often derived from an experience in the group, about which the child is sensitive. The group worker tries at the outset to explain to the children in her group the importance of their behavior in group activity and the interest of the other staff members in learning what takes place in the group setting. Despite this, it is important that the group worker obtain special permission from the child to reveal a specific experience to the other staff members. Otherwise, on learning from his individual therapist or from his mother that the experience was discussed, the child may feel that his confidence had been violated. In some instances he may not give permission to report a particular incident, and his wish will have to be respected, unless he can be convinced that his decision is unwise.

To illustrate, an unstable and immature ten-year-old boy showed evidence of sexual preoccupation in the group. His history revealed that his mother had been very permissive in dealing with her son's sexual interests. She frequently slept with him and allowed him to fondle her, in the stated belief that he needed to know that she loved him. Attempts by the individual therapist to discuss sexual matters with the child were met with marked resistance. The subject, he said, did not interest him and made him feel very uncomfortable. When, after a series of interviews, he maintained his resistance to discussing sex, the therapist decided to talk to him about his behavior in the group sessions. (The boy had tried on several occasions to push up against the worker's body and two or three times had placed his hands on her breasts and buttocks. There was no question about the fact that he was seeking sexual gratification.)

The individual therapist explained to the boy that many of his fears of the dark and of being attacked had their source in something about which he felt guilty or ashamed, very likely his sexual wishes and behavior. He told the child he would be neglecting him if he were permitted to avoid discussing this important subject in the interviews. He then told the boy what he had learned about his behavior in the group. Despite the fact that this information was presented in a way that would be least disturbing to him, the boy reacted with anger and embarrassment. He referred to the group worker as a "big blabbermouth" and threatened never to return to the group. He did not carry out this threat, but for a long time it was difficult for the group worker to reestablish a trusting relationship with him. The matter probably could have been handled more effectively had the group worker discussed his behavior more frankly with him when the incidents occurred and advised him to talk to his individual therapist about it.

The Use of the Group in Treatment

During the past few years, the clinic has used group therapy, increasingly, for children of latency age. The group worker, therefore, has played an active role in explaining to the children the factors responsible for significant behavior demonstrated in the group. Although the group worker usually addresses her remarks to one child, she does so in a way that helps the other children as well. Often, in the case of a child who is not ready for a direct discussion of objectionable behavior, she waits until a child who is better prepared behaves in a similar manner and discusses his behavior with him. In some instances she discusses a certain kind of unacceptable behavior with the group as a whole, not so much to explain a situation, as to indicate that she understands their difficulty in controlling such behavior and that they can count on her to be sympathetic.

During the past year, our group workers introduced a plan for holding individual interviews with each of the children in their groups. The purpose of these interviews is to increase the intensity and scope of the group experience for the child and eventually to translate such individual interviews into total group discussions. These interviews are aimed at helping the child to utilize the group experience more intensely and at preparing its members for later, more comprehensive, personal group discussions.

The group worker discusses incidents which are still fresh and vital in the child's mind, but since the child is removed from the immediate threat and from the more intense feeling of the group experience, he can more comprehensively reflect upon what he is experiencing in the group. Although the child is looking across the desk at the adult, the responsibility for bringing up the problems does not rest with the child. Moreover, since the group worker has lived through the group experience with him, the child's use of a denial is lessened.

The interview offers the child the opportunity to expand upon his difficulties more thoroughly and more personally. For example, a child who does not express himself in the group out of fear of retaliation or ridicule can voice his fears, dislikes, and resentments to the worker alone, without having to face the counterresponse of the other group members. It is then up to the worker to help the child see how these same things could be expressed in the group without the feared results.

The group worker has the opportunity not only to examine problems, but to spell out what her approach will be in helping to solve them, the better to assist the child in understanding the treatment process. She is also in a position to help along or to support whatever changes the child has made, by having more time to point out these changes and to evaluate them. Often children feel that they are changing, but are unable to understand how or why. Helping a child to pin down this feeling can support further change. The group worker can also help the child understand the behavior of other children in the group.

I have referred to difficulties encountered when the experiences of a child in group sessions are not used wisely by the individual therapist. There are countless opportunities for the individual therapist to use such observations without disclosing the source of the information to the child. Often the child will refer to the experiences spontaneously during his interviews, in the wish to understand why certain incidents occurred as they did in the group setting. Sometimes the child describes the experience quite differently from the way the group worker described it. In such cases, the child is encouraged to discuss the experience with the group worker to get a clearer picture of what really took place. The individual therapist frequently gets material from the child that suggests he is unhappy in the group, either because of the other children or because of the group worker. Such material is shared with the group worker, who may be unaware of the child's dissatisfaction.

Our caseworkers have found that the group worker's observations are valuable in casework with the parents. Two of our caseworkers, Mrs. Sylvia Reisman and Mrs. Marilynn Lee, have published a report on their use of group-work observations in our Clinic.[1] They found that the behavior demonstrated by children in the group sessions is familiar to parents, who enjoy discussing material they can understand, especially when they are anxious, confused, and not too sure about the procedures in a psychiatric clinic. A mother can see a relationship between the behavior of her child in the group and his behavior in the home, and she can also connect it with her own experiences and feelings as a child in the company of other children. The psychiatric interview, on the other hand, is unfamiliar to most parents and is often an area clouded with mystery and fear.

Often, the description of a child's behavior, as given by his parents, teachers, and others, is highly subjective when compared to the group worker's observation. The group worker describes specific situations and the child's characteristic responses to these situations, to the other children, and to the group worker. The caseworker, therefore, has a reliable body of information to use in helping parents understand the meaning of a child's behavior and attitudes. She may be able to point out to the parents how their attitudes and feelings, often based on confused thinking and anxiety, affect the child's behavior in the group. Of course, the

[1] Reisman, Sylvia D., and Marilynn Lee, Use of Material from Group Treatment of Child in Casework with Parents, *Amer. Journ. Orthopsychiat.*, vol. XXVI, no. 3, July, 1956, p. 630.

caseworker still obtains significant material on attitudes and defenses from the child's interviews with the individual therapist, and she relies on this material, as she always has. Furthermore, particularly in the case of the inhibited, anxious, or phobic child, it may often be the only way significant material is obtained in our clinic studies.

The following illustrates how the caseworker uses the group worker's observations. A mother, deeply concerned about her eight-year-old son's "violent" temper reactions, against which she had been strongly conditioned by her childhood experiences with an unsocialized, violent brother, was amazed to learn that her boy talked baby talk in the group and tried hard to be approved and babied by the group worker. Discussing this behavior helped the mother recognize that she had overreacted to the child's early manifestations of aggression. Casework therapy helped to lessen the mother's anxiety about her son's aggression and opened the way for her to give him the maternal warmth of which she was capable.

When the child's behavior and attitudes in the group sessions differ sharply from what takes place in the home, the caseworker can discuss with the parents how their fears, standards, and expectations affect the child's feeling and behavior. When the child's difficult behavior in the group has been modified, yet persists in the home, more intensive casework with the parents is indicated. Sometimes, knowing that the group worker has had difficulty in handling a child can be a real boost to a mother whose confidence in her own ability to control her child's behavior has been pretty well shaken.[2]

The withdrawn, inhibited child who lacks confidence in himself usually responds well to group-work therapy. After a period during which the child isolates himself and does not participate, he joins, marginally, one of the many group activities available to him, in which one or two of the more gentle children are involved. He rarely responds well in a group where all the others

[2] *Ibid.*

are aggressive. Improvement rarely occurs without the group worker's careful watching for opportunities to engage the withdrawn child's interest in others and to help him participate at the appropriate time. Working on the theory that a withdrawn child is searching deeply for recognition, the group worker attempts to find some type of activity in which he can excel. It is interesting how often the withdrawn child begins to improve in his ability to relate to other children when he finds, perhaps for the first time, that he can do something—anything—as well as, or better than, the other children. The important first step is often followed quickly by overtures to one or two of the other children, and before too long, the child is an accepted and recognized member of the group. It should be made clear that what takes place in the group rarely explains entirely a child's improvement; many other things are happening to the child and for him, within the clinic setting and outside it, which also contribute to his improvement.

One of the most difficult problems, for which a child is frequently referred for therapy, is aggressive, hostile, and destructive behavior. Such behavior is highly resistant to treatment because it is usually the result of frustration and deprivation, and it provides the child with a way of punishing others for his unhappiness. In some instances, however, where the child has suffered because of his hostile behavior or is deeply anxious because of his fear of being unable to control his hostile aggression, he may be motivated for treatment.

Attempts have been made, in previous studies, to be very permissive in allowing such children to carry out their aggressions and destructiveness, stopping them only when real danger threatened. Such a plan, however, is impossible in our clinic. The children are permitted to yell, scream, pound, run about, climb, quarrel, and box, but they are not permitted to attack each other or the group worker in any way that might cause physical harm, nor are they allowed to destroy or deface the room or furnishings. In other words, the children are allowed to give way to their aggressive feelings but not to their destructive drives.

To manage such a program effectively requires an experienced group worker who can quickly impress on the children her determination to maintain order and her eagerness for them to have fun and healthy outlets, as she tries to help them with their problems. Also, she lets them know that she is strong enough to prevent them from hurting others or themselves and that there are better ways of dealing with unrest and anxiety than by being destructive.

It is possible that a group made up exclusively of hostile, aggressive youngsters from seven to eleven years of age can be handled in this way; however, more than one adult might be needed. Our groups are mixed and contain some children who are neurotic, some who have character problems, and some who are aggressively hostile. Therefore, it is necessary to care for the needs of the nonaggressive children as well as those of the aggressive ones.

Every attempt is made to avoid unnecessary friction and to separate children before tempers flare too high, and harmful objects are kept away from those who do not know how to use them. Each child is told, individually and in the group, that hostile aggression often is the result of fear—fear that someone else may make things better, box better, or get more attention from the worker; fear that someone else at home is more favored or better loved by the parents; or fear that he may never amount to anything. He is told that aggressive, hostile behavior is always self-defeating and will produce more problems for him. He is encouraged to argue, talk, or yell rather than to strike out, and he is given work or play that will help to channelize his aggression. He is praised for evidence of greater control of his temper or hostility and is rewarded with his acceptance by the other children and by the group worker.

The hostile child in the group is more likely to talk about the severity or cruelty of the discipline at home; he needn't hide, for he has already expressed hostility in action. Many of the other children in the group have had similar problems and may be willing, at first, to discuss them with each other. Later, as they feel closer to the worker or find it is safe to trust her, they will discuss their hostilities and hatreds with her, too. By the time the child feels he is a part of the group, he has been motivated to change.

Giving up hostile aggression is rarely possible unless, while group treatment is going on, casework therapy with the parents enables them to recognize the factors responsible for the hostile aggression of the child and to eliminate these factors. However, working with the parents becomes easier as the child shows evidence in the home that his behavior is being modified.

Many children are so hostile and destructive because of their anxiety that participation in the usual group in a child-guidance clinic is out of the question. For these children long-time residence in a treatment center may be necessary, although very exceptional foster parents have at times succeeded in neutralizing the hostility of such a child. Sometimes nothing short of intensive psychotherapy in a residential treatment center will suffice. Careful selection of aggressive children for group participation is important to prevent traumatizing the child and the group. In spite of careful efforts, it is necessary at times to remove an aggressively hostile child from a group.

When a child's difficult behavior has been modified in the clinic group, the next logical step would be to place him in a larger, more general, supervised group, before subjecting him to a group that is not supervised. Although such a program is desirable, it is rarely available. Children who have a tenuous hold on reality usually fail to benefit from group-work therapy, since fundamentally, they lack a capacity to relate to others. One must keep in mind that we see children in groups for one-and-one-half hours once a week and that this may not provide nearly enough time for the effort required to lessen the narcissism or anxiety of markedly regressed children.

Because I have placed so much emphasis on group-work treatment, the reader may get the impression that little can be done with children of latency years in individual therapy, but this is far from true. Many children of latency years can only respond to face-to-face interviews with one adult, who can then prepare them to enter a treatment group. Children usually move from individual therapy to group therapy, but they can also move from group therapy to individual therapy. Frequently, the group worker may decide that a particular child, whose treatment was limited to the group, has reached the stage where he can benefit from individual treatment. Sometimes she may suggest that a child who is not responding to group therapy should be limited to working with an individual therapist.

I have emphasized the use of group treatment in a child-guidance clinic where the individual therapist is not involved, because the demands for service from a community child-guidance clinic are so great that we should attempt, as far as possible, not to duplicate services. Because a child has a neurotic problem does not mean that he must be seen by an individual therapist. Often the child can receive treatment for such a problem just as adequately in the group as by individual therapy. Therapy in a child-guidance clinic is primarily concerned with the strengthening of the child's ego in many ways, and these include dealing with all of the emotional tensions that surround him. Individual therapy is only one of the important aspects of treating a child, and so is group therapy. One of the advantages of carrying on treatment in a child-guidance clinic is that workers in several disciplines can help a child and his parents by working together as a team and by being constantly in touch with each other.

As the number of trained group workers increases, it would be valuable to have the benefit of their services wherever troubled children come together in groups—schools, recreation centers, day nurseries, and small and large institutions.

Group Therapy with Adolescent Boys

Most adolescent boys who are referred to the Wilder Child Guidance Clinic present character problems. Acting-out behavior represents their method of dealing with their tensions. They have a real problem in trying to break parental ties, and defying authority offers a good way to prove to themselves that they are emancipated. When the school and their parents are unable to tolerate their acting-out behavior and law enforcement methods are needed to control them, we are asked for help. Often, by the time we are called, so much hatred has developed between the youngster and his parents that they are all thoroughly embittered.

Such youngsters rarely respond to individual psychotherapy. They see the therapist as an authority figure, bent on depriving them of the only defense they have—acting out. Despite his good intentions, the therapist must struggle to be accepted by the resistant adolescent, and only in a few instances, is he successful.

We soon learned that many acting-out youngsters accept the group program with a male therapist more readily than they accept individual interviews. They enjoy a chance to work with materials and to wrestle, box, and eat. Before long they are willing to discuss their complaints about their parents, the police, and their schools. Problems common to the group, such as hostility to siblings, parents, and authority figures, are discussed. Engrossed by their interest in others' problems, the boys find it easier to discuss their own. Since the group worker often initiates the discussion, they feel free to include him in their remarks. Instead of the group worker asking direct, leading questions which usually meet with resistance, the youngsters ask these questions of each other. The group worker limits himself to pointing out errors in judgment or unwarranted accusations. The boys discuss dating, sexual interests, jokes, and practices.

In several instances because of a particular youngster's sensitivity, it was found inadvisable to discuss some subjects frankly. However, the youngster was given a chance to discuss the subject with the worker in his office, away from the group. This practice has grown so that now each member of the group is allowed some time alone with the group worker.

Some adolescents prefer to receive all their group therapy in discussion sessions and join a discussion group at the beginning of therapy. Others, who begin in the activity group, later prefer to give it up and "advance" to a discussion group.

A group worker who assumes the responsibility of conducting a treatment group with adolescent, acting-out boys must have a long experience with adolescents, enjoy them and their antics, and be able to accept acting-out hostility and criticism from them. He must have the capacity to deal directly with problems of hostile aggression without counterhostility. Youngsters will lose their distrust of such an adult quickly.

In therapy with the group worker, the most defiant adolescent often is able to allow himself the dependency relationship he could not tolerate with his own parents, particularly if his parents did not earn it. Affection from the group worker is more acceptable because of the worker's sustained, honest, and positive feelings and because of the similar reactions of others in the group. This shared feeling dilutes the relationship and makes it more acceptable. When the barrier is broken down by a long, gratifying relationship to the group worker, the way is open to a relationship with other adults.

Section 3 |

THE NEUROTIC
CHILD

CHAPTER 6

General Characteristics
of Neurosis in Children

Research and intensive psychoanalytic studies of children have helped psychiatrists to understand neurotic conflict and illness in children. The work of Anna Freud, Melanie Klein, Hug-Hellmuth, Susan Isaacs, Aichhorn, Zulliger, and others has provided child therapists with a sound theory of the emotional development of children and with a great store of valuable clinical information about childhood neuroses. Child analysis has profoundly influenced the therapy of disturbed children by methods other than analysis, and most well-established child-guidance clinics in this country have psychoanalysts, analyzed therapists, or dynamically trained therapists on their staffs.

Child-guidance clinics have carefully studied large numbers of children, placing particular emphasis on the parent-child relationship and the emotions which produce neurotic conflict. These studies have confirmed the psychoanalytic theories of normal and abnormal emotional development and have provided new information about neurotic illness, character abnormality, and delinquent behavior.

The diagnosis of neurotic illness in children differs from that in adults, since in normal development the child suffers emotionally unsettling experiences which can be mistaken for neurotic symptoms. In the Oedipus period especially, when the child is establishing his emotional adjustment to his parents, night terrors, fear of the dark, and other sleep disturbances are common, but they disappear when the child reestablishes his equilibrium. The same disturbances may appear during a period of marked sibling rivalry or difficulty in establishing cleanliness.

Neurotic illness, however, *can* occur during the early years when the ego is severely weakened by repeated traumatic experiences. The emotional disturbance in this case lasts longer and the symptoms are more intense. These early childhood neuroses are the forerunners of adult neuroses.

A diagnosis of neurotic illness is not based on a few interviews with the child or even on a complete initial study by all the members of the clinical team. New emotional situations which constantly develop in the child, in the family, in the neighborhood, and in the school provoke responses from the child which a diagnostic evaluation must consider. These responses are important in a therapeutic program which depends more upon the proper handling of contributing factors than upon the fact that the child is suffering from a specific clinical entity. In other words, treatment does not depend on clinical diagnosis in itself; it depends upon adequate care for the symptomatic behavior and the deep underlying insecurity and unrest which result from disturbing influences on the child with neurotic illness.

Neurotic illness in a child involves his total personality. The ego, superego, and id are all involved in the neurotic process. Ego disturbances appear in many ways: the neurotic child is inhibited in one or more of his activities involving his play life, schoolwork, participation in sports, and acquisition of skills. Because his ego is weak, the child may be shy, withdrawn, and self-conscious. He feels inferior, inadequate, and insecure and lacks confidence in himself. He is unusually sensitive, cries easily, and seeks someone on whom he can depend. He creates fantasies excessively, is highly suggestible and unstable. His aggression is inhibited.

Sometimes a child's inhibitions are general and permeate many of his interests in a subtle way. He appears to be unusually well behaved until further observation reveals he has been oversocialized. He is docile, neat, and rarely defies authority or shows hostility. He is orderly, anxious about the welfare of others, and dislikes seeing any evidence of cruelty. He is more comfortable in giving gifts to others than in receiving gifts.[1] These manifestations may result from the parents' insistence that the child behave in an oversocialized manner. On the other hand, they may result from repression in the child due to neurotic conflicts in the parents who cannot tolerate any other behavior. In the latter case, the child's behavior represents a reaction formation which ensures continued repression.

One must differentiate at all times between an acute emotional upset, even an excessive emotional one, which can be explained by the reality situation and an upset due to neurotic personality change in a child. The disturbance due to a reality situation will clear up as the situation is solved, but it will persist in the case of the neurotic conflict.

The superego of the neurotic child tends to be rigid and severe. He has exaggerated feelings of shame and suffers excessively from feelings of guilt. His guilt may be related to something he has done in the past or something he wished or now wishes to do. In many instances the neurotic child is conscious of his feeling of guilt and free in expressing it. Often, however, his guilt is unconscious and expresses itself in depression that he cannot explain. Many neurotic children indicate their unconscious guilt by unwittingly creating situations which cause them embarrassment and suffering. The need to punish themselves is the price they must pay to assuage their guilt.

Shame in the neurotic child may so torment him that he cannot make friends with other children or adults. Although it is generally thought of in connection with the superego, shame is more

[1] Isaacs, Susan, "Childhood and After," New York, International Universities Press, Inc., 1949.

intimately related to the ego-ideal.[2] The neurotic child's feeling of shame results from his embarrassment at failing to reach the standards of behavior and achievement expected of him.

The evidences of strong instinctual drives which characterize the neurotic child are his exaggerated need for affection, his excessive sexual interests and activities, his hostility and sadism. The inhibited neurotic child is blocked in the expression of these drives. His drives are insistent, he is unable to tolerate frustration, and he suffers intensely when his wishes are not gratified.

The essence of neurotic conflict is a weakened ego. A weak ego cannot handle its synthesizing function to master instinctual drives.[3] The ego must determine how much of each drive can be allowed expression, how much to block, and how much to modify. It must know what gratifications the superego will allow. It must recognize any impulse which is dangerous to the child's welfare and set up defenses against the impulse. It must search all sources in the outside world for instinct gratification. Unless the ego is strong enough to carry out this synthetic function, the child is in constant danger.

A child's ego may be weak from the very beginning and remain weak all through childhood. The history of such a child will show no periods of normal, healthy development, but a succession of neurotic symptoms and character disturbances. More often the neurotic child's early life is comparatively healthy, until upsetting emotional experiences traumatize him and precipitate him into a state of neurotic conflict. Loss of a parent through death, desertion, divorce, or illness may take place, creating severe emotional tension in the home, and particularly in the child if the loss is a severe blow to him. School failure or subjection to ridicule may seriously traumatize a child who is strongly competitive and eager to win approval through achievement. Acute organic illness frequently

[2] Piers, Gerhart, and Milton Singer, "Shame and Guilt," Springfield, Ill., Charles C Thomas, Publisher, 1953.

[3] Nunberg, H., The Synthetic Function of the Ego, *Int. Journ. Psychoanal.*, vol. XII, 1931, p. 123.

ushers in neurotic illness. The organic illness need not be severe or debilitating; it may owe its pathogenicity to the fact that it occurs at a particularly vulnerable time in the child's life. Most traumatic episodes which precipitate neurotic illness are probably the last link in a series of circumstances which have weakened the child's ego.

The child is likely to be less concerned about his neurotic conflict than is the adult. The adult whose conflict inhibits or blocks him from working efficiently, relating himself to other people, or enjoying life feels seriously threatened. Anxiety mounts when he fears that this is the way he may always be. The child is less concerned, since he is still dependent on his family and does not have to make important decisions for himself. Adults usually consider neurotic behavior in children as something that will clear up in time, and they may fail to show concern unless the behavior persists or worsens rapidly. Parents who are overanxious about neurotic manifestations, particularly when they have suffered from neurotic illness themselves, are quicker to seek help when a child displays neurotic symptoms.

If a child is not suffering severely, he is reluctant to come for therapy. Usually, however, his uneasiness and apprehension about symptoms he cannot control suffice to motivate him. The parents must assume responsibility for getting him to come in for treatment until the therapist has made him realize that treatment is necessary. The child who is neurotically ill and suffers from acute anxiety is anxious for help and looks forward to treatment as the adult does. He tries hard to follow the therapist's suggestions for stimulating productive interviews.

Anxiety is the predominant characteristic of neurotic conflict and lies back of every neurotic symptom. A neurotic symptom will not subside until the anxiety disappears. Neurotic anxiety is the signal with which the ego warns the child that a state of danger exists and that action must be taken or he will suffer from some force in the outside world. The anxiety is unconscious and assumes the same forms in the child and the adult.

Neurotic anxiety may manifest itself as generalized fear or dread. All potentially dangerous situations must be avoided. The child rejects sports involving competitive aggression, overnight outings away from home, swimming, climbing, and many other activities through which he learns skills and prepares himself for adult life. When, in addition, the child avoids situations which might embarrass him or stir up unacceptable wishes, his world becomes even more constricted.

Neurotic anxiety may appear as a phobia or circumscribed anxiety. Freud's classic paper, Analysis of a Phobia in a Five Year Old Boy,[4] provides a comprehensive discussion of the dynamics in a phobic child. Children forced to meet a feared object or situation suffer intense agony although they do not understand what they fear. Intense phobia of a doctor is understandable, since the child fears the doctor may inflict pain. The underlying anxiety regarding the nature of the mutilation he fears from the doctor, however, is not known. Because phobia of school is so frequent a form of neurotic illness, a more detailed discussion is included in a following chapter.

Neurotic anxiety may occur in sudden attacks, with no evidence of external danger. Sudden fear of death, of an uncontrolled impulse to commit suicide or to kill someone, may terrify the neurotic child. Several cases in this category are included in the following chapter.

Through their studies of neurotic children, child-guidance clinics have contributed methods of dealing with those factors which encourage neurotic illness in a child. Eliminating these factors early may prevent later neurotic illness in the child. Treating those factors which produce neurotic conflict in one child, moreover, may prevent the development of neurosis in other children in the same family. Rarely are one or both parents of neurotic children free from neurotic conflict or illness. Their chronic anxiety and insecurity create an atmosphere of emotional tension and confusion

[4] Freud, Sigmund, "Collected Papers," vol. III, London, Hogarth Press, Ltd., 1925, p. 149.

which permeates all of the activities within the family. The parents' inability to tolerate even slight expressions of sexuality or aggression in their child forces him early to repress instinctual drives. Rigid patterns of socialization demand a moral code of the child before he has learned to enjoy outlets needed by and generally accorded to young children. Indecision, rigidity, and concern about minutiae force the child to behave like an adult before he has learned to be a child.

Neurotic parents often respond surprisingly well to casework treatment which helps them see how they are creating problems in their children. As they see themselves repeating patterns responsible for their own inhibitions and anxieties, they become more willing to change. Most intelligent parents today have read good popular articles and books describing the development of neurosis. The caseworker helps them focus their general information on their child and his problems and often initiates a genuine attempt to try new methods. She rarely succeeds in changing the attitudes of neurotic parents who are more seriously conflicted; they require more intensive psychotherapy.

The amount of time spent in the therapy of neurotic children depends largely on the severity of the illness. The severity can be gauged by evidences of ego weakness as expressed in a child's difficulty in carrying on daily tasks, particularly in applying himself to schoolwork or in having an interest in it; in his inability to enjoy play and recreation; in his impaired capacity to develop relationships to others. The length of treatment varies also with the amount of resistance to treatment in the child and in the parents. Treatment continues until the staff has evidence that the ego has improved, the pathologic defenses have been reduced, and the crippling anxiety has lessened. In some instances treatment continues for two or three years, although usually the neurotic conflict can be sufficiently relieved in a year. In all cases treatment is discontinued as soon as it can be done safely, since the sooner the child can get along without treatment, the better. Often the child will indicate when this stage has been reached.

CHAPTER 7

The Child in Acute Anxiety States

Treating neurotic conflicts in children is one of the major functions of the Wilder Child Guidance Clinic. One can only roughly estimate the incidence of the different kinds of neurotic conflicts the Clinic has studied during the past twenty years. In any case such an estimate probably would not reflect the distribution of childhood neurosis in the community.

Generalized neurotic inhibitions in children are comparatively common. Hysterical illness with somatic symptoms is relatively uncommon. Hysterical anxiety manifested by phobias and attacks of acute anxiety occurs with relative frequency. Few children suffer from hysterical depression, but in many more, depression is overlooked because it is masked by other symptoms. Psychosomatic illness occurs infrequently, although psychosomatic reactions to tension are frequent. Hysterical character disturbances with infantile regression are relatively common. Obsessional character problems are less frequent but occur in sizable numbers. Obsessional neurotic illness is uncommon but occurs more often in severe form than is generally assumed.

Neurotic acting out is a common form of expressing neurotic

conflict in our cases. Neurotic aggression and neurotic delinquency, because of the special problems they present in therapy, are discussed in a separate section of this book. The cases to be presented in abbreviated abstracts in this chapter illustrate the comparatively passive forms of neurotic illness in which neurotic suffering is largely internalized.

Sudden attacks of anxiety may occur at any age but are seen more frequently during the prepubertal and pubertal periods of development between ten and fifteen years of age. Children who suffer acute anxiety outbreaks usually have histories of previous periods of anxiety during difficult periods. Several such cases will be described briefly to demonstrate different clinical manifestations and treatment.

The anxiety with which Walter's acute illness began was extreme. His father had brought him to the county hospital because Walter complained of great difficulty in breathing, was gasping for air, and was convinced he was dying. Physical findings were negative, however, and he was referred to the clinic for treatment of hysteria.

Walter already had been referred to the clinic by his school principal. She reported him as a defiant adolescent whose teachers could no longer tolerate his behavior. Such a combination of aggressive sadistic behavior and severe anxiety is fairly common. The anxiety may reflect feelings of guilt at having given way to hostile aggression, or aggression may represent an attempt to act out the underlying conflict.

Walter was fourteen years old and in the seventh grade. He had average intelligence, but his schoolwork was poor because he lacked interest. He was one of several children in a home of poor standards. His father was alcoholic, a poor provider, and a severe disciplinarian. Walter's mother had died the year before, on the eighth of October, from complications following gallbladder surgery. She had suffered from repeated illnesses, many of which were functional, and had been confined to her bed for several months before she died.

During his first interview with the therapist, Walter reclined in a half-sitting position, finding it easier to breathe this way. He began the interview by saying he feared he would die on the eighth of October of that year. He explained that it was his turn to die; his mother had died on that date the year before. He said he had been suffering from abdominal and back pains and difficulty in breathing for several weeks. His mother had had similar symptoms and had been very uncomfortable for a long time before she died.

Walter was upset because he had done so little to make his mother comfortable before she died. He had refused to go on errands, and he had been noisy when she needed quiet. The therapist explained to Walter that his suffering was due to his emotions and that treatment would help him feel more comfortable if he could speak freely about all matters that disturbed him. Walter could not understand how "just talking" would help him, and the therapist explained that if he could express his sick thoughts he would realize that these thoughts were no longer dangerous.

As he was leaving after the first interview Walter asked the therapist if there was any danger that he might die during a choking spell. The therapist quietly assured him that such a danger did not exist, but Walter remained unconvinced. He listened attentively to each explanation of his symptoms the therapist gave, and he often asked for further explanations. At every interview, however, he complained of new hysterical symptoms, and the therapist's questioning invariably revealed that his mother had suffered with similar symptoms at some time during her illness.

When it was clear that Walter was not responding to assurance, the therapist told him that his fear was due to his complete identification with his mother and that because she had died he feared that he had to die. The therapist explained that Walter was afraid because he felt guilty about several things, including his mother's death. Walter replied by giving several examples of his unkindness to his mother. He followed this with an angry outburst against his father and sister. He hated his sister, who kept urging him to leave home so the others could live peacefully. He described the severe beatings his father gave him. He seemed relieved after this outburst, but his discomfort and anxiety persisted.

A few days before the eighth of October Walter complained to the therapist that his mind was a blank. He also said that recently he had awakened during the night and found that he could look straight ahead but could not turn his eyes from side to side. By this time Walter recognized that he was strongly identified with his mother, and he could see that his symptoms resembled her disoriented condition before her death and her death itself.

On the seventh of October the caseworker took Walter for a week's visit to the home of a pleasant middle-aged couple. The foster parents reported that he was uncomfortable for a day or two, but not extremely so. Following this crisis, however, Walter rapidly lost interest in continuing with therapy and, despite the therapist's efforts to convince him of his need to understand himself, withdrew from treatment.

Casework with Walter's father had proved to be fruitless. A family agency had worked with him over a period of years, but they closed the case when attempts to help him failed. He refused to encourage Walter to remain in treatment, since he saw no reason for Walter to come to the clinic. The therapist, therefore, was never able to discuss with Walter the deep hostility toward his mother that had forced him to identify with her in such a punitive way.

At the time Walter left treatment his anxiety had decreased, and he was certain that he could remain well. The family moved from the city, and the therapist did not see Walter again until four years later when he came to the clinic to ask the therapist to help him find a job. Walter had been all over the country, stopping in different states to work long enough to earn his way. The therapist learned nothing to suggest that his panic had recurred, and his emotional adjustment seemed to be good. Walter recalled the stormy period of four years earlier, and when the therapist asked him how he explained it, Walter replied, "I guess I didn't have enough to keep me busy." We may infer that his conflicts were again repressed in the manner characteristic of hysteria.

Walter's therapy consisted primarily of reassurance and clarification. The explanations he received dealt with conscious material, though some of it was just below the level of consciousness. His chance to talk about his fears made them seem less ominous. He needed to recognize that he was not responsible for hastening his mother's death; that his hostility toward his father was understandable in the light of his father's severity and alcoholism; that he really loved his mother. The more favorable evaluation of himself which he gained in therapy helped sustain him in the next four years.

Usually a child who suffers acute panic welcomes any help that promises to relieve anxiety. Occasionally, however, a child is so upset that he fears and distrusts everyone except those in his immediate family upon whom he is totally dependent. When previous treatment has involved a child's removal from home—a procedure which increases an anxious child's feeling of helplessness—his distrust may be even greater. Anxiety is useful as a warning of a dangerous situation. It loses its value as a defense when it grows so excessive that it interferes with clear thinking and acting.

Alan was a twelve-year-old, passive, dependent boy in a state of acute anxiety. He came to the clinic after he had successively feared that he had a brain tumor, meningitis, polio, and heart disease. As a child he had suffered from outbreaks of anxiety and fainting spells. He frequently complained of numbness of the extremities. According to his mother, Alan was transfixed with fear. On the day of his first clinic appointment his mother appeared in the therapist's office to explain that Alan refused to come into the building because he was afraid. Aware of Alan's suffering and extreme passivity and dependency, the therapist went out to the car, where he found Alan sobbing. Alan was frightened and ashamed of his infantile behavior, and he seemed a little angry at the therapist for coming to get him.

After a friendly greeting, the therapist explained to Alan that he had come to the car to let Alan know that he wanted to help him. The therapist added that he knew about Alan's fears and suffering and had suspected that Alan would not be happy about coming to see a new person. He explained that he would not sit by and do nothing because he knew he could help Alan overcome his fears. After a while Alan managed to answer a few questions about his home and school and then agreed to come to the therapist's office for his next appointment.

Alan's resistance at this first meeting characterized much of his attitude during the first three years of treatment. Rarely did the therapist succeed in getting Alan to talk spontaneously about his feelings or symptoms. Anything he said pertaining to his illness came only in response to questions. In spite of his discomfort, Alan would sit for long periods of time without saying a word until the therapist spoke to him.

On rare occasions when the therapist told him that he did not see how he could help Alan unless he could speak more freely, Alan talked briefly about some experience, and on one or two occasions even told a fragment of a dream. He was never able to associate to the dream, and he only looked bewildered when the therapist asked him to tell what came to his mind as he thought about the dream. All he could do was to repeat the dream fragment, adding that nothing else came to his mind. The therapist had made sure that Alan knew what kind of material he needed; he had explained the procedure repeatedly. Although Alan was unable to express his feelings freely, each time he sensed a danger that treatment might be stopped he pleaded to continue.

The caseworker worked with both parents. They were middle-aged, hard-working people, deeply religious, with practically no social outlets except family and church activities. There was little real demonstration of affection among members of the family, rarely any expression of anger, and no discussion of sex. The characteristic family pattern was one of suppression of affect. Alan's father, mother, older brother, and sister were shy, clannish, and weighted down by feelings of inadequacy. All the children had at some time suffered emotional upsets, although none were as serious as Alan's. Both parents tried hard to involve themselves in casework treatment, but neither was able to express his feelings. Each parent had suffered from neurotic anxiety sometime in earlier life. The mother had endured several episodes of hysterical depression, and, like Alan, had feared death. When the caseworker recognized that these parents needed their defenses against expressing feeling, she used her interviews mainly to learn more about Alan's behavior and his responses to therapy.

Alan had been having considerable difficulty at school before coming to the clinic for treatment. He refused to recite because of shyness, even when he knew the answers. The caseworker interviewed Alan's counselor and arranged to have Alan excused from reciting unless he volunteered. Each year the worker had to make the same request after Alan told the therapist that he was still too tense to respond when asked to recite.

After three years of supportive therapy Alan was a strongly built adolescent with a nice sense of humor, attending high school regularly and in most instances enjoying his schoolwork. He played football, baseball, and hockey, though he was not a member of a team. He had lost much of his fear of organic disease. His fear of insanity, which he had admitted during the course of therapy, had lessened. Although Alan continued to be dependent on his family and home, his parents appeared quite content with the progress he had made. They recognized his inability to be outgoing socially, but they excused it as a characteristic family trait.

The therapist had evidence that treatment had strengthened Alan's ego and that at the end of treatment he felt more adequate and better prepared to enjoy life. On several occasions when the staff had discussed stopping treatment because of Alan's failure to involve himself in the therapy, they concluded that he badly needed the support the therapist was providing. Since Alan was receiving no other form of treatment, it was imperative to continue with supportive therapy until his emotional dependency on the therapist lessened.

The therapist tried many times during treatment to inject a discussion of Alan's known hostility to his father. He tried also to get Alan to discuss his interest in the opposite sex. In each case the subjects were discussed briefly, and then Alan dropped them. That Alan did not appear upset by these attempted probes suggests that he felt sure his right to withhold material would be respected.

Alan's treatment was terminated when he felt capable of finishing high school with less discomfort, had few attacks of anxiety, and improved his social life. After graduating from high school Alan entered the university. He dropped out of school when he found the work too difficult and took a job in a retail store. He came in to see his therapist occasionally and seemed to be getting along quite well, although his life was rather restricted, and he had only one or two close friends.

*One evening about four years after the study was terminated Alan called his therapist in great anxiety, to report that his leg had suddenly become paralyzed, although only for a few minutes, and that he was very much afraid he was going to have another convulsion similar to those he had before he first came in for study. He said that, during the study, his great concern had been that he might have another convulsion, although he had had none then nor in the years that followed. He had completely lost his fear until the incident which prompted the telephone call. He was invited to return to the clinic, and the therapist had a series of interviews with him. Alan spoke freely during these interviews, and the material suggested a relationship between the convulsions and his sexual conflict. He agreed that his fear of epilepsy would decrease if he had a complete neurological examination and special laboratory studies, but when, for good reasons, he was unable to keep his appointment for the examination, he made no effort to arrange for another one. He told his therapist later that he had been relieved by his statement that the fear was based on emotional causes. During the weeks and months that followed, Alan's fear lessened and eventually disappeared. He now plans to return to college to enter the professional school he had

* The asterisk here and throughout the book signifies follow-up material from contact with the patient or the parents prior to the second edition.

hoped to enter before. He had been advised at the university at that time not to do so, because there was question of his ability to do well in that profession. The possibility of a recurrence of his anxiety and perhaps panic later on persists because the conflict remains in the unconscious, where it has again been repressed.

To confine treatment to measures of support and reassurance in cases where insight therapy might produce lasting results is difficult for an analytically trained therapist. When situations of this nature present themselves in a psychiatric clinic for children, however, one must gracefully accept the limitations imposed by the child's defensive needs.

Walter and Alan resemble each other in their unreadiness for insight therapy. Walter was seeking immediate relief from a tormenting fear. When his anxiety was no longer warranted, he felt capable of dealing with his life problems without help. Alan was aware of his need for insight but was not ready or able to accept it. His fear of uncovering the basis of his conflicts kept him content when he was free of terrifying symptoms. He knew his vulnerability, but he wanted to leave well enough alone and chance the future. He was confident that he could continue to depend on his mother, especially if his symptoms again developed.

The next three children to be discussed also suffered from attacks of acute neurotic anxiety, but, unlike Walter and Alan, they were eager to understand what caused their suffering. Their participation in therapy was more intelligent, since they realized that their future emotional welfare depended on their uncovering factors responsible for their attacks of anxiety.

Jean, an eleven-year-old girl, became agitated by tormenting thoughts and wishes and was unable to fall asleep unless she could talk them through with her mother. When these nightly talks became increasingly prolonged and Jean began to demand the attention of both parents to lessen her anxiety, she was accepted for treatment. The parents were alarmed by Jean's need to tell them every one of her dissocial thoughts. Many times she awakened during the night and returned to her parents' bedroom to discuss new disturbing thoughts. Both parents were extremely tolerant of these intrusions and showed great patience in answering her many questions.

Jean was sexually preoccupied and frankly discussed her sexual fantasies with her parents. She was perfectionistic, overly neat and clean, and washed her hands frequently. She worried about the way children felt toward her, though she was always well liked by other children and liked them. She showed an early interest in the birth process, and the parents always answered her questions frankly. The parents had always been demonstrative with Jean, especially her father, who was an overdemonstrative person.

Jean was a pretty girl. Shy and reticent at first, she quickly became friendly as she answered questions about school and her friends. The therapist told her he knew that she was worried about several things and asked if she wanted to tell him about her worries. She smiled warmly and proceeded to talk at great length. She spoke freely about her fears, and the therapist told her that her frankness would help him to understand her.

The therapist encouraged Jean to talk about her dreams, which were frequent. Her dreams were highly symbolic and rich in content, but the therapist did not discuss them until he felt that Jean could discuss any subject without becoming overanxious. When she began to talk about the thoughts her dreams stimulated, he watched her reactions carefully and saw that discussing them disturbed her no more than her previous discussion of significant conflicts.

Several of her dreams concerned her being in bathrooms or trying to get into them while other people were there. These dreams led her to discuss the exhibitionistic and peeping tendencies which she had had for several years. She had been aggressive in examining other girls and boys, and she had taken the lead in involving other children in sexual play. Jean spoke about these matters in a hesitant way, largely in response to questions.

Jean had been talking so rapidly and under such pressure that the therapist had allowed her to discuss the kind of material which might have produced even greater anxiety. He had permitted her outpouring because it was similar to what she had told her parents. These thoughts were conscious, and it seemed safe to allow her to express them. Jean had included her father in many of her dreams in a way which left no doubt that he was a strong factor in the production of her sexual fantasies. When she later included the therapist in her fantasies as a sexual attacker, it appeared that the free discussion of sex at the clinic was overstimulating her sexually and threatening her. Despite the fact that casework interviews with Jean's mother failed to indicate that Jean was becoming more seriously disturbed, the discussion of dream material was stopped and the therapist confined his interviews to discussing Jean's relationship to her family, school, and friends. After about three months of interviews Jean grew less tense and anxious at home, her need to talk to her mother lessened, and she went to sleep several nights without stopping to talk to her parents except to say goodnight. As her anxiety lessened the interviews became less frequent, and after about four months of therapy she asked to stop coming in.

The caseworker saw both parents once a week and had many telephone interviews with them during periods of acute disturbance. Both parents were concerned from the outset that Jean was developing a psychosis. Her father, a traveling man, was so concerned about psychosis that he often returned prematurely from a trip because of his anxiety about Jean. Her mother sensed that Jean was punishing her through her illness, forcing her to confine her social life to the home and Jean. The caseworker discussed ways in which both parents could continue with their social life without disturbing Jean too much, though not until Jean's acute anxiety had lessened.

The caseworker was able to lessen the anxiety of both parents by discussing in some detail situations which caused their greatest concern and embarrassment. She advised the father, who was avoiding his relatives because of Jean's illness, to speak frankly to them about Jean's acute disturbance as an adolescent phase which she would overcome. If he could stop thinking of Jean's illness as the beginning of mental illness, he could convince his family of this fact. The worker agreed with the parents that Jean's sexual interests were exaggerated but explained that this was not uncommon in disturbed adolescent girls seen at the clinic. The interest of these other girls in sex lessened after a year or two, and so would Jean's. The worker was not certain of such a favorable prognosis, but she was certain that the lessening of her parents' anxiety was needed before Jean could be less anxious.

When the family moved from the city soon after, the caseworker kept in touch with Jean's mother by mail and learned that Jean was getting along fairly well. She enjoyed her schoolwork and had new friends. Every once in a while for a few evenings Jean would come to the mother's bed and have to report her thoughts. The parents offered her an opportunity to see a therapist, but Jean told them this was unnecessary and that she could get along without help.

In treating Jean, the therapist attempted to offer her a cathartic outlet for her disturbing fantasies. Even though she had told these same fantasies to her parents, she needed to discuss her thoughts with someone less anxious than her parents, one who could deal with her thoughts objectively. Jean learned in therapy that her fantasies were safe and that she was in little danger of acting them out. The therapist explained to her that some of her present disturbing wishes represented earlier childhood cravings which would give her little satisfaction now. He assured her that the anxiety she was having at night and her need to report everything to her parents would lessen and disappear.

*Four years after the study, Jean finished high school with a B average and enrolled in a state university, after working during the summer to earn part of her college expenses. She is still hypersensitive and tends to worry, but not excessively. She eats and sleeps well, and at no time has she had a recurrence of the severe anxiety and panic she suffered when she came to the clinic. She has many friends, does some dating, is interested in athletics, and has considered studying to become a social worker. She still confides much to her mother, who describes her as a kind and thoughtful girl.

One of the chief problems confronting the staff in Jean's case was the difficulty in establishing a clinical diagnosis. The picture was very much like those of other adolescents with acute panic at failure to master instinctual drives. Jean, however, was more aggressive than the others. She had acted out sexually without any evidence of guilt about sex. Younger children tend to act out aggression during the day and suffer anxiety during the night, but such a pattern is infrequent in neurotic adolescents struggling with their sexual drives. Their acute anxiety is accompanied by sexual inhibition and a withdrawal from sexual activity and interest.

However, the most varied reactions occur during the preadolescent period when the ego struggles desperately to regain the state of equilibrium enjoyed during the period of latency. The ego mobilizes the many forms of defense, among them repression, sublimation, reaction formation, and acting out.[1] The activity of the superego increases, so that anxiety and suffering mount. Often the picture which results is difficult to differentiate from a beginning psychosis, and in some instances, as in the case of Jean, the final diagnostic evaluation must wait until the pubertal period has passed.

Jean's reaction to describing disturbing material raises the question of how much sexual material can safely be discussed with neurotic youngsters. In general, the therapist, in keeping with his tendency to allow children to choose subjects for discussion, waits for them to introduce the sexual theme. Some reference of the child to a quarrel with a boy friend or to false accusations made by the parents when a girl has stayed out too late at night usually begins it. At times children indicate in many ways that they are concerned about sexual matters, but they are too inhibited to intro-

[1] Freud, Anna, "The Ego and the Mechanisms of Defense," London, Hogarth Press, Ltd., 1937.

duce the subject. When a child comes to the clinic because of anxiety that can stem only from sexual conflict and he avoids the subject for a long time, the therapist finds a way to help the child discuss sexual matters.

Sexual matters are not discussed routinely with neurotic children. The causes of sexual conflicts responsible for neurotic suffering are deeply repressed and, with few exceptions, will not be uncovered by methods of therapy used in child-guidance clinics. Sexual problems are discussed when the child is confused or upset by conscious sexual wishes, misunderstandings, and fears. Discussion clarifies the child's thinking, relieves anxiety, and eliminates unnecessary fear.

The danger of introducing a discussion of sex with children who are neurotically conflicted, however, has been exaggerated. The procedure is safe when the usual precautions in dealing with emotional material are observed. Occasionally, however, a child becomes acutely disturbed by a discussion of sex in spite of all the precautions that are taken. A preadolescent boy, after several months of interviews, indicated a strong interest in examining feminine undergarments on clotheslines. He told about having stolen a few of these garments, and he appeared ready to talk about sexual matters. The therapist thought it was important to discuss sex with him, since there was the danger of his being caught stealing. The therapist knew that this boy had a real sexual problem, from the history given by the mother. He had been discovered by the parents in the act of masturbating on two occasions and had been punished. After a general discussion of sexual matters, the therapist referred to the subject of masturbation. At the mere mention of the word masturbation, the boy became acutely anxious. He was angry and accused the therapist of taking away his chance of getting well. He would never be able to come to the clinic again. Such a violent reaction was unexpected and is the only instance of this kind in the author's clinical experience.

Another reaction of a somewhat similar nature occurred in a fifteen-year-old boy with marked phobias. He was seen three times a week for several months, when he began to discuss hostile death wishes against his father. The hostility grew in intensity, and it appeared that rapid strides were being made toward working through an important conflict. As this was happening, however, it became evident that the patient was developing a traumatic reaction. He was grimacing excessively, raising his voice to a high pitch, and laughing inappropriately. It was obvious that his ego could not tolerate his recognizing such hostility toward his father, whom he loved and upon whom he was dependent. The technic of treatment was immediately changed. The patient was told that the hostility toward his father was exaggerated. He was reminded of the many positive statements he had previously made about his father, which were evidence to the therapist that he loved his father dearly. The boy was noticeably relieved by this discussion, and in a few days the acute reaction subsided and the picture changed.

There are few set rules to guide a therapist for all cases of acute neurotic suffering in children. Treatment must always proceed cautiously, assessing the ego reactions at all times. The responses of the child to all discussions are observed by the therapist during the interviews and by the parents between interviews.

Eileen, a gentle, soft-spoken, pretty adolescent girl, thirteen years old, asked of her own accord for help because of a sudden panicky fear of death. She was very bright, an excellent student, well liked by boys and girls, and previous to this outbreak of panic had been a gay, lively girl. One night she was seized suddenly by a fear that something terrible was happening to her and that she would die as a result. She had tried desperately to figure out what she feared and what precipitated the fear but had failed. Her married sister, who had previously been at the clinic, suggested that Eileen come to the clinic.

A few weeks before Eileen's illness her mother had remarried. Remarriage was forbidden by the church to which Eileen and her family belonged, since her father, who had been mentally ill for over ten years, was still living. The mother, however, considered him dead, and felt free to remarry. Eileen, a devout girl, could not share her mother's feelings in this matter, though she tried. She was strongly dependent on her mother, and she hated her step-father for throwing her into a state of religious conflict.

Eileen disclosed these facts in the first few interviews. She quickly developed a strong positive relationship to her therapist and was hopeful of discovering the cause of her dreadful symptom. She reported frequent dreams, many of them involving anxiety, and the therapist used the dream material to stimulate discussion of anxiety material. He discovered that Eileen was associating freely to elements of the dream. The following significant conflicts came to light during treatment, largely through the use of dream analysis.

Eileen had mixed feelings about her mother. She had been aware for some time that her mother was sexually promiscuous but refused to believe that her mother would be disloyal. Her mother had told Eileen that in the eyes of the church her father was dead, and Eileen had learned that this was not so. Her resentment mounted, she felt hostile to her mother, and she felt she was alone in the world. She ceased to care whether she lived or not and developed a wish to die, along with a fear of dying.

During therapy she became conscious of deep death wishes toward her father. If he died, her mother's marriage would be blessed and they could live together in peace on earth and later in heaven. The wish that her father might die seemed less terrible to her when through her interviews she recognized the reasons for it.

She realized that she had a strong sexual attachment to her stepfather and had felt very close to him until he married her mother. She then began to hate him violently and to wish he would die. Her mother's marriage would then dissolve and she would again have her mother for herself.

As Eileen understood these conflicts she became more comfortable. On two occasions she suffered milder attacks of panic, but after ten months of treatment her fear of death disappeared and she remained well. A follow-up study two years later revealed that she had suffered no recurrence of hysterical anxiety. Six years later a relative who brought her own child to the clinic for study reported that Eileen was very well and had been working for two years after completing high school.

Treatment in this case was limited to Eileen. She had been accepted for study on an emergency basis because of her extreme panic, and her mother had not been seen. She responded so well to early treatment without the mother's participation that the staff decided to continue in this way. Eileen's treatment consisted largely of insight therapy. The strong positive relationship to the therapist, whom she accepted as a good father figure, facilitated therapy.

Anna Freud [2] has drawn a clear picture of the defenses set up by the ego during the period just before puberty in the development of boys. All the methods of defense learned by the child come to his aid during this period when the sexual instincts develop rapidly and demand expression. The ego's strength is taxed, and its other responsibilities suffer. The ego is in danger of being overrun by the instincts, and anxiety develops. When the danger is great, states of panic develop. Two methods of defense which occasionally occur during the pubertal period are intellectualization and the ascetic reaction. Both these defenses were used to some extent by the adolescent boy whom we shall call Carl, who became acutely disturbed by neurotic conflict.

Carl was thirteen years old when his study began. He had become panicky one evening when an older sister used perfume and lipstick. He had opposed his mother's use of cosmetics for several years, but suddenly their use severely upset him. He cried and sobbed all night. The next day he appealed to his minister at a Luther League meeting to urge his sister, who had previously been a member of the League, to stop the use of cosmetics. Recognizing the neurotic nature of Carl's upset, the minister suggested a clinic study to the parents.

In his early interviews Carl avoided any discussion of his particular symptom. He confined his remarks to his work in school and his interest in natural phenomena. He and his father enjoyed dis-

[2] Freud, Anna, "The Ego and the Mechanisms of Defense," *ibid.*

cussing philosophy, and Carl was especially pleased that his sister was not included in these discussions. When an opportunity arose to talk about Carl's anxiety, the therapist explained the function of the clinic in lessening anxiety in children who were conflicted. He told Carl that many of his remarks suggested he was suffering from a good deal of anxiety, and that his parents had told the caseworker about some of the things that bothered Carl. Carl listened attentively, but he did not refer to his problem during that interview.

Carl began his next interview, however, by telling the therapist that some of the boys in his church group enjoyed talking about "dirty" subjects. They would tell each other off-color stories and had tried to interest him. They knew that he was strongly opposed to such stories, and yet they repeatedly asked him if he would join them in their fun. He became upset now whenever he saw them collect in groups, and he had almost decided to stay away from the group meetings, but he was deeply religious and enjoyed discussions with the more serious members of the group. He knew also that he could not escape such boys, since the boys in his neighborhood and at public school behaved the same way. Carl, who was very bright, suggested that there was something wrong in his point of view, since he was so outnumbered by boys who were interested in sex. The therapist agreed with Carl that his attitude was unusual, since it caused him emotional suffering. He explained that there must be reasons for Carl to feel as he did about sexual matters, and that the interviews would help the therapist and Carl understand his overreacting to the boys' interest in sex.

The therapist explained to Carl that some of the causes of his concern were in a part of his mind of which he was entirely unaware. He briefly described the nature of the unconscious mind and explained in a simple manner how reaction formation develops as a defense. He told Carl that dreams often contain clues to the underlying causes of conflicts, and he suggested that if Carl dreamed he try to remember them and report them in the interviews. Carl's dreams interested him as an intellectual exercise at first, then as they began to contain frank sexual material he was surprised and concerned. The therapist discussed pubertal development from a physiologic and psychologic point of view and helped Carl to recognize that his sexual interests were a part of normal development. Carl agreed that sex was a normal part of life, but insisted that it was not for him. He remained firm in his decision to stay away from boys who were sexually preoccupied.

Shortly after the use of dreams in therapy began, Carl told the therapist about his distaste for perfume and cosmetics. He described one dream in which a boy he saw at school was wearing cosmetics. Dangerous situations appeared in this dream, and Carl referred to these, but he said nothing of the boy with the cosmetics. The therapist recognized that the boy in the dream reflected Carl's anxiety problem, but he made no attempt to discuss this with him. The therapist also suspected that Carl was expressing a relationship between sexuality and castration anxiety. The cosmetics used by his sister and mother apparently had stirred up a strong sexual wish in him. Early in life Carl must have been conditioned to believe that an interest in sex was dangerous. The dream demonstrated that the danger consisted of changing a boy into a girl. Since such a danger had to be avoided at all costs, the most effective defense Carl's ego could adopt was to repress his sexual interests. To guarantee that the repression was maintained, Carl developed a reaction formation so that he overreacted to anything which stimulated a sexual interest. While he could consciously deny sexual wishes, unconsciously his ego recognized their presence and developed the neurotic symptoms as a defense.

It is difficult to think of acute neurotic suffering as a defense. Its defensive nature here can be understood only when Carl's present suffering is compared to the unconsciously recognized danger of castration which he would suffer if his incestuous sexual wishes were expressed. His sister's and his mother's use of cosmetics, therefore, precipitated the reaction of panic.

The therapist explained to Carl that he probably learned early in life that sexual interests were frowned upon in his home. He very likely had indicated a lively interest in sex and may have had an unfortunate experience or series of experiences ending in his rejection of sex. How or why this happened the therapist did not know, he explained, but he was sure that something like this had happened. He told Carl that he would have to accept the fact that sexual interests were neither reprehensible nor dangerous, unless the social laws pertaining to sex were involved. Sex was a normal part of life; without it, animal life could not exist.

Carl was impressed by this discussion. He was apologetic as he told the therapist that he still felt sex was dangerous. As the interviews continued, however, the therapist saw that Carl was less troubled by the fact that his friends were sexually preoccupied. He mixed more with them, and he was less contemptuous of them. His parents reported that Carl was more carefree and less tense. Although he was still unwilling to tolerate his mother's use of cosmetics, his family sensed that he would soon find even this acceptable.

During his next few interviews Carl admitted that he had had sexual thoughts and wishes for some time. He refused to accept these thoughts and spoke of them as fantasies over which he had no control. His manner of speaking about sexual fantasies, however, was decidely different from his behavior when treatment began. He was more tolerant and less self-condemning of his interest in sex. The therapist assured Carl that as he became more secure, he would feel less threatened by sexual thoughts, aware of the fact that he was strong enough to master his sexual impulses. Carl was now more relaxed in the interviews and occasionally even humorous. The panic state of his illness had disappeared.

Casework with Carl's parents did not add much to the therapy because of their resistance to involving themselves in treatment. The mother had suffered from gallbladder disease and had difficulty in getting to the clinic. The father did not want to come in to discuss himself, although he was willing to talk about Carl. Both parents had for some time felt closer to their daughter than to

Carl whom they could not understand. The worker emphasized Carl's assets and impressed the parents with the therapist's high evaluation of Carl.

Reference was made to Carl's ascetic defense. This consisted of a marked preoccupation with religion and an avoidance of opportunity for pleasure when it interfered with religious observances. It was clear that his religious fanaticism was helping him to control his deep sexual urges. His minister had recognized that Carl's religious interests were overcompensatory. He was pleased when later Carl's attitude toward religion was a sounder one.

*Four years after the study Carl had improved considerably. He entered a college in California, planning to major in philosophy. His intense interest in religion decreased, and he became genuinely interested in a girl, to the surprise of his parents. He had learned to get along better with boys and girls. In recent months his ability to keep up his very high grades at school lessened, and the parents were concerned about this. Carl discussed his problems with his counselor at the college, and they agreed that he should have additional psychotherapy. He was referred to a psychiatrist at the university.

CHAPTER 8

The Child with School Phobia

Closely resembling acute panic states is a clinical condition which has been called "school phobia." The term itself refers to a state of acute anxiety about going to school, and the word "phobia" suggests a localized or circumscribed anxiety related to school attendance. Usually, however, a child who dreads going to school has anxiety about other activities. School phobia is common among children studied in the child-guidance clinic. The condition usually appears suddenly and dramatically in youngsters who seem to have been making a good school and life adjustment at the time. The following is a typical example:

Anne, an attractive twelve-year-old girl, very bright, popular in her class, outgoing and fun-loving, one evening informed her parents that she did not feel able to go to school. She was afraid to go but didn't know why she was afraid. She had been uncomfortable in her classes for several days, had been unable to concentrate on her studies, and was dizzy and nauseated at school.

Her parents reacted in a manner typical of parents of children with school phobia. They discussed with Anne the happenings of the past few days in school and asked about the subject matter, her teachers, and her schoolmates. They tried to learn something about her recent social life, especially to discover any unfortunate emotional experience. When they found nothing to explain why Anne should have a dread of school, they suspected that she was withholding facts from them.

The next morning when it was time for Anne to leave for school, her parents became anxious. Her father was annoyed by what he termed "nonsense"; there was nothing to fear. Anne admitted as much. He had to go to work. He became angry as Anne started to cry, and he insisted that she put on her wraps and come along with him to school. When the mother acted as though she felt he was doing the wrong thing, he became more annoyed; the mother's behavior increased his doubts about what he was doing. Realizing that this was no time to change his mind, however, since that would only confuse Anne more, he got into the car with her. Anne cried all the way to school, saying she knew she could not make it. Her father assured her she would get along well as soon as she was at her desk with all her friends around her. Anne and her father walked up the school steps, but as they approached the entrance Anne grew pale and vomited. Realizing that he had made a mistake, her father returned home with her.

Anne remained at home that day feeling miserable. Her mother tried to cheer her, assuring her that her feeling must be a part of some acute illness that would soon pass, but Anne knew better. She was certain this was not a physical illness; that it had something to do with her deep feelings. She felt tense, upset, and worried. What bothered her most was that she hadn't the slightest idea of what was frightening her, and yet she knew that something must have produced such a sudden change in the way she felt. She had no interest in play, in prospective parties, in the many things that had meant so much to her before. She felt that this change in her would remain for a long time and that she had lost her grip on things.

Her parents called the family doctor, who examined her but failed to find anything to explain Anne's peculiar behavior. He thought perhaps Anne's oncoming puberty partially explained her emotional upset, but he did not think it enough to account for the change. He suggested a more complete physical check-up and, if that failed to show any pathologic circumstances and Anne's behavior persisted, a psychiatric consultation. The parents were alarmed by the suggestion that Anne see a psychiatrist, until their doctor assured them he did not think that Anne was having a "nervous breakdown." He discussed the role of the psychiatrist in the treatment of functional illness, and the parents agreed to refer Anne to the child-guidance clinic for treatment.

Anne's parents were more considerate than most parents of children with a school phobia. Usually, driven by their anxiety, parents first urge their child to go back to school, beg him, then try to bribe him with gifts. When these methods fail they often resort to punishment, in the belief that the child is being willful and stubborn. When parents become panicky about the child's not going to school, their anxiety intensifies the child's suffering. By the time they bring the child to a clinic on the advice of the school or school social worker, the child feels ashamed of his helplessness and guilty about the anxiety he has caused his parents. Absence from school has made him feel that he is behind in his schoolwork and will never be able to catch up with his classmates. In bringing their child to the clinic the parents are primarily interested in getting him back to school and less concerned about the child's emotional illness. They feel that his return to school will start the recovery which will develop on its own momentum.

The caseworker's treatment of the parents in the first interview sets the stage for future therapy. She informs them that the clinic staff is as eager as they to get the child back to school and will do what it can to accomplish his return. She emphasizes, however, that the staff is not interested in having the child in school before he is emotionally ready to be there, the staff having learned that returning such a child too soon always fails and intensifies his feeling of failure. The caseworker encourages the parents to turn over to the staff the responsibility for getting their child back to school, hoping to lessen their anxiety so that they can give up their ill-advised methods with the child. The parents, having been unsuccessful in their own attempts, are likely to accept this proposal, but rarely are they able to avoid some form of persuasion or criticism. Most parents finally yield during the course of casework therapy as they begin to realize that their methods are harming their relationship to their child.

For many reasons related to their own deep anxiety or their unresolved hostility to the child, neurotically conflicted mothers are unable to modify their ways of dealing with a child who continues to be unable to go to school. A mother who is dependent on her child for satisfying her emotional needs may suffer anxiety each time the child leaves for school. She may fear the loss of the child's love as he becomes attached to his teacher, or that a danger may befall him on the way or at school. The child quickly senses his mother's anxiety and he becomes anxious and begins to fear going to school. Casework therapy is directed toward solving these problems in the mother; if casework fails to change her attitude, more intensive psychotherapy is required.

All children with school phobia suffer from neurotic illness. Certain factors, however, must be present to explain why the child's inability to go to school is such an important part of the manifestation of the neurosis.

School attendance requires the child to leave home and his mother. Often he must leave his mother alone with a feared rival for her affection, perhaps a newly born brother or sister. The child may fear that his mother is in danger of being attacked by an alcoholic father who has been brutal; by a father with whom the mother frequently quarrels; or by a fantasied attacker. The child's fear of the mother's being attacked probably stems from an unconscious awareness of sexual activity between the parents.

The child may fear danger in going to or from school from a threatening bully or a sexually menacing boy. He may fear that a boy or girl may arouse sexual longings that produce guilt. He may be afraid of animals. The loss to a rival of a friend on whom the child has developed a dependent love relationship, or the shame of going to school with a mentally retarded sibling or one who has earned a poor reputation in school, may sufficiently disturb a sensitive child to make him want to avoid confronting his school-mates.

Difficulties in the school itself may upset the child enough to make him dread it. A strict or complaining teacher, a seriously conflicted teacher, an undisciplined class, poor achievement in school work, real or fancied problems associated with going to the toilet are some of the factors frequently mentioned by children with school phobia. A shy or withdrawn child may find reciting extremely upsetting. The child who works slowly may be threatened by a teacher who demands speedy performance. A child may fear failure, especially failure to satisfy demands of a parent to achieve beyond his capacity.

Any of these factors may make going to school painful or frightening for a child. Often the child recognizes these precipitating factors and reports them in his interviews with the therapist, although he may be too embarrassed to discuss some of them. In such cases he may invent reasons for not being able to go to school if he feels threatened by the fact that he cannot really explain his dread of school. A combination of precipitating causes may contribute to any particular child's inability to go to school. Any one of the causes enumerated, however, may operate in a child without producing a school phobia. Other factors responsible for production of neurosis in a child also must be present. The occurrence of one of the precipitating factors at a time when a child is especially vulnerable may determine whether or not a school phobia will develop.

In the general population of the child-guidance clinic, boys outnumber girls from two to one to five to one. In the case of school phobia, however, more girls than boys appear among the cases.[1] Some form of psychosomatic symptom is usually associated with school phobia. The most frequent complaint is abdominal

---

[1] Klein, Emanuel, The Reluctance to Go to School, in "The Psychoanalytic Study of the Child," vol. I, 1945, p. 263.

pain which may be accompanied by vomiting and dizziness. These symptoms usually disappear on days when the child is not required to go to school. School phobia may appear after an acute illness which need not be severe. The regression which is associated with illness is often enough to upset the child's emotional balance. The child who unconsciously needs to be at home with his mother has found that during the course of this acute illness he has had his mother largely for himself. When he has longed for this, the illness may so condition him that he cannot give it up. Strongly competitive children are often threatened by having missed a few days of school, fearing that their competitors have gained an advantage over them.

Treatment

As in other forms of neurotic illness, school phobia may represent a comparatively simple conditioning in which the precipitating factor owes its strength to special conditions. When this is the case, once the precipitating factor is recognized and eliminated, the school phobia may promptly disappear. The ego of such a child is relatively strong, and the difficult reality situation does not produce serious regression.

Anne, for example, who was mentioned earlier, had only four clinic interviews before her father removed her from treatment. He objected to the clinic's plan for long-time therapy, and said that he was not concerned about Anne's emotional health since she had always been so well. He wanted her back in school, and he thought he could find some quicker way of managing her return. Disregarding the caseworker's reminder of Anne's previous reaction when he tried to force her to go to school, he arranged to have the family doctor talk to Anne, give her some medicine to strengthen her, and return her to school. The caseworker acknowledged the father's right to use his own methods, and Anne was withdrawn from clinic treatment.

Later the referring doctor told the therapist that the father had insisted he give Anne some medicine to "strengthen her nerves" and assure her she would be better off if she returned to school. The doctor saw no other alternative and advised Anne to return to school even though it would be difficult for a while. Anne went back to school, was attending regularly and seemed to be getting along well. Psychological tests at the clinic had shown Anne to have very superior intelligence, and her achievements were correspondingly high.

The family doctor, who felt it unfortunate that Anne had lost the chance to discover what caused her acute neurotic illness, kept in touch with the therapist. Anne apparently regained her emotional health and continued to do well in high school and college. She married, had children, and from all reports has made a good emotional adjustment.

Anne's attack of school phobia may have been a transient neurotic episode which cleared up in a short time because of Anne's strong, relatively mature ego. Her defenses enabled her to deal adequately with whatever situations precipitated the illness. Anne's history prior to the development of the school phobia contained fewer evidences of emotional disturbance than were present in the more long-standing cases known to the clinic. Another possibility must be kept in mind; in spite of the fact that Anne seems to have made a good emotional adjustment, one would have to know her intimately to be certain that she has not been suffering from less obvious forms of neurotic conflict.

Darryl came to the clinic when he was ten years old for treatment of a school phobia. A few months before, Darryl had had a severe headache at school and was unable to concentrate on his work. His teacher, whose gruffness he feared, was annoyed with him and shook him in the presence of the other children, while accusing him of making no effort to do his arithmetic. When he got home that day he had a fever, and he was in bed for a week. When his illness subsided he dreaded the idea of going to school, and the thought of returning produced abdominal pains. He complained about his math teacher especially, but the others were difficult, also, he said.

Both parents were sensitive and withdrawn and had a limited social life. According to the mother, the father was a kind and gentle person who cried easily if anything went wrong with her or the children. Since the father's family had a history of psychosis, he was badly frightened by Darryl's refusal to go to school. The caseworker quickly assured him that Darryl's illness bore no relationship to psychosis, and the father was visibly relieved.

Darryl had always been a very shy child. His mother told the worker that if, on returning home from school, Darryl saw a car parked outside and knew the family had visitors, he would stay outside, close to the house. The mother explained that he came by this behavior honestly, since she had behaved in the same way as a child. Darryl's history contained several indications of acute neurotic episodes. Because Darryl had been unable to return to school for several months the previous year, he had failed and was repeating the fourth grade. The family was certain that a change of school would solve the problem, but Darryl was happy at his new school only a few weeks before the symptom of school phobia returned.

After a few interviews Darryl grew quite fond of his therapist and looked forward to visiting him. The therapist told him he might feel better if he could get to school for at least part of the day. He explained that although he might be uncomfortable at school, his feeling of accomplishment would make up for this discomfort, that he would feel stronger, and that this strength would eventually help him to get back to school. The therapist told Darryl that he would continue to work with him and arrange for help with his schoolwork if he needed it. Darryl was certain that he could return for a part of the day. His conviction that he could get back to school persisted over the week end until Sunday night when, according to his mother, he paced back and forth, declaring it was just impossible for him to return to school. On Monday morning he was ashamed to return to the therapist and admit failure. He had a severe headache on his way to the clinic and almost vomited in front of the building. The therapist admitted to Darryl that he had made a mistake and misjudged his progress. He decided that a longer period of therapy would be required before Darryl would be strong enough to venture returning to school.

Treatment interviews with Darryl continued for about two months. He talked a good deal about school, his home, and his early life experiences. He dreamed frequently and recited these dreams. He talked about an interest in playing with doll clothes and doll houses and of his need to hide them whenever any boys came to his house.

Because Darryl was so afraid of the possibility of failing at school again, the staff felt that he would develop more ego strength by being tutored in his schoolwork. Darryl was happy at this suggestion and came to see the tutor three times a week for a period of several months. The tutor was an excellent teacher but was neither trained nor interested in dealing with emotional problems, and the therapist continued to see Darryl from time to time. The next fall, when school began, Darryl was prepared to return, felt confident in his ability to compete with the others in his class, and got along very well.

Four years later, however, the father brought Darryl back to the clinic and wept as he reported that Darryl's trouble had returned. Darryl's mother had been severely ill and the family had been worried about her. Darryl became increasingly uncomfortable, was unable to concentrate on his schoolwork, and lost interest in going to school. When he tried to do his homework his pencil fell out of his hand several times and he threw it away in disgust. Actually, Darryl was suffering an attack of acute chorea (St. Vitus' Dance). The parents were directed to their doctor. Darryl was confined to his bed for several months, recovered fully and returned to school.

The clinic received reports from Darryl's parents for several years. His acute neurotic illness did not return.

Doris, a bright eleven-year-old girl, who lived with her widowed mother, developed a school phobia following an attack of flu that had kept her home a week. She remained out of school for two

months before vacation began. She returned to school in the fall
for a few days, but withdrew because of a recurrence of the school
phobia. Doris and her mother lived in a small apartment. The
mother, who had always been a passive, dependent woman, clung
to Doris for emotional support. She tried to do most of the planning and thinking for Doris and allowed Doris to dominate and
control her in return. Doris seemed to enjoy the attachment, but
the therapist saw considerable evidence that she resented the
binding tie. This symbiotic relationship between Doris and her
mother was reflected in the mother's complaint when she referred
Doris to the clinic, "We won't go to school."

The mother was in therapy with a psychiatrist who had recommended that she bring Doris to the clinic. He told the caseworker
that the mother resisted the study and felt ashamed of her inability to deal with the problem. He felt that the mother was
afraid that treatment would lessen Doris's dependency on her.
He had been trying to lessen the strength of this tie for some time
but had been unsuccessful. When the school social worker visited
the home, the mother told her she was sure that Doris would
have nothing to do with the child-guidance clinic. After several
interviews with Doris and the mother, the school social worker
told the mother frankly that Doris was prepared for the study
and that it was the mother who was blocking it. Doris came to
the clinic a few days later.

She was reticent at first in her interviews with the therapist. She
cried frequently as she talked about her dread of school and about
the death of her father, to whom she had been strongly attached.
After a short series of interviews the therapist asked Doris if she
would like to try getting to school for just a short time, perhaps
only going to the principal's office for a half hour or so and then
returning home. He suggested that this might make her feel less
fearful of school and help her eventually to return. Doris at first
was shocked by the suggestion, but then said she would like to
try going back for a short while. The mother expressed a strong
interest in this early attempt to get Doris to return to school but

Doris failed to get there. The mother's unconscious need to keep Doris at home successfully interfered with her conscious plans to have Doris return to school. On three mornings the mother overslept; another time the mother had an important errand and Doris had to go along with her; once the mother had to take Doris to the dentist. Casework with Doris's mother was limited, since she was in therapy with a psychiatrist. The caseworker kept in close contact with the psychiatrist, who suggested that the worker not discuss the mother's part in keeping Doris out of school. He had recognized the mother's need to keep Doris close to her, but had avoided discussing it with her since she was already overburdened with guilt over her failure with Doris.

During the next two months the therapist devoted most of his interviews with Doris to discussing her relationship to her mother. The therapist explained the mother's unconscious need to cling to Doris, and he helped her to clarify her negative feelings toward her mother. The therapist encouraged Doris to look forward to the not-too-distant future when she would have her own home and family.

When a little later it grew apparent that Doris would not be able to get to school without help from outside, the staff evolved a new procedure. The school social worker, who already knew about the clinic treatment program, attended a treatment conference. The staff decided that Doris might respond to firm pressure from the outside which the mother could not provide. Doris needed extra help from a kind person eager to help her, but able to remain firm. One morning, shortly after the conference, the school social worker appeared at the home and announced that Doris was going to school on that day. Ignoring tears and threats of illness, she helped Doris into her clothes and drove her to school. Although the struggle disappeared after the second day, she repeated this performance for a week until Doris felt she would be able to continue alone.

The result was good. The clinic received daily reports which indicated that Doris was getting along well and showed no signs of excessive emotional tension or new neurotic symptoms. Doris continued in therapy for a few weeks and then dropped it, feeling that she could get along without further help.

*After her return to school, Doris never had a repetition of anxiety in relation to going to school. She graduated from high school, in the upper section of her class, and entered the nursing school at the state university. Her mother's strength improved, and she took a job as a secretary; she has remained relatively well, emotionally, and is pleased at Doris's decision to go into nursing.

A year after Doris's treatment, the clinic found another opportunity to try the procedure which had helped Doris return to school.

Ruth, a twelve-year-old girl in the seventh grade, had also developed a dread of school after an illness of ten days just preceding the summer vacation. Her neurotic illness was apparently more severe than some of the others, since even during the summer vacation she was withdrawn and afraid of all social contacts away from home. As the beginning of the school year approached, her anxiety became intense.

Ruth had always been very close to her mother. She resented her brother, born when she was six, and in the last year or two, she told the therapist, she had felt quite hostile to him. She pointed out to her parents and to the therapist that her parents gave her brother many privileges she had been denied.

Both parents were acutely upset by Ruth's inability to go to school, her father particularly so. He warned her mother against a clinic study, arguing that it would only emphasize to Ruth that she was sick. He accepted the study grudgingly after he failed through his own devices to get Ruth back to school.

Casework with both parents was directed toward lessening the mother's acute anxiety and the father's resistance to treatment. Not until several months after the study had begun was the father convinced that Ruth was not "pulling the wool" over the clinic's eyes and that the study was really needed.

After four months of therapy the clinic staff had little evidence that Ruth was making much effort to return to school. She remained in bed till almost noon daily, and she was not interested in doing school assignments sent home to her. The staff felt this might be another situation where the patient would respond to pressure in getting back to school, and the school social worker agreed to bring Ruth to school to remain for a brief period. Her parents were happy to cooperate in this venture, and they said nothing to Ruth about the plan until the school social worker arrived at the home early one morning. Ruth became panicky; she fought efforts to help her into her clothes and screamed and carried on in such a way that the school social worker grew convinced that Ruth was not ready to return to school. The parents agreed that Ruth was not ready and the plan was dropped. Fortunately, Ruth, who had worked very well with her therapist up to this time, did not resist further therapy, which continued for several months.

This case is mentioned here to illustrate a different reaction to the use of external pressures. In any such case, the worker must be prepared to give up the method as soon as it is evident that using pressure will have a negative effect on the child or on the future plan for therapy.

*Ruth is now twenty years old. She graduated from high school with honors. She is, at present, employed as a secretary and enjoying her work, and in the spring she is to be married. "Ruth is happy and is getting along well," reports her mother. There was no recurrence of symptoms after her return to school; she lost all her apprehensions. She has many interests and, as far as her mother can see, is in all respects emotionally well.

The differences in behavior and in response to therapy of children with school phobia are due to variations in the conditioning and precipitating factors which contribute to the illness. The amount of regression, the extent of the dependency, and the duration of the illness are related mainly to the ego strength of the child and the emotional maturity of his parents.

The greater the child's secondary gain from his illness, the more he will resist therapy. He will stay away from school as long as the precipitating factors of his illness continue; the clinic staff, therefore, must make a continuous study of all the major forces which influence the life of the child and his parents.

A child's unconscious need to remain at home in order to dominate his parents may not lessen until he discovers the reason for his need. As has been noted in the discussion of cases, the child may need to keep his parents for himself until his need to dominate them disappears and he can finally acquire a feeling of security and of being loved. Although this overdemanding period may be trying to the parents, it may be lifesaving to the child in his future love relationships. Usually, mothers who spontaneously sense the importance of meeting this need in the child cooperate best during the treatment of a child.

Fathers of children with school phobia are particularly interested in their treatment. They are concerned about the future life adjustment of their children, and they consider school attendance to be related closely to their function as disciplinarians. Fathers are particularly helpful in the treatment of children whose mothers are weak and passive.

Girls with school phobia tend to be subtly aggressive in spite of their shyness, the boys passive and withdrawn. In one group of twelve children with school phobia studied at the Wilder Child Guidance Clinic, three of the four boys enjoyed playing with dolls. In spite of their embarrassment they had great difficulty in stopping this play. One of the boys became frankly homosexual in later life; another continued with his feminine interests. The boys in this group had suffered early pronounced infantile fears and inhibitions. Reference made to the later development of these boys does not imply that boys with school phobia tend to develop pathologic emotional adjustments to life. School phobia, however, does reflect a neurotic relationship between mother and child in which both suffer from separation anxiety. A study by Johnson, Szurek, and Falstein [2] found that mothers of children with school phobia suffered from unresolved emotional relationships to their

[2] Szurek, S. A., A. Johnson, and E. I. Falstein, Collaborative Psychiatric Treatment of Parent-Child Problems, *Amer. Journ. Orthopsychiat.*, vol. XII, July, 1942, p. 511.

own mothers. Our studies also indicate that the phobic child is unable to give up his dependency tie to his mother because of her clinging to him. Neither the mother nor child knows what is taking place but both behave as though they were unconsciously aware of each other's deeper needs. Somewhere in therapy, each must learn of these needs and of the mixed feelings in their inter-relationship. The child in particular must learn to recognize his resentment of his mother for keeping him tied to her.

The mother's inadequately resolved relationship to her mother may help to explain the preponderance of school phobia in girls, since mothers find it easier to attempt solving their problems through a female child.

A child's fear of one teacher often spreads to other teachers, then to the whole school. Emanuel Klein [3] refers to the oral fear of being devoured by the school which is characteristic of children with school phobia. He recommends that such children be re-turned to school as soon as possible, to prove to themselves that the school is not so dangerous as it appears to them in their un-conscious fantasies.

In all school phobia cases known to the Wilder Child Guidance Clinic, the school staffs cooperated in treatment and permitted the children to return to school for any period of time they wished. Many of the teachers send work to the children's homes and often send notes of encouragement to the children. Without this co-operation from the school, treatment of school phobia is extremely difficult.

The acute panic of many children with school phobia is difficult to describe. Their embarrassment at not being in school, their need to hide from other children while going on errands, their lack of an explanation for school absence when their friends call them, and the gradual loss of friends add to their anxiety and shame. One frail boy who defied his father's order to return to school locked himself in his room. His father in desperation called a policeman who consented to carry the boy to school. Although terrified of the policeman, the child fought and kicked him until the policeman

[3] Klein, *op. cit.*

told the father he was making a mistake and that there was some doubt that his son would be able to remain in school after he got there. Some of the more panicky children beg the therapist to stop referring to the day when they will be able to return to school. The mere mention of school provokes tears and trembling.

The clinging, demanding behavior of children with school phobia is characteristic of children with so-called "oral character" make-up. Typical of such children is a strong element of cruelty. They show a lack of consideration for their parents' anxiety or for the amount of work to which their parents are subjected because of the school phobia. The tired, exhausted, pained expression of the parent of a child with school phobia, particularly in the early stages of the study, reflects his deep suffering and feeling of helplessness.

Most children with school phobia have been overprotected by their parents all along. Many find they can get what they want during their attacks of panic, and this may provide a motive for perpetuating staying away from school. At times they may malinger and provoke counterreactions from the clinic staff as well as the school authorities. A premature use of coercive measures before the ego of the child can tolerate returning to school may result. The therapist must realize that malingering in a child is due to emotional conflict which requires understanding and help to prevent the use of punishment. In spite of efforts to act wisely, mistakes will occur in attempts to return the child to school. The ill effects of these mistakes can be largely neutralized by stopping the unhealthy measures.

The therapist must know the child's ego strength in order to determine his readiness to return to school. Usually the child does not volunteer to return, and often the parents are unprepared to manage his return without help from the clinic staff. A child who has not been kept up to grade in his schoolwork will find it easier to return if he learns that the school will take special measures to help him. He must feel that those who urge him to return or demand it are aware not only of his insecure feelings, but are more certain than he is of his ability to meet this challenge. When, despite attempts to assure him that return to school is a constructive step, he considers it to be a form of punishment, the child is usually not ready to return, and he does not remain long at school.

Many children with school phobia, especially those with deep feelings of guilt and an unconscious need for punishment, require child analysis for their future adjustment. The inordinate, clinging, greedy need in a child for the constant presence of his mother reflects unconscious guilt feelings toward her. A child so totally dependent on a love object is not readily prepared to bring into consciousness his hostile feelings toward that person. The therapist who does not analyze the child, therefore, finds it difficult to get the child to admit hostile feelings toward his mother. Instead, the therapist must depend on other ego-strengthening measures to lessen the child's need to cling to his mother.

Many of the parents also require analysis, particularly those with an unconscious need to keep their children tied to them. Parents who have a deep unconscious hostility to their children, or who have other unconscious conflicts which produce a need to fail with their children, may not respond to any therapy but intensive anlaysis.

During the past several years the Judge Baker Guidance Center has conducted a series of studies on several aspects of school phobia in cooperation with the schools.[4,5,6,7] The child-psychiatry

[4] Coolidge, John C., Pauline Hahn, and Alice L. Peck, School Phobia: Neurotic Crisis or Way of Life, Amer. Journ. Orthopsychiat., vol. XXVII, no. 2, 1957, p. 296.

[5] Waldfogel, Samuel, John C. Coolidge, and Pauline Hahn, The Development, Meaning, and Management of School Phobia: Workshop, Amer. Journ. Orthopsychiat., vol. XXVII, no. 4, 1957, p. 754.

[6] Waldfogel, Samuel, Ellen Tessman, and Pauline Hahn, A Program of Early Intervention in School Phobia, Amer. Journ. Orthopsychiat., vol. XXIX, no. 2, 1959, p. 324.

[7] Coolidge, John C., Mary Lou Willer, Ellen Tessman, and Samuel Waldfogel, School Phobia in Adolescence: A Manifestation of Severe Character Disturbance, Amer. Journ. Orthopsychiat., vol. XXX, no. 3, 1960, p. 599.

team consulted with the teachers and found that they were often able to recognize school phobia early in its development. By instituting remedial measures, the members of the team succeeded in attenuating the severity of the illness. In their articles the team cautioned against allowing the child to have school help in the home in those instances in which the child was unable to return to school. Allowing a teacher to work with the child in the home prolonged the child's inability to separate himself from his family. Of particular interest was their finding that emotional rejection of the child was not an important factor in the development of school phobia. More often, the mothers of children with school phobia suffered from a fear of being inadequate as mothers, and their child's refusal to attend school was final proof to them of their inadequacy. The team made many practical suggestions for working with parents and school personnel, and their published articles deserve careful consideration.

Fortunately, however, many parents find through casework therapy an opportunity to express their deep dependency needs. This outlet may lessen their need to keep their children emotionally dependent on them, and the child's return to school may be facilitated. In some cases, also, the caseworker may help a father to recognize his wife's dependency needs and modify his behavior toward her, so that her need to cling to her child dwindles.

CHAPTER 9

The Child with Depression

Children suffer from neurotic depression more often than is generally believed. Depression in a child is frequently overlooked, since the child, unlike the adult, usually is active and able to maintain an interest in his activities even while depressed. He is rarely so deeply depressed as the adult; he has less cause for a feeling of hopelessness. The depressed adult suffers not only from the discomfort and unhappiness which belong to the illness, but he is tortured also by his inability to explain his suffering and his terror about the future. The child, still dependent upon others, does not need to concern himself with the future, and he retains his capacity to relate himself to situations or persons. In exceptional cases, however, the child may present the picture of deep depression like the adult's.

A child's grief, following the physical loss of a love object upon whom he has depended for emotional support, usually lessens quickly when relatives or close friends or a social agency provide emotional support. Sometimes, however, a child continues to be depressed for a long period when a fixation or pathologic tie to the lost love object prevents his displacing his attachment onto others. In most cases the child's fixation results from the adult's inordinate need to keep the child dependent upon him for his own emotional outlets. Usually therapy succeeds in loosening the child's abnormal fixation, and his normal resiliency helps him in this struggle to free himself.

More frequently the child is deprived of the love of a parent without the physical loss of separation. An unwanted child who lives with his rejecting parents continuously feels unloved. A parent's emotional rejection always creates feelings of unhappiness and emptiness in a child and often produces depression. These feelings seriously disturb the child's stability, interfere with his emotional development, and prevent his becoming socialized. The most severe forms of neurotic illness and criminal behavior have their origin in the parents' early rejection of the child.

Frank, conscious rejection of a child produces disturbances in behavior and often physical disturbances as well. These are usually so marked that the parents need help with the child and call in a nurse, physician, or social worker to assist them with the problems the child presents. Since professional people today are aware of the dangers of allowing a child to continue in life rejected and unloved, many of these children are referred for study much earlier than in the past. The clinic makes every attempt to modify the parents' attitude toward the rejected child before the damage becomes irreparable. If the parents cannot change their attitude, the clinic directs treatment toward removing the child to a setting where he can find acceptance and love.

In most cases rejection is only one part of an ambivalent attitude which the parents have toward their child. An ambivalent parent accepts and rejects his child at the same time because he both loves and hates him. The greater his love for the child, the less the child feels the rejection. The parents' positive feelings about their child bring them to the clinic to seek help when he develops symptoms; their negative feelings interfere with the therapeutic plans the clinic initiates.

Feeling unloved is the chief cause of neurotic depression in children. Although the primary feelings of the depressed child are unhappiness and dejection, a great deal of hostility is also present, and the amount of hostility depends on the extent to which the parents reject the child. His hostility is much greater when the parents show favoritism to another child in the family. The child's excessive, unconscious hostility and his unconscious death wishes toward the parents result in sadistic, irritating behavior. A vicious circle thus develops in which the child seeks affection to neutralize his depression and yet is forced to be hostile and rejecting toward those from whom he seeks love.

The process of becoming socialized presents the child with many prohibitions and frustrations, but a child who feels secure and loved can retain his equilibrium in spite of them. The rejected, depressed child, however, already conditioned by repeated frustrations, usually finds it difficult to accept further denial. The depressed child withdraws libido from the activities which a child generally enjoys. He does not enjoy play with other children, he is unenthusiastic about gifts, and he does not enjoy eating. Withdrawal in itself is not infallible evidence of depression in children, however; many children either by nature or as a result of conditioning prefer to play by themselves or to seek the company of only one other child. They are happy and content with reading and other inactive pastimes. Some depressed children, furthermore, do not withdraw but manage to cover their depression with restless activities which mask their unhappiness. When such children are denied outlets, their depressed feelings become noticeable, a process similar to that in the so-called "holiday depression."

Children in their latency years may be depressed without being aware of it. A nine-year-old boy, referred because he was unable to concentrate on his schoolwork in spite of superior intelligence, could not explain to the therapist why he felt tense and restless. His mother had had several spells of hysterical depression. She was certain that her son had not known of her depressed states, but this was hardly possible since her depressions were often severe. The boy told the therapist that something bothered him "way down inside" that made him feel vaguely unhappy. He could think of nothing in his life to make him feel unhappy. After a series of interviews with his therapist, to whom he was strongly attached, his general feeling of unhappiness lessened considerably, although nothing in the material presented in therapy explained his depressed feelings.

* This boy, whom we shall now call Earl, was referred for study again when he was seventeen years old, because he continued to be quiet though not really withdrawn. He enjoyed reading and being by himself. Although he had friends whom he saw rather frequently, he did not really need them to be content. He felt uneasy about the prospect of joining a club of adolescents, but his parents insisted that he do so, and he planned to go along with the idea. He was a bright student, attended high school, but did not really enjoy schoolwork. He had made no effort to date girls, but had no serious objection to marrying later on. He did not appear to be really depressed, but he did not experience the zest for living he recognized in his friends. He explained that returning to the clinic was his own idea, because he felt he needed help. However, he said little spontaneously and only discussed questions raised by the therapist. He admitted later that he probably would not have come in had his mother not shown concern about his lack of social drive. He added that he, too, thought he had problems. He agreed with his mother that he had trouble in relating to people, but he doubted that this problem would be solved through his interviews; the therapist agreed with him. He was told in the last interview that he was making a reasonably good adjustment, despite his lack of drive to spend more time with others. He was fairly content with his present feelings about life and would very likely continue to be. Rorschach tests, given in the first and second studies, revealed evidence of moderate depression and pathologic reactions to the father figure. In his closing interview the therapist told Earl that, if he felt he needed help later on or had any feelings of chronic dissatisfaction, it would be well for him to be analyzed.

Earl presents the kind of problem so well described by Edith

Jacobson in her article on normal and pathologic moods.[1] She believes that moods represent a cross section of the entire ego, lending a uniform coloration to all its manifestations. Moods may result from a provocative experience which cannot be sufficiently relieved by channels of discharge, and so they persist. The long history of Earl's vague symptoms suggests that early infantile influences played a part and that they were very likely related to the mother's depression. The mother reported that she was always strongly identified with Earl. The hostile component in Earl's depressive mood was reflected in his sarcastic, bitter remarks to his peers, references to feelings of failure and unworthiness, and quarrels with members of his family, especially with his mother and sister.

Whenever symptoms of depression in a child are vague and ill-defined, the therapist must be careful to rule out physical factors that may produce fatigue or general debility. Careful physical examination often reveals chronic foci of infection, especially of the sinuses, that have been overlooked. Clearing up these infections may give the child sufficient strength to counteract the effects of emotional conflict. Physical factors in themselves rarely produce depression. They may, however, be an important link in the chain of circumstances that produces not only depression but other neurotic symptoms. The danger of overlooking physical factors and the effect of insufficient food and rest is avoided when the staff keeps physical as well as psychologic factors in mind at all times.

When children are removed from their homes, they often grow depressed and need considerable reassurance, especially during the early part of their stay in a new home. Their depression is due to their uncertainty and anxiety about their future, the traumatic separation from their own home, and their concern about what is happening to their parents and siblings. Usually the depression decreases after they grow accustomed to the foster home and feel

[1] Jacobson, Edith, Normal and Pathological Moods—Their Nature and Functions, in "The Psychoanalytic Study of the Child," vol. XII, 1957, p. 73.

secure there. If the depressed feelings persist, and the child continues to be apathetic and sad, treatment is necessary.

Dave, a ten-year-old boy, lived with his nine-year-old brother
in a foster home where he was not happy. He had no foster father
in the home, and he badly needed a father figure, since his father
had deserted the family six years previously. One year later his
mother had been committed to an institution for schizophrenic
illness, and she was still in the hospital at the time Dave was
studied. Dave's problems were bed-wetting, temper outbursts, and
hysterical, uncontrolled laughter. The referral did not mention that
Dave was depressed.

At times he was a nuisance at school, occasionally striking at
children, although he never really hurt them. His schoolwork was
poor because he could not concentrate, but he was a bright boy
and his achievements were up to grade.

The group therapist at the clinic found him withdrawn, and
although he was friendly with other children, he tended to leave
them and remain by himself in some activity. She described him as
pensive and deeply unhappy.

His individual therapist described Dave as a sad boy, chronically
depressed, and unable to find anything that he thoroughly enjoyed.
Before too long Dave made clear that his real problem was concern about his parents. His eyes welled with tears as he talked
about his mother, who apparently was not improving in a hospital,
so far as he was able to learn. No one had ever told him why she
was placed in the hospital, although a few of his remarks made
it obvious that he realized she was mentally ill. He had heard
nothing at all about his father and said that no one seemed to
know where he was.

Dave felt that he was not supposed to talk to the agency worker
about his mother. Whenever he had asked questions about her,
he had decided from the way she answered him that she did not
want to talk about his mother. Dave was starved to talk about his
parents, and he told the therapist that he prayed every night that

the family be reunited. He included some discussion of his parents in every interview.

Dave responded well to therapy. The clinic worker discussed with Dave's placement worker some of the material he had revealed in the interviews. After several interviews with Dave about his mother, the agency worker arranged for him to visit his mother at the hospital. She discussed the occasional reports her agency had received about his father, and answered all Dave's questions about him. Dave reported to his therapist his visit to his mother, and arrived at the conclusion that it was unwise to think about reuniting the family, since his mother was much too sick. He realized, too, that his father could not or did not want to come back to his family. The clinic arranged to remove Dave and his brother to another foster home with a foster father as well as a foster mother, and in a short period of time Dave was making a much better emotional adjustment. His schoolwork improved, and his relationship to the agency worker responsible for his care was much stronger. His depression vanished.

The increasing trend for social workers to discuss emotional problems with children under their care is fortunate, since many of the problems referred to child-guidance clinics in the past could have been treated by trained caseworkers. The caseworker responsible for the emotional welfare of children must permit them to talk freely about problems which concern them. Children placed away from their homes are often discouraged from talking about their parents when the caseworker cannot give them positive reports about their parents. The child will probably benefit from any information about his parents that the worker can give him, providing that she presents it in a way to provoke the least anxiety. The child is better able to plan his future on the basis of unpleasant facts than on the bizarre, unreal fantasies which he may create about his parents. Most children are anxious to find out about members of their family from whom they have been removed; they are eager to know what is happening to them. Since they know that their worker does have information, the fact that she does not talk makes them suspect that her information is all bad. The child in a foster home usually can accept negative data about his parents, since similar behavior was the cause of his removal from them. In reporting facts as she knows them, the worker helps him to deal with reality and assures him that he can depend on her in other ways as well.

A frequent characteristic of neurotic depression in children is a deep feeling of self-reproach and unworthiness that resembles the depression of adults. Children may find life unbearable if they feel they will never find happiness again, if they lose their capacity to love and feel loved by others. Adults who suffer from hysterical depression occasionally recall that as young children they felt there was little in life to make them happy. One woman in her thirties who had always felt rejected by her cold, narcissistic mother, explained that as a little girl she used to ask herself, "Why should I go on living? What's the sense to this?" She was certain she was not more than six or seven years old when she felt this way. Her feeling of futility about life persisted up to the time she sought therapy for her neurotic illness. Ferenczi [2] referred to a feeling of aversion to life and chronic pessimism in individuals who early sensed they were unwanted.

Frequent accidents in children, as in adults, reflect unhappiness and often an unconscious wish to die. A ten-year-old child, who had been seriously rejected, was moved repeatedly from one foster home to another because of his chronic irritability, temper outbursts, and deep unhappiness. A clinic study revealed that he was deeply depressed and hostile. He felt very much alone and unloved, and stated frankly that he saw little sense in going on this way. Shortly after the study began the agency notified the clinic that the boy had slipped on the top step leading down to the basement and had died as a result of a broken neck.

The clinic had studied several children who attempted to take

[2] Ferenczi, S., The Unwelcome Child and His Death Instinct, Int. Journ. Psychoanal., vol. X, 1929, p. 125.

their own lives because of severe depression. Occasionally the attempts were not serious, and the motives were based on a dramatic need to attract attention and sympathy. In these cases the staff tried to determine why the child had to resort to such radical measures to gain attention. Usually some wish to die was present, although the wish to live predominated.

Many motives may lead a child to attempt taking his own life. Zilboorg,[3] who made a comprehensive study of suicides of the young in different cultures, believes that children of prepubertal and pubertal age take their own lives when their egos are too weak to master their anxiety from their heightened sexual drives. Boys particularly, he feels, are threatened by their homosexual impulses which represent their effort to deal with the heterosexual drive. Behind this anxiety lies a fear of castration and a wish to destroy themselves before someone else destroys them.

Zilboorg mentions the fact that in some cultures adolescents may develop such strong fears of punishment or ridicule that they take their own lives. We have noted at the clinic that sensitive children who run away from home often explain that they had stayed out too late or had done something wrong and were afraid to return home because they would be punished. Questioning in these cases has revealed that parents did not use severe punishment. The children, however, were unconsciously hostile toward their fathers, felt guilty about their hostility, and unconsciously feared the most severe kind of punishment. Not until this deep anxiety in relation to the father was lessened did the running away stop. We may postulate that the child who takes his own life because he fears punishment suffers from even more severe terror of the father.

Several children seriously attempted suicide and would have succeeded were it not for accidental discovery and prompt medical attention. One ten-year-old boy took a fatal dose of sedative medi-

[3] For a general discussion of the dynamics of suicide see: Zilboorg, Gregory, Considerations on Suicide, with Particular Reference to that of the Young, *Amer. Journ. Orthopsychiat.*, vol. VII, no. 1, 1937, p. 15.

cation and after being unconscious for several hours slowly recovered. He had lost his father in an automobile accident the year before and had never recovered from the depression which followed his father's death. Despite a strong conscious wish on the part of the mother to have her son receive treatment, he refused to accept therapy. From the history that the mother gave, the therapist learned that the boy had mixed feelings about his father and a very strong attachment to his mother. Apparently he sensed that he might learn more about his relationship to his father than he dared to learn. He responded well to a strong friendship with a young man who had known his father well and who could give him time and attention, but he persisted in rejecting therapy, even at the suggestion of his friend.

A twelve-year-old boy ran away with his brother from the home of his father and stepmother to the home of his mother and stepfather. He was an unstable, aggressive boy who very quickly outlived his welcome with his stepfather. When his behavior became difficult, the stepfather spoke of returning him to his own father's home. Realizing that his stepfather was serious about his threat, the boy attempted unsuccessfully to take his own life. When he returned home from the hospital, his mother and stepfather, who had blamed themselves for the boy's attempted suicide, indulged him in every way. Soon his difficult behavior returned, and the boy was referred to the clinic for study. In spite of the therapist's efforts to gain his cooperation, the boy had little motivation to continue in therapy. The child was certain that he would never again feel that he wanted to die. He knew that he would never have to return to his own father, and he was convinced that he could modify his behavior sufficiently to remain in the home of his mother.

Neither of these boys was able to accept therapy. In each instance the therapist had tried to help the child understand his motives for suicide in order to prevent its recurrence. Both boys were threatened by the prospect of stirring up the morbid feelings which prompted the wish to die and wanted more than anything else to avoid such a discussion. Perhaps in both instances the boys achieved their desired purpose by trying to die. Recognizing their parents' grim determination never to offend them deeply again, never again to deprive them, they may have felt certain their problems were solved and they had nothing more to fear.

Stanley was studied two years after publication of the first edition of this book. He is included here because we had an opportunity to work with him for a long period of time, in contrast to other cases, where long-time treatment had not been possible.

Stanley was a twelve-year-old boy who attempted suicide because he felt life was not worth living. His father had died three years earlier, and Stanley blamed himself for his father's death because he had insisted that his father take him out for a drive, when his father was tired and wanted to rest. An accident occurred in which the father was killed, but Stanley was not hurt. When his mother remarried, Stan could not accept his stepfather.

Stan was an exceptionally bright boy who insisted on making his own decisions, a situation his mother was unable to accept. When Stan refused to accompany his scout troop on an overnight trip, his mother, determined that he do so, kept insisting that he take the trip and finally called the scout leader, who came over and talked with Stan. That evening Stan swallowed a bottle of sedative pills; he was taken to the hospital and was unconscious for forty-eight hours. A few weeks later he came to the clinic for a series of interviews. It took some time before he was able to accept the idea of therapy, but finally he was able to talk quite freely. He had felt, he said, that life was not worthwhile if he had to continue under the domination of his mother, whose opinions he did not respect. During the course of therapy, he occasionally got involved in delinquencies, together with other boys his age, which became increasingly serious. At times he showed little feeling of guilt about these escapades; at other times he seemed eager for help.

The caseworker found the mother to be a very insecure, unhappy woman, not content with her marriage, but too weak to

separate from her husband. During casework treatment, she gradually became stronger, aware of many of her emotional problems,
and able to improve her relationship to her husband and to her
son.

Since Stan seemed to want a young person as therapist, the
change was made. The second therapist made less effort to get
at underlying conflicts. In a short time Stan seemed very close
to him. He came in regularly for his interviews and talked freely,
and within a short time, his schoolwork began to pick up and, for
the first time, was commensurate with his intellectual ability.
There were one or two minor episodes of stealing, and then his
delinquency stopped completely. After he had been known to the
clinic for about two-and-one-half years, therapy with Stan was discontinued. Therapy with the mother continued for several months
longer.

CHAPTER 10

The Child with Obsessional Neurosis

One of the most vexing problems in therapy concerns the treatment of severely neurotic children, ill for a long time, whose illness is due to deep unconscious conflict, and for whom the only prescribed therapy is child analysis. Obsessional neurosis in children, for example, is due to specific unconscious material which must be uncovered to cure the child. In view of the scarcity of trained child analysts in all communities, and the high cost of such intensive therapy, it is essential that other methods be discovered for treating the obsessionally neurotic child and his parents.

The writer, a trained child analyst, has accepted nine children suffering from severe obsessional neurosis for therapy at the Wilder Child Guidance Clinic, hoping to discover forms of psychotherapy other than intensive psychoanalysis. Most of these children were seen two or three times a week. In some cases the interviews were limited to once or twice a week, and after a year of therapy to once a week. In two cases the children were seen three times a week for two years. One child was seen six days a week for a period of three months as a part of his therapy, which lasted much longer. None of these children can be said to have received intensive analysis.

The diagnosis of obsessional neurosis in a child depends primarily on the presence of ceremonials or rituals which he cannot control. He is obsessed by the need to repeat acts over and over again. He becomes annoyed when anyone attempts to stop him from performing these bits of behavior, although he knows that what he is doing does not make sense. Touching all objects in sight, washing his hands frequently, repeating acts a specific number of times are common forms of rituals. He is totally unaware of why he behaves in this manner. He may explain that behaving in this way will bring him good luck, or he may fear that if he does not behave in this way he will suffer bad luck.

The obsessionally neurotic child is often subject to peculiar throat noises, spitting sounds as he speaks, blocking on certain words, or a habit of placing dirty objects or body secretions in his mouth. He has a marked interest in his bowel movements, in the buttocks, and all excretory products. He tends to put objects in specifically assigned places and wants his possessions to be in an exact order, becoming anxious if the order is changed. Frequently he is preoccupied with obsessive thoughts which frighten him because of their sinister character and because he cannot understand why he has them. Typical of such thoughts is the fear that he will poison one of his parents, or that his food is poisoned.

Jean, who was described among the cases of acute anxiety in Chapter 7, was subject to compulsive hostile thoughts about her sister and felt compelled to confess these thoughts to her mother. Jean, however, was not nearly so enslaved by the need to repeat acts as were the other children in the group of obsessional neurotics. It is interesting that she was the only obsessionally neurotic girl treated at the clinic; all the others were boys.[1]

The child cannot escape performing his rituals. He behaves as

---

[1] Freud referred to the fact that hysteria occurs more frequently in females; obsessional neurosis in males: Freud, Sigmund, "The Problem of Anxiety," New York, The Psychoanalytic Quarterly Press, and W. W. Norton & Co., Inc., 1936, p. 110.

though he is receiving a command from his psyche to carry out acts which have a definite function for him. These acts substitute for his instinctual drives which would be much more disturbing if carried out. For example, the child touches many objects instead of touching his penis or striking out aggressively at someone else. The washing of the hands symbolically represents his removing the contamination from unconsciously having touched the penis or the anal area. Placing objects in a specified manner seems to act as a reassurance to the child that his body is intact and has not been damaged. Other ceremonials, such as retracing of steps, which was manifested by several of the children, represent undoing an act which unconsciously represents a violation of oversocialized standards. The entire picture is that of a child being punished by an overly severe conscience for unconsciously permitting himself instinctual gratifications through his symptoms. The picture may change within a short period of time, one ritual giving way to another, due to intervening differences in the dynamic picture, but the new ritual is equally relentless and must be performed.

Readers who are acquainted with obsessional neurosis in the adult will recognize the similarities between the obsessionally neurotic child and the adult. Certain differences, however, appeared in the children of the group treated in the clinic. In contrast to the marked passivity and withdrawn behavior of the adult with obsessional neurosis, the children in this group were active, productive, and in one instance, destructively aggressive. Whereas interfering with the rituals of the adult tends to produce severe anxiety and tension phenomena, the child mildly protests and seems to suffer much less. The total amount of anxiety suffered by the obsessionally neurotic child is actually much less than in the case of the adult, probably due to the child's dependency on his parents who support him in many ways, and to his ability to find other outlets, even though his illness may be well established.

Ideally, the child with obsessional neurotic illness should be thoroughly psychoanalyzed. Ideally, so should the parent or parents whose neurotic conflicts contribute so heavily to the child's neurotic illness. The analysis of obsessional neurosis in adults and children is discussed in the psychoanalytic literature. Freud's article on this subject in the "Collected Papers" is especially valuable.[2] The modified analytic treatment of the children in the clinic group consisted of interpretation of ritualistic behavior whenever the therapist had evidence to justify interpretation. Dream material was used as much as possible for the interpretation of unconscious drives and wishes. Fortunately, most of the children in our group dreamed richly and associated well to their dreams. Even some of the children of latency age in the group associated well to dream material. When they did not dream the children often made up stories and, as a rule, they were better at telling stories than most children with whom this technic is used. Their rich fantasy life probably accounts for this.

These children seemed to understand interpretations better than other children seen at the clinic, and they often volunteered their own interpretations. They were outspoken about their fantasies of attacking, torturing, and killing. They did not hesitate to attack verbally and ridicule the therapist, especially when they were unable to accept an interpretation. During brief periods of acute anxiety and guilt, the therapist often needed to interpret their deep hostile wishes and fears of castration and death which accompanied their destructive fantasies. Castration anxiety was particularly prominent in these boys, and it is not surprising that three of them frankly stated wishes to have been born girls instead of boys. They were deeply identified with their mothers, and although they needed to deny the significance of the penis, they fantasied at the same time that their mothers had male genitals. Two of them expressed wishes to have children of their own. They expressed marked hostility to girls, and many of their fantasies dealt with torturing girls and exposing them to embarrassment and ridicule. The therapist repeatedly interpreted the unconscious wish and need

[2] Freud, Sigmund, Notes upon a Case of Obsessional Neurosis, in "Collected Papers," vol. III, London, Hogarth Press, Ltd., 1925, pp. 296–372.

to be castrated as a punishment for their wish to attack and castrate others, particularly their fathers. An abundance of material in the dreams and fantasies supported this interpretation.

Ordinarily, in the intensive therapy of neurotic children who do not suffer from obsessional neurosis, interpretations of unconscious material are delayed until the analytically trained therapist is quite certain that the child is prepared to accept the interpretation. Usually, the therapist waits until the child can almost make the interpretation himself.

The same caution was not exercised in the case of the obsessionally neurotic child. To be sure, interpretations were never made unless the material revealed justified them, but the therapist did not wait until the child was entirely ready for them. Frequently the child resisted the interpretations, as stated above, but the therapist made them nevertheless, not only to lessen anxiety but to stimulate the uncovering of more unconscious material.

Occasionally the children in the group accused the therapist of putting stupid thoughts into their minds, forcing them to think too much about matters which only made them sicker. In each instance the therapist met the attack with a detailed description of the material the child had presented spontaneously and which had occasioned the interpretations. Such attacks were generally short-lived and often later in the same interview the child presented more of the kind of material which he had just complained about.

Resistance to treatment was marked in most of these children. Although all attempts to uncover unconscious material produce resistance, it was more marked in the obsessionally neurotic group. Two of the boys called upon "little men" [3] inside themselves to help their resistance. They reported that the little men were opposed to their giving up secret information. For a while treatment had to be concentrated on a devaluation of the little men in favor of the therapist who, as the child's ally, was dedicated to helping him.

Fortunately, most of the children in this group quickly became

[3] See the case of Ralph in this chapter, pp. 152–164.

friendly with the therapist. For a long time they had felt helpless to deal with their disabling rituals, and they welcomed the therapist's cooperation in an attack on the enemy. Before long, however, they became less concerned about their problems and, consistent with their general feelings of dependency, turned over the responsibility of their getting well to their therapist. The therapist handled their resistance by interpretations and often scoldings and a reminder that treatment would continue only as long as the child indicated a wish for help.

On many occasions in almost every case, when the child felt he could never get well, the therapist found supportive treatment essential. At these times he assured the child that he would stand by with help and that the child, like many others with the same illness, would respond to treatment.

It is difficult to state to what extent the improvement in some of these children was due to the uncovering of unconscious conflict. It is hard to escape the impression, however, that this was the determining factor in their improvement.

A Case of Obsessional Neurosis

Ralph was ten years old when his father brought him to the clinic for study because of marked enuresis, restlessness, and severe temper tantrums. Ralph's mother objected strongly to the study and warned Ralph that his friends would criticize him if he accepted psychiatric help. His mother had been subject to depressions for many years and had given up any hope of getting well. She was embittered, felt hostile to her church, refused to allow their parish priest to visit the home, and discouraged her children from going to confession or to Mass. The children had little respect for their mother's opinions and continued with their religious observances.

During his first visit with the psychiatrist Ralph gave the impression of being a bright, alert little boy, restless and undernourished. He spoke rather warmly about a brother younger than himself, an older brother, and an older sister. He was very fond of his father but had mixed feelings about his mother who stayed in bed most of the day, complained about everything, and cried a great deal. He thought she was "crazy about two-thirds of the time." About one-third of the time, he said, she was kind and thoughtful.

He described a habit he had for about a year of opening and closing doors many times to make sure that they were closed. He felt that certain numbers were lucky and that he was compelled to repeat some actions a given number of times to avoid bad luck. He asked the therapist why he had to repeat these acts. He had fantasies of being attacked by gangsters, fighting with them, and frequently overpowering them, but often being overpowered himself. He asked if the therapist thought he was crazy.

The therapist did not think he was at all crazy. He explained that Ralph was being driven by thoughts which were in a part of his mind which Ralph could not control. Perhaps in the study the therapist and Ralph could discover what these thoughts were, for then the need to carry on his rituals would no longer exist. The therapist said he was certain that Ralph had many worries and fears and that, as time went on, Ralph would find it easy to talk about them to the therapist.

Ralph reported [4] that each time he touched an object with one hand he had to touch the same object with the other hand or else that hand would feel sad. When he closed a door an even number of times the odd numbers felt bad, and he often found great difficulty in determining the number he should use. He had been having some very "bad thoughts," especially about his mother, wondering if she was going to die. He added spontaneously that sometimes he even hoped she would die, and that upset him.

The therapist sympathized with Ralph's suffering from such horrible thoughts. He suggested that these thoughts frightened Ralph because he feared some kind of punishment. Ralph ad-

---

[4] The period of time between contacts will not be stated. This will vary from a few days to weeks.

mitted that he constantly feared that terrible things would happen to him.

Ralph would like to be a gangster himself, he said, and kill his enemies. At times he felt he was being followed by someone who was "after" him. He found himself looking over his shoulder repeatedly to see if someone was following him.

The therapist suggested that Ralph wanted to be a gangster so he would not have to fear the older boys or be afraid of robbers at night. He pointed out that only one part of him wanted to be a gangster; the other part was kind and thoughtful of others. The therapist had learned about his kindness from his father and school teacher.

Ralph reported a great interest in sex. He told of having frequent erections and of playing with his penis. In discussing genital differences he revealed that he thought a woman had a penis extending back toward the anus and this was why she sat down to urinate. One concept of sexual intercourse he mentioned was that the woman "puts her penis into the bad man's" anus. He had derived this concept from seeing dogs stuck to each other following the sex act. An older boy had explained pregnancy to him as the result of a man's "putting his penis into a woman's back." This disturbed Ralph who wished, he said, that the stork theory were the correct one.

The therapist explained sex differences and sex relations in dogs and people as vaginal, not anal. He told Ralph that his guilty concern about sex was mostly a result of misinformation and sexual practices he had learned from others.

Ralph had shown considerable interest in feces in several interviews. He believed that the baby was born by way of the anus. The therapist asked him to close his eyes and describe what came to his mind when he thought about feces, and he fantasied that the feces came out under great pressure "strong enough to knock over a brick wall." During this interview, Ralph for the first time mentioned feminine interests he had had for some time. He even thought it would be nice if he had been born a girl. The therapist decided not to take up this subject with Ralph at this time, since it would have little meaning to him. He again explained the birth process to Ralph, pointing out, as he had before, that the baby made its exit by way of the vagina. Ralph made several later references to the birth process, and, in spite of the explanations, continued for a long time to refer to anal birth.

Preoccupation with anal material and the special significance of the anus as an organ is characteristic of obsessional neurosis. Freud demonstrated this clearly in his early studies of neurosis and attributed the etiology of obsessional neurosis to a fixation of the libido at the anal stage of libido development.

Ralph reported that he was unhappy while the therapist was away on vacation. His habits grew much worse. On several occasions he had tried to control his habits but he felt "empty and uncomfortable" whenever he tried to stop them. During this interview he talked about the fun he had with his friends. He enjoyed being outside and playing and had many friends. He referred again to his lucky number, which had changed three or four times since the beginning of treatment.

The therapist tried to determine from Ralph's dreams and fantasies what caused him to select any given number. The numbers seemed to stand for people. On one occasion when the therapist felt he was gaining insight on why a certain number was chosen, the number changed.

Ralph described spending long periods of time making up long and involved stories. He would come home from school, go to his room, and continue with the fantasy he had left off the day before. He preferred this occupation to playing outside. His fantasies failed to reveal much to the therapist. They dealt largely with wish fulfillment; in the fantasies Ralph was the strong man overcoming his enemies. Ralph recognized that he was overcompensating for feeling small, weak, and sick.

Ralph on several occasions mentioned a "little man" inside of him who seemed to know how events were going to turn out. The little man would laugh at him and warn him that he was not going to be successful in an examination at school or that he would not be invited to a certain party. When the little man was silent, Ralph usually was going to have good luck. Occasionally the little man was wrong, and Ralph felt very happy about that.

The therapist again discussed with Ralph his good and bad self. Most of one interview was devoted to discussing his conscience, his guilt at his destructive wishes, and his need to punish himself. Much of his guilt was associated with his hostility and death wishes toward his mother and, to a lesser extent, toward his father. The therapist told Ralph that he could see that his good self was growing stronger and that before long it would overpower his negative self.

Ralph began to resist therapy. He associated less well to dream material and often came late for his appointments. His resistance then changed to an outpouring of sadistic fantasies of bloodshed and killing. People were thrown down elevator shafts and tortured.

Ralph was so agitated during this entire interview that the therapist made no attempt to interpret the material. He told Ralph that he must be having a great many negative thoughts at this time, but that he had the strength to control his impulses, and the therapist was not at all worried about him. The therapist arranged to have Ralph come in daily during this period of acute anxiety.

Ralph continued to have fantasies of overwhelming destruction. Cities were destroyed; buildings toppled over; posts and trees were cut down; people were cut in half. Death was everywhere. During this period Ralph personified inanimate objects. He had to treat each object with consideration or he thought it would feel insulted and humiliated. He personified the inner organs of his body and described them as in continuous quarrel with each other. Ralph seemed lost in an orgy of destruction.

The therapist recognized repeated evidences of castration anxiety in these fantasies. Ralph had previously referred to his castration anxiety, but the therapist had found no good opportunity for

*interpretation. Now the therapist felt that unless he could explain
to Ralph why he was so anxious and preoccupied with this subject,
Ralph would become even more disturbed. He discussed castration
fears with Ralph and related these fears to his masturbation and
sexual preoccupation. He told Ralph that his wish to have been a
girl reflected a deep wish or need or fear of being castrated. Perhaps
he wished to be like his mother, feeling that he deserved this for
his hostile fantasies about her.*

The problem of castration anxiety in the neurotic children
studied in the clinic needs amplification here. Conflict growing
out of the fear that something may happen to the genitals as punishment for sexual wishes and fantasies is rarely absent in neurotic
boys. Neurotic girls express this conflict through envy of the penis
they lack or in a shadowy belief that they formerly possessed a
penis which was removed as a form of punishment.

The passive, effeminate boy who would like to be a girl, and
the homosexually conflicted child, have unconsciously accepted
castration as a fact. The neurotic child with severe anxiety fears
castration as punishment for his deep hostile wishes toward his
parents, with whom he is in sexual conflict. His dreams provide
abundant evidence that castration anxiety is a major concern to
him. The tough acting-out youngster, the bully, the delinquent,
is often overcompensating to assure himself that he is strong and
powerful and not deeply castrated. The child who feels he must
exhibit his genitals to girls or women is attempting to prove he
still has a penis.

Since castration anxiety is unconscious and the child does not
understand it, the therapist cannot discuss the subject with him,
except during intensive treatment when the goal of therapy is the
uncovering of unconscious material. In clinic cases the therapist
will discuss the emotional factors that have precipitated the
castration anxiety in the child. He encourages the child to talk
about his present and past feelings toward his parents, discusses
the child's feelings of hostility and rivalry toward his father and
his feelings of inadequacy and inferiority. He helps the child see

that his deep anxiety is closely tied to these emotional experiences, without ever referring to castration as such, and without referring specifically to the fear of genital injury or loss.

The child's dreams are useful in these discussions since they usually include sexual material and help the child to talk about sex. If the child's relationship to the therapist is strong enough, or if the anxiety is sufficiently disturbing, the child may be able to talk to the therapist about masturbation and in some instances describe his masturbation fantasies. Such material is intimately related to his castration conflict.

During this period of therapy, casework with the parents is directed toward helping them understand the child's need for approval and responsibility. His parents must help him feel adequate. The caseworker discusses their attitudes toward sex and attempts to relieve their anxiety about their child's sexual interests. She discourages them, however, from actions which the child could interpret as seductive toward him, since these stir up his conflicts. Through these interviews they learn to recognize the destructive effect of arbitrary, strict demands on the child.

The child with castration conflict is encouraged to express his hostility rather than to react submissively. He is helped to enjoy active sports, supervised by strong male figures with whom he can identify.

The treatment of Ralph's castration anxiety differed from this process, however; since he was seen frequently, his treatment was intensive, and the therapist was attempting to uncover unconscious material.

Ralph was quick to grasp interpretations related to dream material. He associated well to dreams and felt free to argue with the therapist whenever an interpretation did not make sense to him. On this occasion, when the therapist discussed castration anxiety, Ralph listened attentively and seemed to accept without question the therapist's remarks.

Ralph's mother tried to encourage him to stop treatment. She pointed out to him that he was no happier now and that his bed-wetting persisted. Ralph told the psychiatrist that his mother was totally unaware of his compulsive rituals; he had never wanted to tell her about them.

The therapist told Ralph that his mother was very sick and that he hoped her attempts to interrupt therapy would not succeed, since continuing treatment would prevent his suffering like his mother.

Ralph had been thinking a great deal about pregnancy. He asked the therapist why boys his age could not become fathers, and the therapist explained spermatogenesis. Ralph was certain that if he ever had sex relations his habits would become infinitely worse.

The therapist pointed out to Ralph that his compelling need to carry out rituals often was a form of penance. His sexual thoughts and wishes made him feel guilty, and his rituals, which interfered with his happiness and made him so uncomfortable, represented in some way the price he was paying for having sexual thoughts and hostile, aggressive feelings toward his mother. This was why he feared that having sexual relations would intensify his habits.

The therapist suggested to Ralph that he feared sex because he felt some terrible punishment would follow his giving way to sexual feelings. He was afraid that he would be castrated, and his dreams suggested that castration was equivalent to being destroyed. Perhaps the punishment was to be so severe because his sexual wishes were directed toward members of his own family.

Ralph had developed a ritual of going back and forth to his bed half a dozen times before he could get into it. The therapist explained to Ralph that he feared getting into bed because he associated it with sexual activity and he was fighting against the temptation to masturbate and to fantasy sexually.

Ralph had repeated Oedipus dreams. Again he began to resist treatment, and came late. He reported one dream in which the therapist was killed. This dream contained considerable sexual material, with much obscene language and incidents of men urinating on women.

Ralph had been in treatment for more than a year, and he was in a state of negative transference. The therapist suggested that Ralph probably wished he could withdraw from treatment because he was deeply threatened by the therapist. Sexual material had threatened Ralph all along. Now he was suffering the double threat of having increased sexual fantasies and being obliged to relate them to another person. Perhaps he felt that through the interviews the therapist was trying to seduce him into sexual activity. The therapist reemphasized his interest in helping Ralph control his sexual impulses, since he knew that Ralph would suffer if he lost control. He discussed the changes associated with puberty and explained how Ralph's increasing sexual drive might frighten him.

Another matter which disturbed Ralph was that the therapist opposed his mother's wishes regarding his coming to the clinic, and continued to insist that her advice be ignored. The therapist discussed Ralph's negative transference relationship in some detail because he feared that Ralph might otherwise leave treatment. A child in a negative state of transference believes that the therapist is a dangerous, menacing, or seductive person who must be avoided. Ralph had been able to accept the therapist's interpretation of his hostile aggression since he had already recognized his hostility to his mother and occasionally to others in his family; but he was disturbed by the sexual material discussed in therapy, especially when he began to realize it was related to his mother. He was upset by his mother's denunciation of the therapy and felt guilty about defying her wishes.

Ralph listened attentively to the therapist's explanation about his negative reaction to treatment. His quick perception of unconscious behavior and his strong tie to the therapist helped him to overcome his negative reaction to therapy.

Ralph's resistance persisted after this interview but it grew less intense. An active struggle developed between the clinic and Ralph's mother, however, and Ralph was in conflict about defying his mother. His rituals became quite marked, particularly those involving taking off his shoes. He had great difficulty in going to bed. He was still taking several trips to the door or even into the next room and back to his bed. He reported that he now hated going to sleep because his habits occupied so much time before he could get into bed.

By now Ralph felt that the bed was a place of danger and conflict. He repeated little prayers over and over before getting into bed, in the hope that prayer would help him get into bed more quickly.

Ralph dreamed that his teacher gave him permission to have sex relations. All the boys and girls in the room were carrying on sexual activity. He told his teacher that his mother opposed his having sex relations, but she told him it was all right to go ahead. The therapist noticed that Ralph felt no anxiety in this dream.

He realized that Ralph was becoming less conflicted about sexual matters, and that he no longer had to take his mother's injunctions too seriously.

Ralph's habits grew less frequent. One night he was able to go to sleep without performing his rituals. The next night he doubled the number of rituals to make up for what he missed. Then he missed two nights, then four nights. At this time he said, "To heck with making up for the missed habits."

It was now summer. Ralph had been in treatment for one and a half years and was being seen daily for interviews, since he had more time to come to the clinic. He reported that his mother often threatened suicide. He used to be terrified as a little child when she threatened to kill herself; now he often wished that she would die. When she told him to stop coming to the clinic he would become furious. "I got so mad I could fight any kid on the way coming over to the clinic. I could *kill* him."

Ralph had reported earlier that when he was younger he had been a good fighter. Since then, however, he had become afraid of fighting. The therapist explained that his fear probably developed when he began to feel hostile toward his mother and wish for her death. He then displaced his death wishes about his mother onto other people toward whom he felt hostility. He probably avoided fighting with other children because he was afraid he might kill them.

Ralph was looking better. He was more cheerful. He talked about being almost ready to get into fights again. This year, when the therapist took his vacation, Ralph's rituals did not increase. Some were still present, but they were less compelling. Ralph was playing football and enjoyed it, although he was not yet secure enough to fight other children.

When his mother's illness grew worse, Ralph's rituals reappeared to a moderate degree. He again talked about the little men inside him who were struggling against him. Ralph was now coming to the clinic once a week. Occasionally he missed appointments. His rituals relating to going to bed reappeared.

The therapist repeated his explanations and interpretations. He suspected that his mother's illness had stirred up an excessive amount of guilt in Ralph and told him so. Ralph's rituals persisted for some time.

He grew better again. His rituals lessened. He became attached to girls. When he fantasied having sex relations with them it no longer disturbed him, although at times he wished he did not have sexual thoughts. He again mentioned a "little man" inside of him who had first appeared when Ralph was about seven years old. At that time the function of the "little man" appeared to have been to keep Ralph from having pleasure.

Over the mother's objections the clinic staff decided to have the clinic worker visit her in her home. The worker saw the mother once a week for some time, but stopped coming when the mother told her she had no interest in continuing the interviews. Ralph's mother blamed all her trouble and Ralph's on organic factors. She felt that Ralph was as sick as ever and that the clinic had not helped at all. During this time Ralph reported to the therapist that when he told his mother that his pajamas were just slightly moist since he was wetting less during the night, she answered,

"But they are wet, that's enough." When his pajamas were entirely dry she said to him, "But you are not drinking water in the evening. Your bladder is empty. That's no trick."

Ralph was finally able to see that nothing about the clinic would possibly satisfy his mother. He acknowledged that it was silly for him to feel bad about defying her by coming to the clinic.

Two and a half years after treatment began Ralph felt much better and looked better. He still retained some rituals, although he often spent weeks without performing them. Occasionally he still felt that the "little man" inside him was trying to keep him from enjoying himself. His interviews were spaced further apart.

After three years Ralph was still having occasional spells during which he needed his rituals. He looked well, was enjoying himself, and felt more secure. Treatment stopped.

Four years later, when Ralph was seventeen years old, he dropped in to see the therapist. He had become deeply religious and was considering entering a seminary to become a priest. Most of his rituals had disappeared, although occasionally he needed to perform a few of them for a day or two.

When Ralph was twenty years old he came in for another interview. He had not entered the seminary. He was feeling well, was sociable, and enjoyed his friendship with young women. Although he had difficulty in making decisions because of his ambivalent feelings, he was much more comfortable and could probably make a comparatively good adjustment to life. The therapist told Ralph that he probably would get along well. He suggested, however, that at a later time, when he could afford it, Ralph might well have further psychoanalytic treatment.

*Ralph, now in his early thirties, has a professional career and is doing well. He is unmarried, but gets along well with women and is eager to be married. He has many friends of both sexes. Since his mother's death, he has been living away from home and has made a good social adjustment. He feels that, although he still has conflicts and is under a moderate amount of tension, he is managing to maintain his work without interruption. He feels his strong religious beliefs and participation in church activities have helped him to maintain the gains he made in therapy ("I'll never be able to thank you enough."). The ritualistic touching of objects and the ceremonials are gone—except those which are part of his religious observances. His chief problem is procrastination ("I get to very few places on time, and this is not good."). He has not felt the need for psychiatric help; however, he indicated that, if his tensions did not lessen, he would seek further therapy.

The clinical picture of obsessional character, which Ralph presented in his last interview, raises the question of whether therapy changed his illness from a disabling neurosis to a more easily tolerated character disturbance. Follow-up studies of children suffering from established obsessional neurotic illness will help to determine the later course this illness takes and the extent to which this is affected by different forms of therapy. Nor is there information available at the present time regarding what happens to children who suffered from well-established obsessional neurosis during their latency years but were not treated.

Because there are so few follow-up reports on children who have suffered from disabling obsessional neurosis, I am adding brief accounts with follow-up reports on two additional boys who were given long-time analytic therapy in our clinic.

When he came to the clinic for the first time, Fred was nine years old. He was living with his parents and his older sister and was referred to us because his peculiar habits in the schoolroom disturbed the class. He made loud throat noises, had a facial tic, touched youngsters as they walked by him, and quarreled with them. He had no friends. The parents reported numerous compulsive habits. At first they believed he did these things to irritate them; later they realized that he could not control his habits. He refused to walk behind people because he said he couldn't stand looking at their "backsides." He often touched objects, such as door knobs, dishes, and even the ground, with his mouth. He washed his hands often after touching things, and yet, he would put his finger into his nose and then into his mouth. He often repeated an act many times. He was insolent to his parents, had a terrible temper, and got into fights occasionally, even though he did not like to fight.

In his first interview with his therapist he admitted a marked fear of losing all control. He reported a dream in which he received shocks through an electric socket and yet continued to put his finger into the socket although fearful of being electrocuted. He described being bothered by terrible thoughts: "When I walk behind people I think of them sticking their fannies in my face, and I think of licking them where that stuff comes out—that makes me sick."

Fred was eager for any therapy that might lessen his disturbing symptoms. Although he complained that seeing the therapist two or three times each week kept him from his friends and play, he soon became very cooperative and remained so throughout most of his three years of psychoanalytic therapy.

A few months after therapy began, he was placed in a group which he enjoyed. He presented serious adjustment problems in the group, and the group worker needed great patience in order to protect the group from him, and him from the group. From his group experience, he learned how to live more peacefully with other children. He remained a member of a group until the close of his treatment and often referred longingly to his group experience.

Casework with the parents was intensive from the outset. There were always problems in the home, in the neighborhood, and especially, in the school, that had to be met. Fred's aggression against the parents and school was so serious that we frequently felt that foster-home care or residential-treatment care would be required for him. Fred, an unusually bright and gifted boy, seemed to sense when his parents were about to take radical steps, and managed to modify his disturbing behavior each time such a move was contemplated. After a year or so the parents were better able to deal with Fred's aggression and compulsive symptoms, especially as Fred began to respond to group and individual therapy.

After about two years of intensive therapy Fred was easier to handle at school. His schoolwork and attitude improved, and he enjoyed achieving. He liked scouting and soon did outstanding work both in school and in his scout troop. As his conflict lessened he had much more energy available for work and play. The ritualistic behavior gradually dwindled, although there were occasional brief periods of a moderate return of his "habits."

After treatment stopped, the parents came in for visits two or three times each year, and Fred came in about once a year to see his therapist. He had become very fond of the therapist and the feeling persisted.

*Recently, his parents reported to us that Fred was a junior in high school, was considered an exceptional student, would very likely win a scholarship to college, and was hoping to do research in science. He had a part time job which he was enjoying, was well liked by his fellow students, and was an officer of his class. He had become quite interested in girls and did some dating. Although he still had flare-ups of temper, they subsided quickly. According to his parents, the family as a unit was getting along fine, and Fred and his sister were good friends.

Gunther was studied at the clinic for the first time twenty years ago, when he was twelve years old. At that time he had the classic symptoms of an adult obsessional neurotic. Gunther was filled with anxiety, depression, and a feeling of having lost the power to control his movements and his thoughts. He had severe inhibitions which made it necessary for him to retrace his steps and, on several occasions, to return to a window into which he had looked in order to "pull himself out of the window." He was unable to recross the floor of his home if another person had moved over the area before he did. He used large quantities of toilet paper, trying to determine which piece to choose but unable to come to a decision, and he had other anal symptoms as well. His possessions had to be in a certain order in his room, and he feared that, if his compulsions were not followed, his dog, whom he loved dearly, might die. These were by no means all his symptoms. He was in analytic treatment for two-and-one-half years, during which time he was seen three times a week; however, during occasional periods of crisis, he was seen daily. Treatment was discontinued when he had improved sufficiently to be tolerable at home. Although he was far from well, some of his most difficult rituals and ceremonials had disappeared.

Casework with Gunther's mother was not so intensive as it was with Fred's. Even though she despaired of ever having a healthy child, she did finally take matters into her own hands and ordered Gunther to do what he insisted he could not do, and she was frequently successful. On several occasions he sat in one place, without moving all day, because his mother refused to make special adjustments for him. This behavior was not a catatonic symptom—he was in communication at all times—but he insisted that certain acts be performed in certain ways.

Gunther finished high school and later graduated from a state university. I saw him on the street occasionally and once had a few interviews with him. His symptoms persisted, but were nevertheless sufficiently modified to enable him to go on with his education.

*I telephoned Gunther late in 1960 and found that he was married and had three children. The oldest was four-and-one-half years of age. He was working for a clothing supply company and was getting along "fairly well." Although he had periods of marked tension, he never had been so upset that he could not work. He often wondered whether he should have more psychotherapy, so that he could get over his trouble entirely. I explained that this would only be possible if he had a complete analysis. Gunther said that complete analysis was not possible because of the cost and that he would have to make a go of it as he was. There was nothing to indicate the severe anxiety, depression, and feeling of being enslaved by rituals which I have seen in obsessional neurotics, and from which he suffered when he was twelve years old.

Treatment of the Parents
of the Obsessionally Neurotic Child

One of the first things parents of obsessionally neurotic children want to know is how to control their child's aggression and ritualistic behavior. They are troubled at being unable to handle him and afraid of harming him further by using their former methods. The caseworker can tell them very little, however, until she knows the child and the family better.

As she grows familiar with the situation, the caseworker can recommend when to use reassurance and persuasion as an aid in controlling rituals. She can encourage the mother to experiment with different forms of suggestion to see their effect on the child's control of his rituals. To make these suggestions, the caseworker must be in close contact with the therapist to determine what rituals the child may be able to modify. She must always be sure that the mother is not demanding too much of the obsessionally neurotic child, since he may have a very limited capacity for change.

Many of the parents of the children studied at the clinic found they could make their children more comfortable by giving them active help to overcome some rituals. One child, for example, was unable to decide which sheets of toilet paper to use and spent a long time examining each sheet, covering the floor with toilet paper. Scolding him only made him more anxious. He felt that all the other sheets would miss the ones he selected. When the therapist's interpretations failed to change his behavior, the caseworker suggested that the mother tear off a few sheets of toilet paper for the child, in this way assuming the responsibility for whatever guilt he felt. This suggestion proved to be effective.

One boy was unable to walk to the opposite side of a room when someone had crossed the path he had proposed to take. The therapist could not learn why this boy was blocked so seriously, and he suggested that the caseworker tell the mother to reassure the boy that nothing would happen to him if he crossed the room. Perhaps she could even cross the room with him. If this failed, she could have the person who had crossed the boy's path retrace his steps, thus "undoing" the action which had thrown her son into a state of conflict. The mother found that this undoing action was occasionally necessary, and lessened the problem materially. (See the case of Gunther.)

Such magical undoing of an unconsciously dangerous act is a characteristic defense mechanism in obsessional neurosis. When this boy looked into a window he had to return to look into it again before he could leave it. He feared that otherwise he would have to remain in the room overnight. Only part of him felt this danger; if necessary he could have gone away without retracing his steps or looking into the window again, but he would have been tense and uncomfortable until he returned to undo the act. From the boy's remarks about this ritual, the therapist could conclude that he was punishing himself for observing some sexual activity in which he tried to involve himself. Explaining this to the boy, however, did not lessen his need of the ritual, which undoubtedly had many other unconscious components.

The contribution which the caseworker makes in helping the parents to live from day to day during the time the therapist is attempting to discover the underlying factors which make the child behave as he does is a very important one. Her contribution is applicable to all forms of neurotic illness in children and serves the purpose of helping the parents to struggle with the behavior occasioned by the neurotic conflict.

The caseworker helps the mother deal with the school problems which, in the case of the obsessionally neurotic child, can become very involved. If the child is aggressive and hostile, or if his rituals are pronounced in school, the caseworker may need to have frequent interviews with the teacher, the principal, the school social worker, and the parents to solve disturbing problems and keep the child in school. The caseworker can usually count on the cooperation of school personnel if she is careful not to make demands which the school cannot meet. A child who is determined to control the school through his hostile neurotic aggression can make it impossible for a teacher to carry on her work with the other children in the class. One boy fought a great deal with other children at school, and he was expelled when he defied the teacher in front of the other children. He threatened to burn down the school and run away from home. His mother was terrified by his aggression until the caseworker assured her that she could arrange for placement of the boy away from home. Further interviews with the mother, however, showed the worker that removal was not necessary so long as the mother could be sure that the worker was ready to help her to deal with the boy's aggressive behavior. The worker's reassurance gave the mother sufficient strength to stand up to the boy and control his aggression. As she began to understand her own emotional conflicts, her anxiety about her son's aggression diminished. Parents as well as the school can demand conformity of an obsessionally neurotic child in a kindly but firm manner; if the child is too sick to respond, insistence on conforming can be withdrawn. The caseworker must caution the teacher as well as the parents against the use of measures which the child interprets as an attack or as ridicule.

In several cases in our group the staff was convinced that without active support, assurance, and help in managing their affairs, particularly as they related to the everyday problems of their sick child, the mothers would have collapsed emotionally. This was especially true of those parents who themselves had obsessional character traits. The constant bombardment of the ritualistic behavior of their child continuously stirred up their own repressed conflicts.

Both parents must be strong and emotionally secure to deal effectively with a child's hostile aggression in the home, particularly when he is strongly negativistic. The child may require removal from the home, since rarely are both parents of an obsessionally neurotic child free from neurotic illness. Carefully chosen foster parents who are familiar with neurotic aggression may be able to deal more effectively with such children.

A valuable resource for dealing with the hostile aggression of the obsessionally neurotic child is a residential treatment center where a trained staff can work with sick children. While in the treatment center the child continues his therapy for obsessional neurosis with the individual therapist. In extreme situations, when the parents are so disturbed and worn out by the child's neurotic illness, or are so neurotically ill themselves that they cannot handle the many problems which the child presents, the child may have to be removed from his own home during the entire period of therapy. In such cases the parents must receive intensive psychotherapy for their own illnesses.

Much of the superficial behavior of the obsessionally neurotic child is determined by the emotional make-up of his parents. Overprotecting, indulgent parents will handle the ritualistic behavior of a child differently from parents who have always demanded conformity. Rejecting parents will treat an obsessionally neurotic child quite differently from the way warm, accepting parents will. An only child with obsessional neurosis will have to face quite different problems from those of a child in a large family. A neurotic parent will behave differently from an emotionally healthy parent toward neurotic illness in a child.

The therapist who treats an obsessionally neurotic child and the caseworker who works with the parents must plan on years of effort to obtain a satisfactory result under the most favorable conditions. Improvement may result sooner, but it cannot be expected. Many periods of disillusionment occur during the treatment of obsessional neurosis in children when the staff may see little value in continuing with the child. These periods gradually disappear as the child again becomes motivated to give himself to therapy.

Obsessional neurosis has been discussed in some detail because many of its features characterize the treatment of all chronic neurotic conditions which have developed a firm hold on the personality of the child.

Author's Note

In all the cases of neurotic illness described, the children suffered incapacitating anxiety and discomfort. The ego, which normally seeks to gratify basic needs without conflict, failed to perform this function. The problem in therapy was to strengthen the ego, enabling it to function adequately. In some cases the ego had never performed adequately at any time in the child's life. To effect a change in the ego the clinic staff first had to determine the chief sources of the disturbance and then develop a plan of therapy to reduce as much as possible these disturbing factors.

Eliminating neurotic symptoms was only part of the treatment goal in making a healthy child of a neurotic one. Ego-strengthening devices, the uncovering of unconscious conflict, and the removal of external pathogenic factors were necessary before the neurotic child could make an adequate adjustment. The therapy of the child's total life situation was directed toward ensuring his continued emotional health.

The child with a psychosomatic illness was not included in the discussion of the neurotic child, because of the small number of such children referred to the Wilder Child Guidance Clinic. They usually are treated by the pediatrician or general practitioner who calls in the child psychiatrist in resistant cases requiring hospitalization. In time, physicians may refer children with a psychosomatic illness earlier, as they learn to recognize the significance of emotional factors in the life of the child.

For most of the neurotic children described, therapy was not directed toward solving the underlying unconscious causes of the neurotic symptoms. Such therapy was limited to a small number of children. Instead, the Clinic's aim was to make it possible for the child to tolerate emotional stress and live more comfortably even under difficult conditions.

Section **4**

THE CHILD WITH LEARNING PROBLEMS

The Child with Reading Disability

The problem of reading disability is so frequent (affecting 10 to 15 per cent of school children), so disabling in its severe forms, and so complex in structure that it warrants special consideration in a book devoted to emotional problems of children. Learning to read is the first task the child encounters in school, and his success or failure in performing it may determine his future attitude toward learning and toward school. A young child with average intelligence, or better, who has great difficulty in mastering this skill, while others about him read with ease, may soon begin to feel inadequate and to lose confidence in his ability to learn. Many such children are so convinced of their own stupidity that considerable supportive help is needed before they can be satisfied that they are really able to learn.

Because the literature on reading disabilities is so extensive, covering a period of more than fifty years, the recent book by M. D. Vernon,[1] which thoroughly and intelligently reviews the literature and evaluates the important studies from her own rich background and experience, is very welcome.

[1] Vernon, M. D., "Backwardness in Reading," New York, Cambridge University Press, 1957.

Professor Vernon found that there is no clear-cut evidence of any innate, organic cerebral condition which produces reading disability, except in a very small percentage of cases. Cerebral dominance, as an explanation of the disability, is still accepted by many educators but rejected by others. Dr. Abraham Fabian,[2] who reported on this aspect of the problem, states that cerebral dominance as well as left-handedness is as common in good readers as in poor ones.

My interest in reading disability began in 1927, at the Institute for Child Guidance, where Samuel Orton had come to talk to the staff on the subject of cerebral dominance. Afterwards the Institute conducted a study to determine whether visual disturbances were responsible for reading disability. The findings suggested that they were not. Others have conducted similar studies of hearing disturbances and brain damage. Most investigators who have worked with the problem of reading disability have come to the general conclusion that there is no single isolated cause and that an attempt to isolate a single cause constitutes an oversimplification.

Considerable controversy has arisen over the role teaching methods play in producing reading disabilities. It is difficult to determine this from the literature because of changes in methods, uncertainty about what each method includes, and the impossibility of assessing accurately a teacher's skill. Some teachers use one particular method efficiently; others do best with another. It would seem, therefore, that one is not justified in concluding that reading disability results from any one specific teaching method.

In the most severe forms of reading disability the child is almost totally illiterate and unable to understand the very basic processes of reading. One may speculate, as some have,[3] that such conditions are related to physiologic or pathologic defects in

[2] Fabian, A. A., Reading Disability: An Index of Pathology, *Amer. Journ. Orthopsychiat.*, vol. XXV, no. 2, April, 1955, p. 319.

[3] Pasamanick, B., and A. Kawi, Prenatal and Paranatal Factors in the Development of Childhood Reading Disorders, Monographs of the Society for Research in Child Development, vol. XXIV, no. 4, 1959.

the cerebral cortex. I have wondered at times about the possibility of a hereditary factor in such children, since occasionally we see children with severe reading disability who have parents and blood relatives with a similar disability. Several with whom we worked intensively and for long periods failed to overcome completely their difficulty in reading. Although they learned to analyze words well, they worked slowly and stumbled over all the difficult ones. Professor Vernon also found that long-time therapy with children whose reading disability was severe failed to overcome completely the reading difficulty.

Fabian [4] published an interesting study of severe cases of non-readers, in wards for disturbed children at Bellevue Hospital. He found that, when presented with horizontal figures, 76 per cent of the children rotated them to a vertical position. He then tested five hundred and eighty-six children of school age to determine the incidence of this phenomenon and found that 51 per cent of the six-year-olds rotated figures from the horizontal to the vertical position and 22 per cent of the six-and-one-half-year-olds also rotated the figures. However, the percentage dropped quickly at seven years and was practically absent by seven-and-one-half years. He suggested that this tendency placed a serious handicap on the six-year-old reader and pointed out that many children of adequate intelligence, who show severe reading retardation, achieve, in striking contrast, marked success in arithmetic, since the symbols and various operations are vertically directed. He argued that this factor must account for the differences in proficiency of children to learn the two subjects and proposed that we might do better to hold off teaching children to read until they are seven years old.

Dr. James Cunningham [5] reported a situation in a community where children were allowed to enter the first grade and to begin

[4] Fabian, A. A., Vertical Rotation in Visual-Motor Performance—Its Relationship to Reading Reversals, *Journ. Educ. Psychol.*, vol. XXXVI, no. 3, p. 129.

[5] Cunningham, James M., Psychiatric Case Work as an Epidemiological Tool, *Amer. Journ. Orthopsychiat.*, vol. XVII, no. 4, 1948, p. 659.

learning to read at five years of age. When these children entered the second and third grades, the child-guidance clinic in the community had a rapid increase in the number of children with reading problems. Later, when kindergartens were established and reading was begun at six years of age, the number dropped sharply.

The children, who are referred to our clinic because of reading disabilities, vary from those who improve rapidly with a little help to those who have problems that are so complex and who have become so disabled by their inability to read that long-time intensive therapy is needed to help them. Many were never able to read; others read well for a while and then, because of illness, inability to concentrate, or lack of interest, failed to learn one or more of the essential steps and became confused when exposed to more complex processes. Their frustration led to a real learning problem. Brief periods of review in the areas they did not understand helped some children to surmount their fixation and to return to a favorable learning situation. Those who did not respond needed special help with their reading and with their emotional problems as well.

Many problems, even some of the more serious ones, can be met in the school if the teacher is trained to deal with learning problems, if psychologic help is available for a thorough clinical study, and if a school social worker is provided to make a study of the child's home. Arrangements are needed for complete physical and neurologic examinations, during which hearing and visual tests should be made. A study of the home will reveal whether the parents are hindering the development of effective work habits. For example, they may fail to demand that the child meet his responsibilities; they may demand too much of him, so that he feels he cannot satisfy them or enjoys blocking their efforts; or they may demand too little of him, so that he finds it unnecessary to work. Many parents do not realize the importance of establishing good work habits and of active participation for the child; they are fearful that frustrations may be harmful to him. A recent book on discipline and achievement, by Phillips, Wiener, and Haring,[6] emphasizes the importance for mental health of good discipline in the children's inner lives. The book is addressed to schoolteachers and contains suggestions for helping the child meet daily and hourly demands for effort, work, and accomplishment. The child's success in doing what is expected of him gives him a good concept of himself as an active and effective person.

Many children are unmotivated to learn because they have lived for years under chronic tension and frustration. They act out their hostile aggression against all forms of authority and fail to achieve the status of socialization. Since they do not enjoy school because it is work, they fight it and do not learn. I recall a group of difficult, aggressive children with reading disability, who responded very well to a tutoring program under the direction of Dr. Mary Grace Arthur. The program was financed by WPA, and the primary effort was directed toward remedial reading, with little planning for casework and with no direct psychotherapy. The tutors were devoted to their task and in general were warm, kind, and firm teachers. When a child showed definite progress in reading, he was given a gift of a small box of chocolates, and I recall my amazement at seeing a formerly defiant, aggressive youngster blush in embarrassed pride as he accepted his little gift. It is no small achievement to motivate such a child to a point where he takes pleasure in academic progress. This experience suggests that there are few better ways to motivate a child than by developing a close, warm relationship with him. Unfortunately, too few of our acting-out children have access to individual treatment, as the high incidence of reading disability in our underprivileged groups reflects.

Many older antisocial youngsters, despite average intelligence, are so far behind in their reading that one must question the value of spending much time in attempting to teach them read-

6 Phillips, E. Lakin, Daniel Wiener, and Norris Haring, "Discipline, Achievement and Mental Health," Englewood Cliffs, N.J., Prentice-Hall, Inc., 1960.

ing skills. Time would be better spent in vocational training, for which they may be better equipped and which could give them a greater feeling of competence.

Few children with severe reading disability do not present emotional problems. They feel inadequate because, in our culture, children are expected to read. Despite real efforts to deal with the reading problem, few school systems can provide needed services, and the number of backward readers is increasing rapidly. In most cases the parents, not understanding why their child cannot read, often accuse him of not trying, blame the school for poor teaching, and fear that their child will never be able to learn. The problem is compounded by the child's feelings of inadequacy, by the parents' emotional reactions to the child and to the teacher, and by there being so little help available.

The largest number of children, referred to our clinic for inability to read or learn, suffer from neurotic conflicts. Often the inability may be the only apparent clue to the child's possible neurosis, and the condition may come to light for the first time during the study, when the emotional factors in the child and in the home are recognized.

My studies of children with learning problems, over the years, have impressed upon me the importance of sublimation in learning. When the ego is strong enough to make sublimation possible, learning is pleasurable. When the strength of instinctual drives is such that little energy is left for sublimation and learning, the child fails to learn and gains little pleasure from his efforts. This is frequently the situation in cases of neurotic conflict. The discussion that follows contains references to symbolic material which may not be familiar to the reader. I am, therefore, quoting from Jones's classic article on the theory of symbolism,[7] which so clearly describes the meaning of symbols in unconscious thought processes. Jones describes a symbol as a repre-

[7] Jones, Ernest, The Theory of Symbolism, in "Papers on Psychoanalysis," London, Balliere, Tindall & Cox, 1923.

sentation or substitute for some other idea from which it derives a secondary significance not inherent in the symbol itself.

It represents the primary idea through having something in common with it. . . . It is sensory and concrete, whereas the idea represented may be relatively abstract and complex. . . . It is more primitive and represents a reversion to a simpler and earlier stage of mental development. . . . It is a manifest expression for an idea that is more or less hidden and secret. The person using it is not conscious of what it represents. . . . Symbols are automatic, spontaneous, unconscious. . . . The affect investing the symbolized idea has not proved capable of sublimation.

Waelder, in discussing sublimation,[8] cites the following from Freud's "Five Lectures on Psychoanalysis," published in 1910,

"We know of a far more expedient process of development [i.e., more expedient than repression, says Waelder] called sublimation, in which the energy of the infantile, wishful impulse is not cut off, but remains ready for use—the unserviceable aim of the various impulses being replaced by one that is higher, and perhaps no longer sexual. It happens to be precisely the components of the sexual instinct that are specially marked by a capacity of this kind of sublimation for exchanging their sexual aim for another one which is comparatively remote and socially valuable. It is probable that we owe our highest cultural successes to the contributions of energy made in this way to our mental functions."

Hartman,[9] in his study of sublimation, relates the stability of ego function to its ability to resist regression and sexualization. He adopted the term *neutralization* for the change of both libidinal and aggressive energy from instinctual to socially useful forms. Unless this change can be made, the ego's ability to master reality remains weak. Pearson[10] stresses the importance of

[8] Waelder, Robert, "Basic Theory of Psychoanalysis," New York, International Universities Press, 1960, p. 122.

[9] Hartman, Heinz, Notes on a Theory of Sublimation, in "The Psychoanalytic Study of the Child," vol. X, 1955.

[10] Pearson, Gerald, A Survey of Learning Difficulties in Children, in "The Psychoanalytic Study of the Child," vol. VII, 1952, p. 322.

the ego's mastery and its ability to withhold attention from other subjects that try to intercede in the learning process. When instincts become overly demanding, the child becomes distractible, except to the drives. We have encountered several instances of such inhibitions to learning in adolescents with deep sibling rivalry. We have seen similarly dramatic, total inability to learn in very bright adolescents who for years had excelled in scholarship, until the driving aggressive force with its strongest competitive components made further neutralization of instinctual drives impossible.

According to Hart,[11] sublimation consists of a lessening of the aggressive components of pregenital drives. These are the ones that need modification. It may be that the failure to sublimate aggression accounts for the marked inability of aggressive youngsters to learn to read. The ability to form sublimations is proportionate to the ability to endure frustrations, which in turn depends on a warm, positive relationship to the parents. Only under such conditions can a child forego pleasure and accept frustration and reality. His capacity to love allows the child to identify with his parents and thus to sustain his sublimation. In this way the child learns to master reality, an important step in maturation. When the demands of the parents are met in fear instead of with love, repression and reaction formation result. The success of sublimation depends on the absence of repression, for sublimation requires that energy from instinctual drives be released to the ego for socially acceptable goals, such as education. If the drive is repressed, its energy is no longer available to the ego. Sublimation therefore depends on a relatively strong ego and a tolerant superego, so that repression may be avoided.

Investigations of reading disability by psychoanalytically trained therapists have suggested ways in which unconscious emotional conflict may inhibit a child from learning to read.

Phyllis Blanchard was one of the first psychoanalytically trained

[11] Hart, Henry, Sublimation and Aggression, *Psychoanalyt. Quart.*, vol. XX, no. 3, 1948, p. 389.

therapists to make a careful study of the emotional factors involved in severe reading disability.[12] She studied seventy-three children with unimpaired intelligence, whose reading abilities were from one to six years below their mental ability and grade placement. They were taken from their classrooms, away from the scene of discouraging competition, and were tutored by carefully selected teachers who could form warm relationships with children. Those who responded to this measure continued until their reading improved. Those who failed to respond were diagnosed as suffering from emotional conflict, requiring psychotherapy, and were given treatment.

One of Dr. Blanchard's children appeared to be a well-adjusted eleven-year-old boy who, she felt, would respond readily to tutoring. When tutoring failed, however, he was placed in intensive therapy. For a while he read fairly well; then, suddenly, he was unable to recognize words and made numerous errors. He would stop reading and start weaving a fantasy which had been stirred up by the material he was reading. In this way he described his mother's leaving him to go to work, his mother's leaving him for an operation, and a teacher's leaving for an operation from which she never returned, so that he never learned what happened to her. He showed considerable hostility and guilt toward these people who had deserted him. There was an apparent relationship between his reading difficulty and his emotional conflict.

In one of Dr. Blanchard's cases, a boy, with marked hatred for his sister and mother who favored the sister, expressed his hatred through the use of play material. He was using a toy printing set to print, with many errors, the names of wild animals. In the course of his printing he suddenly panicked, afraid that the letters would reach up and bite him, and begged the therapist to put away the printing set and paper.

Normal aggressive drive is required for carrying on all activities.

[12] Blanchard, Phyllis, Reading Disabilities in Relation to Difficulties of Personality and Emotional Development, *Mental Hygiene*, vol. XX, no. 3, 1936, p. 384.

Aggressive components are a part of eating, playing, sexuality, protection, escape, relationships to others, and learning. Children who are deprived of affection and security and who are, therefore, chronically frustrated react with hostile aggression, which is often excessive and leaves little aggressive energy for learning. In our culture we may expect boys to react to frustration more aggressively than girls, and this may help to explain the high incidence of reading disability and general failure to learn among severely deprived boys. It is especially noticeable in institutions for delinquent boys and will be referred to later in connection with a study by Fabian.

In some instances the opportunity for externalizing aggression may be blocked, and the ego may attempt to find expression for aggression, symbolically, in reading. Dr. Blanchard refers to the frequent failure of children with reading disability to establish masculine identification. They cannot deal adequately with aggressive impulses and suffer guilt over hostile, destructive, and sadistic feelings. She feels that the problem of dealing with aggression, which is greater in boys, helps to account for the frequency of reading disability in boys.

Bessie Sperry and her coworkers [13] selected a group of boys with reading disability who expressed fear of falling. Their study revealed a relationship between motor activity, restlessness, and reading disability. These boys asserted their masculinity and autonomy through successful motor activity, and they seemed to have abandoned any attempt to solve their problems at the level of symbolic thought (through learning), because it was too intimately related to their unconscious conflicts.

In 1930 Strachey [14] noted a direct connection between unconscious factors and difficulty in reading. He stated that, when underlying instinctual drives are not sublimated but retain their

[13] Sperry, Bessie, Nancy Staver, Beatrice Reiner, and David Ulrich, Renunciation and Denial in Learning Difficulties, *Amer. Journ. Orthopsychiat.*, vol. XXVIII, no. 1, 1958, p. 98.

[14] Strachey, James, Some Unconscious Factors in Reading, *Int. Journ. Psychoanal.*, vol. XI, 1930, p. 322.

original character, reading will meet with hindrances. His material suggested that the oral libidinal components were predominant in the unconscious background of reading, especially the oral sadistic component.

In their work with children, Sylvester and Kunst [15] found a specific connection between reading disability and the evolution of the exploratory function. These children lacked the courage for the active curiosity which is required to master reading. Sylvester and Kunst found that, when the child's zeal to explore was blocked, he often interpreted exploration as unacceptable and dangerous. If, on the other hand when the exploratory function was overindulged, the child also found exploration threatening, presumably because he had seen more than he could assimilate without anxiety. Reading then became a danger that had to be avoided.

Melanie Klein [16] stated that castration fear is the basis for all early and subsequent inhibitions and that the repression of the active masculine component in both boys and girls provided the chief basis for inhibitions to learning. Research in this area is needed to determine the situations that foster increased castration anxiety in those who develop reading disability. Perhaps we will then be in a position to explain why more boys than girls have reading disability.

In contrast to the cases in which the conflict is primarily in the child, Bessie Sperry and her coworkers [17] studied a group of boys who were unsuccessful in their learning because of specific emotional factors in their parents. School failure enabled them to secure some dependent satisfactions from their parents. In spite of their conscious efforts, the parents' unconscious conflicts pro-

15 Sylvester, Emy, and Mary Kunst, Psychodynamic Aspects of the Reading Problem, Amer. Journ. Orthopsychiat., vol. XIII, no. 1, January 1943, p. 69.
16 Klein, Melanie, The Role of the School in the Libidinal Development of the Child, Int. Journ. Psychoanal., vol. V, 1924, p. 312.
17 Sperry, Bessie, David Ulrich, and Nancy Staver, The Relations of Mobility to Boys' Learning Problems, Amer. Journ. Orthopsychiat., vol. XXVII, no. 3, 1957, p. 640.

duced in one of their children the conviction that he could be secure only through failing.

The implication in these and in other studies from the psychoanalytic literature is that inhibition in reading results when a child attempts to express his unconscious sexual and aggressive impulses symbolically by way of the reading of letters and words. This occurs in children when sublimation is either unstable or incomplete. It is more likely to occur when the child is threatened by castration because of repressed incestuous fantasies. The ego recognizes the attempt to find this outlet through the reading process and inhibits learning.

The cases cited in a study by Dr. Abraham Fabian [18] more clearly resemble the larger percentage of children with reading problems, observed in child-guidance clinics and social agencies. Fabian studied material from several sources where reading disability was discovered and was convinced that the most significant factors were psychological.

In his studies Fabian defined reading disability as more than a 25 per cent deviation from the norm for the child. He found such disability in 10 per cent of the children in several second grades, with 95 per cent of them being boys, though the sexes were evenly divided in his samples. In his child-guidance clinic population, 33 per cent of the children had reading disability; of these 66 per cent were boys. In a placement agency for very disturbed children, 62 per cent showed reading disability; of these two-thirds were boys. In an observation unit for disturbed children at Bellevue Hospital, 73 per cent had reading disability; of these, 84 per cent were boys. Fabian concluded that reading disability was one facet in a complex picture of personality difficulty and could be used as an index to the extent of the pathologic condition of the child or of the conditions to which he had been subjected.

Most of the children we have treated at our clinic for reading disability had problems in motivation. Their deficiencies stemmed

[18] Fabian, A. A., Reading Disability: An Index of Pathology, *Amer. Journ. Orthopsychiat.*, vol. XXV, no. 2, April 1955, p. 319.

from living conditions that made learning impossible as well as from conflicts within themselves that prevented sublimation for learning. Great efforts had to be directed to their parents who suffered from emotional problems of their own. When casework made it possible to modify the conflicts and attitudes of the troubled parents, the child was in a much better position to learn and to receive help in bringing his work up to grade. During the process of giving him this help with his school subjects, he was given the emotional support and encouragement he needed in order to want to work and learn. By the time the child was well on his way, his parents were in a position to give him the support required to sustain his efforts.

When the parents' attitudes could not be sufficiently modified, we had to depend on the encouragement of teachers, who had followed our treatment efforts and were willing to provide the added support. Individual therapy with children was necessary to clear up misconceptions about their parents who, they believed, preferred other children in the family, demanded perfection beyond their ability, and in many ways were dissatisfied with them. Usually the children were somewhat justified in their beliefs about their parents, and they needed help to understand their parents' feelings. In most instances the child's conflicts were confined to conscious and preconscious levels and could be resolved in due time. When the conflicts were unconscious, our efforts were directed toward giving the child some insight to his problems, in weekly interviews. Improvement in these cases, however, came only partly from insight. More often the child responded to the support of and management by the therapist, an identification with the therapist's educational goals, and the improved attitude of the parents.

When weekly interviews fail to result in improvement of the neurotically conflicted nonlearner, more intensive therapy is necessary. In many instances child analysis will be required to permit the release of pathologic libidinal fixations, to lessen guilt and anxiety, and to strengthen the seriously weakened ego. I feel it is very important to continue remedial help with school subjects while therapy is in progress, since rarely is the child prepared to do the work of his classmates even after some improvement in his emotional state. The mistake is often made of delaying remedial work because the problem is largely one of social or emotional conflict.

One cannot stress too much the importance of well-trained, warm, understanding, capable teachers in all grades, but particularly in the early ones. Liss [19] points out that each teacher unconsciously assumes a parental role with her pupils, whether she teaches for her own essential satisfactions or for the creativity and sublimation which gives power to others. Her way of teaching has been conditioned by her concept of the parental role in her own life experience. Tulchin [20] feels that the child who is very backward in reading does best with a teacher for himself. He stresses the need for flexibility in remedial work with any child, for changes may be indicated at each tutoring session, especially during the initial stages of therapy, when so much depends on overcoming resistance. Reynolds [21] advocates daily periods of remedial work for children with learning disabilities, to maintain gains. Knowing the child very well through frequent contact helps the teacher to determine at what point individual psychotherapy may be required.

Early recognition and treatment of the child who has shown evidence of reading disability are essential. Since so much of his future feeling about education and school depends on his enjoyment of learning, everything possible must be done to ensure his success in reading. The help may come from changes in the parents and in the school or from direct treatment of the child's emotional conflicts.

A child who has been backward in reading for a long time has

[19] Liss, Edward, Motivations in Learning, in "The Psychoanalytic Study of the Child," vol. X, 1935, p. 100.

[20] Tulchin, Simon H., Emotional Factors in Reading Disabilities in School Children, *Journ. Educ. Psychol.*, September, 1935, p. 443.

[21] Reynolds, Maynard, Professor of Education, University of Minnesota, in a talk to our staff, 1958.

been emotionally traumatized and needs special instruction. His feelings of failure and confusion often can be lessened only by an individual teacher, who can deal with the child's own particular emotional and educational needs. Dr. Beulah Ephron [22] reported the case of a child whose mother had read to him for sixteen years, in an unsuccessful effort to improve his reading. Interviews with the mother revealed that she had always resented having to read to her son and had obviously not given him the deep affection her behavior implied. He was assigned to a reading therapist who was soft and maternal and who found great enjoyment in the success of each one of her students. She introduced the activity with these words: "Let me read this story to you; I would *so enjoy* reading it." This was true, she did enjoy reading to him. The results were almost immediate and astounding. The improvement was so marked that the boy's teachers wondered what had happened to effect such a change.

In general, parents are not effective in tutoring their children in reading. They are usually impatient with careless errors and annoyed when the child repeats a mistake which had just been corrected. Much of this irritation results from their anxiety about the child's ability to learn. However, there should be no hard and fast rule for parents who attempt to tutor poor readers. I have known many patient, untiring parents who have worked effectively, and their children developed confidence in their ability and finally learned to read.

Despite the efforts of a great many educators, research workers, and clinicians, a satisfactory solution to the problem of reading disability has not yet been found, largely because so many different factors influence it. Research studies must continue until methods are discovered which will lessen the suffering that results from a child's inability to learn to read.

[22] Ephron, Beulah Kanter, "Emotional Difficulties in Reading," New York, Julian Press, Inc., 1953, p. xiv.

Section 5

THE CHILD WITH PERSONALITY PROBLEMS

In his "New Introductory Lectures" Freud wrote:

"The thing which is so hard to define but which we call 'character' must be thought of as belonging entirely to the province of the ego. We have already learnt something of which it is that creates this thing called character. The incorporation of the early parental function in the shape of the superego is no doubt the most important and decisive element; next come identifications with the parents of a later date and with other persons in authority, and the same identifications as precipitates of abandoned object-relations. We can now add to this list, as contributions to character-formation which are never absent, the reaction-formations which the ego acquires, first in making its repressions, and later in a more normal way in repudiating undesirable impulses." [1]

[1] Freud, Sigmund, "New Introductory Lectures on Psychoanalysis," trans-

Character problems and disorders have been studied by psychoanalysts for approximately the last quarter of a century. Research on the ego, particularly its mechanisms of defense, has given us a clearer insight into the emotional factors in learning problems, character disturbances, and dissocial acting-out behavior. This information has proved invaluable to child-guidance clinics in their work with youngsters with behavior problems.[2] Anna Freud's valuable studies of the ego in children are described in her book, "The Ego and the Mechanisms of Defense." [3]

The chief function of the ego is to maintain constant conditions in the organism, a state of emotional equilibrium or homeostasis.[4] The child with a strong ego supported by a healthy constitution, good health, and accepting, loving, mature parents is well prepared for a satisfactory emotional adjustment to life. When the ego is not under attack by a tyrannical superego or crippled by early emotional traumata, it can repress dangerous drives which jeopardize the child's existence. It can make effective compromises between dynamic forces, preventing the need for excessive repression and reaction formation, and in so doing can keep available the energy which might otherwise be needed to repress instinctual drives. A strong ego can give these drives a maximum amount of safe expression without producing anxiety and illness. It uses the healthy defense mechanism of sublimation, or helps the personality face the impulses and deal with them by self-control or renunciation. It attempts to change the person's environment to permit the drives some form of expression.

By contrast, a weak ego develops defenses which themselves

lated by W. J. H. Sprott (International Psychoanalysis Library, no. 24) New York, W. W. Norton & Company, Inc., 1933, p. 125.

[2] See "The Psychoanalytic Study of the Child," edited by Ruth S. Eissler, Anna Freud, Heinz Hartmann, and Ernst Kris, vol. V., 1950, and vol. VII, 1952, New York, International Universities Press, Inc.

[3] Freud, Anna, "The Ego and the Mechanisms of Defense," London, Hogarth Press, Ltd., 1937.

[4] Alexander, Franz, "Fundamentals of Psychoanalysis," New York, W. W. Norton & Company, Inc., 1948.

cause suffering. Excessive repression beyond the ego's tolerance, reaction formation which usurps energy, projection of the conflict which creates problems, and masochistic self-punishment are a few of the unhealthy defenses a weak ego may set up. Defense mechanisms develop early in the child's life and become absorbed as an integral part of his character structure.

It is difficult to classify abnormal characters as specific entities because the criteria overlap. The terms used to describe children in this chapter are not categories of particular character make-ups, but refer rather to outstanding personality traits in children whose behavior sets them apart from others. Such children appear in a child-guidance clinic frequently enough to warrant individual consideration since they often require different methods of treatment. While neurotic conflicts contribute to these personality problems, the clinical picture is not one of neurotic disturbance or illness. It is the ego's unusual response which marks the child as being different and which is responsible for his being referred for therapy.

The Withdrawn Child

A child withdraws from other children and adults to seek safety. Actual or fantasied demands made on him by other people stir up discomfort or anxiety; early experiences or physical injuries or humiliations have conditioned him to feel inferior. He dares not expose himself to situations which resemble those that traumatized him. Since other children, similarly hurt or offended, react with tears or tantrums or aggression against the offender, the traumatic incident itself does not entirely explain the withdrawn behavior.

Often the pattern of withdrawal is present in one or both of the child's parents, who may be self-effacing and have few social contacts. They refer the child for study in the hope that treatment will eliminate the kind of behavior which has caused them so much suffering.

Since the essential problem in these cases is withdrawal from activity with other children, group therapy is the method of choice to help the withdrawn child learn that other children are friendly and safe. The group should be small and include children who are not aggressive or destructive. Another withdrawn child may help the patient feel at ease, especially if he tends to withdraw from the group therapist also. As he realizes that the group experience is relaxing and makes few demands of him which he cannot meet, the withdrawn child may find it possible to relate himself

slowly to others, having learned with the help of the group therapist that he can do some things as well as the other children.

Five-year-old Roy would not utter a word at school. His kindergarten teacher occasionally succeeded in getting him to participate
in a game, but he was painfully ill at ease and quickly withdrew.
The other children wanted him to join them, but he rejected their
offers and they finally gave up.

When the individual therapist at the clinic attempted to talk
with him he grew so tense that he was immediately taken down to
the therapeutic group. He was ill at ease there and stood against
the wall and watched the other children at play. After several
sessions in the group the individual therapist joined him in the
playroom and slowly interested him in small tasks. By degrees
Roy's rigidity lessened and he let the therapist put his arm about
him. When asked questions about members of his family, he
answered 'yes' or 'no' by shaking his head. Within a few weeks
he allowed the therapist to teach him to make plaster molds
and occasionally whispered a few words in response to questions.
His rigid posture disappeared and so did his pained expression
when he tried to answer simple questions.

Roy was encouraged to join the other children in play and
then to talk and sing with them. The parents, also shy and withdrawn, reported that Roy enjoyed the group and looked forward
to his trips to the clinic. He had never enjoyed attendance at
the kindergarten, overwhelmed by the activity of the other children and aware that he was failing to do what was expected of
him.

Roy ate and slept well and showed no fears. He was happy at
home, played with the other children in the family, and talked to
them and to his parents. His behavior changed abruptly as soon
as he left his home. Roy did not give the impression of being
neurotic; he was an inhibited child.

*Roy is now eleven years old, and his father reports that he is
doing very well. He has improved every year and gets out and
plays with children. His teacher reports that he behaves like all

the others in the room, even making faces at them when her back is turned. He spent a week at camp last summer, was shy the first couple of days, and then had a fine time. The father attributes Roy's improvement to his therapy with the psychologist at the clinic. He is still not the outgoing go-getter his brother is, but is able to make friends and defend himself if other boys go after him. He has been active in a Little League baseball team and did quite well.

Many more instances can be cited of children who avoid activities which at one time caused them unhappiness. They withdraw from athletic contests, expecting that they will be beaten; they avoid popularity contests and running for office for the same reason.

The mechanism of limiting participation in activities is one of the methods to avoid a painful reality which Anna Freud [1] described in children. The very young child avoids painful reality by fantasy and through play. As he grows older he is less able to tolerate such methods and looks for another way of dealing with situations. He begins to avoid activity in which he feels he will fail and suffer pain. Anna Freud refers to this behavior mechanism as a restriction of the ego, and regards it as preliminary to the development of a defense. The ego is able to give up this method of avoiding reality if the conditions become more favorable.

Rudy, a fourteen-year-old adolescent boy, illustrates the mechanism of ego restriction. Although he was physically fit and presumably capable of participating in sports, he refused to enter into them with his contemporaries, and preferred to stand watching on the sidelines. He avoided all athletic activities and withdrew to his home where he read a great deal. He carried books around with him wherever he went and was nicknamed "Professor" because he read so much. Rudy had strong feelings of inferiority and preferred to play with younger children whom he could excel and dominate. He turned down a chance to go to camp because he

[1] Freud, Anna, "The Ego and the Mechanisms of Defense," London, Hogarth Press, Ltd., 1937.

knew that the counselors would not tolerate his withdrawal from competitive sports. He is now in treatment, is aware of his problem, and is determined to find out why he has to exclude himself from competition.

Rudy's withdrawal is not a neurotic symptom. The restriction of his behavior is not based on an avoidance of guilt-producing conflict. If forced to enter into competition with his peers, Rudy would feel ashamed because of his ineptitude, not guilty because he was doing the forbidden. He would be recreating a situation which at one time had caused him pain and embarrassment.

In contrast to Rudy, an obsessionally neurotic adolescent boy with homosexual conflict came to the clinic because he was almost completely unable to relate himself to others. He was ill at ease with them and could not get away from them fast enough. He avoided all competitive games that children his age enjoyed, partly because he lacked physical vigor and had poor coordination. The chief factor in his inhibition, however, was neurotic and was reflected in his fantasies while watching a football game. He imagined that a huge machine was crossing the gridiron and crushing the players in its path. When he listened to a broadcast of a football game, the shouting of the spectators was evidence that the crushing was taking place.

Nonneurotic withdrawn behavior based on inhibition responds comparatively well to therapy. Reassurance and other ego-strengthening devices which encourage self-confidence will lessen a child's feelings of inferiority and provide him with sufficient courage to make an effort to participate. The therapist helps the child accept a little pain and humiliation and to expect poor performance in the beginning. He stands by the child in therapy until inhibition is overcome.

Withdrawn behavior calls for therapy when it jeopardizes a child's development, when the child is dissatisfied with his behavior, and when his parents or others are disturbed by his withdrawal. All withdrawn behavior is not inimical to a child's welfare. The therapist must consider the constructive aspects of avoidance which protect the child from physical and psychologic pain, and he can help the parents understand this. When restriction of the ego results in the child's avoiding one activity after another, however, the ego may become functionally impaired and the child's development will suffer. There is the further danger that reality will become more and more difficult and the child may regress into a neurotic illness.

Withdrawn behavior which is due to neurotic inhibition will not clear up until the factor responsible for the anxiety and inhibition is understood, or until the ego is strong enough to carry on the activity without conflict.

CHAPTER 13

The Overprotected Child

Overprotection almost always results from an intense, all-embracing relationship between the parents and child. In most instances the mother overprotects the child, beginning early during the period when the child is helpless and dependent. The mother's overprotective attitude often develops during her pregnancy while she eagerly looks forward to a longed-for gratification. In many instances the mother attempts to keep the child exclusively for herself, and is successful in doing so when the father is passive and dominated.

A mother who cannot see the ill effects of overprotection on her child's future adjustment is overreacting to her own narcissistic needs. Levy [1] found such mothers decidedly unresponsive to therapeutic efforts by caseworkers and psychiatrists.

Both parents are more likely to overprotect the child when they have waited many years for a pregnancy; when a child has suffered a serious illness or accident in early life, especially involving the brain; or when they have previously lost a child whom the overprotected child replaces. Under such conditions the child becomes overvalued and treasured.

---

[1] Levy, David M., "Maternal Overprotection," New York, Columbia University Press, 1943.

The behavior of a child who has been markedly overprotected varies with his mother's treatment of him. The dominating mother tries hard to mold the child as she wishes him to be. The indulgent mother abandons the child to his own emotional development, making only weak attempts to modify his behavior. [2]

The child who has been overprotected but controlled at the same time usually does not present disturbing behavior to his environment. His binding dependency on his mother prevents his making contacts with other children and so he has not learned the art of relating himself to them. He feels different and isolated, and resents his mother whom he blames for his unhappiness.

The child who has been overprotected and indulged presents a serious problem in adjustment. Accustomed to having his own way and to feeling secure in the protection of his mother, he will continue to live on the basis of the pleasure principle. He will be unable and unwilling to accept frustration and will lack the capacity to give of himself to others. He is unmotivated for therapy that attempts to get him to relinquish his drive for pleasure and accept the reality principle. Casework with his parents is no more rewarding, since in most instances parents who have permitted a child to develop in this manner are immature and incapable of involving themselves in prolonged treatment.

Neal came to the clinic for the first time when he was eight years old. He demanded his own way at home, in school, and with his friends. He had been indulged since early childhood. He began to rebel openly when his brother was born, and he demanded from his mother the same attention she gave to the baby. He refused the usual foods his mother served, so she prepared foods which he ordered, fearing that he otherwise would become undernourished and sick. Neal soiled himself frequently and wet his bed. He feared the dark and awakened often from frightening dreams. His attacks on his brother became more and more violent and at times he beat him mercilessly.

Neal's mother was a hard-working, neurotic woman, guilty in

[2] *Ibid.*

her relationship to her parents and siblings, whom she allowed to dominate her. They ridiculed her inability to control Neal and warned her he would develop into a gangster if he did not learn to behave. After trying ineffectually to control Neal's behavior, the mother gave up in despair.

Neal's father was a kind, passive laborer, somewhat dull and unconcerned about Neal's behavior. He was certain that Neal would outgrow this "childishness" and saw little need for clinic treatment. Repeated attempts were made to have him come to the clinic. The school found Neal a behavior problem, he refused to work on any assignments and was cocky and clownish in the classroom. The other children disliked him.

Neal showed no interest in therapy, although he was fond of the therapist and enjoyed his clinic visits. He blamed his difficulties on the school and on his mother, whom he ridiculed as inconsistent and stupid. The mother filled her interviews with complaints about the school, her husband's refusal to punish Neal, and Neal's cruelty to his brother. She recognized that she had indulged Neal excessively until the new baby was born. Now he refused to permit her to behave differently, and she felt helpless in dealing with him. After a few weeks of complaining to the worker, the mother decided that she had had as much help as she wanted at that time and so treatment was discontinued.

Neal was referred to the clinic again when he was eleven years old. He was still intensely jealous of his brother and cruel to him. He ignored his mother's attempts to control his behavior, defied her, and laughed at her. His soiling persisted and he had asked permission to talk to the therapist again to see if he could learn to control his soiling. He was no more motivated to carry on treatment than in his first period of treatment. He came late for his appointments and wanted to play rather than discuss his problems. Neal's mother impressed the caseworker as being more helpless with Neal than she had been previously. She had given up any hope of changing his behavior; someone else was going to have to do that. She rejected a plan to place Neal away from home, and insisted he was going to have to learn to behave at home or pay the penalty.

Neal's behavior, as described, continued for several years. He made unreasonable demands, that were met by the mother. The agency caseworker visited the home repeatedly and got a clear picture of the quarrels between the mother and Neal, which usually ended by their screaming at each other and Neal's running out of the house. The father remained passive, not entering into the quarrels. The caseworker noted that the mother made many unnecessary demands on Neal, which irritated him, and she suggested that Neal be allowed to assume greater responsibility for himself. She convinced Neal's mother that there were ways of dealing with Neal's problems, without help from a caseworker, and demonstrated that talking quietly to Neal and using reason were more effective than emotional outbursts.

*Recently the caseworker learned that Neal is in the Navy. His difficult behavior persisted, though before he left for the service, he was arguing less with his parents, but he still insisted on having things done for him. He writes often to his parents and is homesick, and when he visits them, he is very pleasant.

Fortunately, all parents who overprotect children do not have unalterable personality needs. They are amenable to change when helped to realize that their overprotection of the child may be more harmful than helpful.

Dale suffered from encephalitis when he was two years old. He was unconscious for thirty-six hours during his illness and was not expected to live. He was moderately paralyzed for a time after the illness. He was the second of two children, and both were dearly loved by the parents. Dale's illness disturbed and frightened his parents, and in spite of the warnings of their physician, who tried to point out the dangers of overprotecting Dale, they continued to overprotect and indulge him for the next two years.

Dale was five when he first came to the clinic, and his right hand was still weak. He rarely used it in his play with small objects. His treatment was mainly confined to the preschool therapy group which he attended twice a week for ten months. His parents described his behavior at home as obstinate, destructive, and extremely restless and uncontrolled. He had no fears, according to the parents, and often ran out into the street in the midst of traffic. His early behavior in the clinic was in marked contrast to this, and he showed a real capacity to control his aggression. He played nicely with the group and was considerate of the other children.

Difficult behavior like Dale's is often attributed to organic complications following encephalitis, so-called "postencephalitic behavior." More often than not this behavior is the result of overprotection and indulgence by anxious parents who fear the effects of frustrating a child who has suffered from brain damage.

At first Dale's parents had difficulty in applying limits to his aggression. Their concern lessened when they realized how easily the clinic staff controlled him, and they began to see that their attitudes were contributing to Dale's uncontrolled behavior. After several months of casework treatment the mother reported that she was slowly gaining in her ability to be firm with Dale. Within a short time she reported that Dale allowed her to put him to sleep without a struggle, and she had believed previously she would never achieve such a feat. After eight months of treatment the mother felt that Dale had improved sufficiently so that she no longer needed to come in for regular casework interviews. She continued to see the caseworker every month, allowing Dale to come regularly to the group, until Dale was playing nicely with other children in the neighborhood and was ready to enter school.

*Dale, now eleven years old, is in the fourth grade in a parochial school. He can read and spell, but is having difficulty with arithmetic. He is not a behavior problem in school and gets along quite well with other children. He has grown a great deal, and in spite of his physical handicap, he plays baseball and hockey and enjoys these sports. He becomes frustrated at home and has temper reactions, but they are by no means as frequent as they used to be. He still pounds his head when he is very angry. He is able to sleep by himself and no longer insists that someone sleep with him. For a while he was taking a mild tranquilizing medication, but it was not administrated routinely.

Dale's mother feels more comfortable in managing his behavior and is doing better with him, although his father continues to be quite protective. The mother is concerned about high school and the possibility of a vocational choice for Dale. She would like the clinic to reevaluate Dale when he is in the seventh grade.

Parents often overprotect a child because they unconsciously reject him. Unable to tolerate the fact that the child was unwanted, they repress their hostile feelings and not only accept him but give him an exaggerated amount of attention and affection. Overanxiety in such instances often accompanies overprotection, and both are reaction formations set up by the ego to keep unconscious hostility from consciousness. A careful observation of the parents' handling of the child and the way they deal with problems and discipline discloses their ambivalent feelings. Their overprotection has a sadistic quality which punishes and limits the child. They will not permit him to skate or swim because of the danger involved, even when danger is ruled out. He must follow rigid health rules because his well-being demands it, although none of his friends is subjected to these precautions.

Parents who overprotect their child because of unconscious rejection usually are tense and uneasy during interviews. Their hostility to the child is often close to the surface, stirred up by the rebellion or neurotic behavior which brought him to the clinic. When allowed sufficient time, they will be able to discuss their hostility frankly with the caseworker. This is well illustrated in a case August Aichhorn reported in seminar in 1930:

Gretel was a seven-year-old girl brought into court on complaints of neighbors that she had been severely beaten by her father. The beating had taken place at an evening meal when Gretel refused to eat her food. The father was very angry because, according to him, the mother was doing so much for her child, was over-solicitous about her, and Gretel was unappreciative. They had tried different methods to get her to eat and when she stubbornly refused the father had beaten her.

Aichhorn first spoke to the father, who left the impression of being a hard-working, kindly man. Aichhorn felt that the father, seeing the child react defiantly to a very lax mother, wanted to use stricter methods in order to help his daughter. He then spoke to the mother, who was a pleasant person and appeared to be very fond of the child. She reported that the father was ordinarily a mild and kindly man but lost his patience when greatly provoked.

When Aichhorn spoke to the child about her activities with her mother during the day, she described how from the moment she got up, her mother ordered her to do things. "Your shoes need shining." "Have you brushed your teeth?" "Let's see the back of your ears." Her briefcase was examined to see if all her books were there. When she returned from school the mother asked, "How was your work?" "Did you behave?" "Did you get good marks?" "What are your assignments for tomorrow? Let's see if you can do them." If Gretel was not able to do the work for the next day's assignments well she had to repeat it at home.

Aichhorn commented that this mother was mishandling her child without physically touching her. Gretel's refusal to eat was a protest against her treatment during the day. She was trying to show her father what pressure she was under, but he misunderstood and sided with the mother.

Aichhorn called the mother in again. It was useless to ask her why she reacted this way to the child because she did not know. He learned from her that she had only one child. He asked her if she had ever lost a child or if she had ever had a stillborn child. She answered "No," and began to cry. She explained that she was not the mother of the child but her stepmother, adding that the child did not realize this nor did the social workers know it. "I cannot allow my husband or anyone else to say I have neglected this child and that nothing will ever become of her because she has no mother." This explained to Aichhorn why she had to be conscientious, but it did not explain why the mother had only one child. He told her that she was hiding something, and she admitted that when they were married she and her husband decided not to have any more children because "children of two marriages never get along well." When Aichhorn asked her if she was satisfied with this arrangement she said she was not but that there was nothing she could do about it.

Aichhorn concluded that the mother was not a kindly, loving woman with this child; she was overacting to an unconscious wish for the death of the child so that she could have children of her own. He decided that the best solution to the family problem was for the mother to have a child of her own. Even though this might traumatize Gretel, the stepmother could feel more kindly toward her and could be a much better mother for her.

In spite of the mother's objection to Aichhorn's talking to the father, because she did not want him to know how she felt, Aichhorn did talk to the father. He, too, was anxious to have more children, but he did not want the stepmother to know how he felt. The matter ended in the parents' agreeing that it was to their own and to Gretel's best interests that they have children. This was the surest method of stopping the overprotection which Gretel could not tolerate.

Unconscious hostility or guilt based on deeper underlying conflicts often are not revealed in casework interviews, and a mother who rejects her child because of an unresolved incestuous conflict may require psychoanalytic therapy before she can gain sufficient insight to relinquish her overprotective measures.

In many instances overanxiety, which usually accompanies overprotection of a child, has no relationship to the mechanism of unconscious rejection. The caseworker or therapist must be careful not to imply that a mother deeply rejects her child or has unconscious hostility toward him unless facts substantiate this. Excessive neurotic anxiety about a child may express a deep need for punishment because of unconscious guilt feelings unrelated to the child. For example, a deeply religious mother whose church forbids the use of birth-control measures, or who has performed self-induced abortions, may suffer from neurotic guilt because of these practices. Because she dearly loves her child, her guilt takes the form of anxiety that something may happen to the child she loves, and she overprotects him in consequence.

The Effeminate Boy

With few exceptions the effeminate boy feels out of place with other boys. He is unable to accept himself because his behavior is unacceptable to his parents. Parents find it hard to remain complacent about effeminate behavior in their son. Aware of the rejection he will meet away from home, they may begin early to attempt changing his behavior by offering him boys' toys when he indicates a preference for girls' toys.

The most difficult problems arise when parents are overly concerned because their son is not a "real" boy. Conditioned by his own life experiences with this problem, a father may decide early that he will not ignore his son's feminine interests until it is too late. He overlooks the fact that his anxiety may intensify rather than lessen effeminate behavior. The child may be conditioned to continue with behavior that has brought him so much attention, and behavior patterns which might otherwise have been temporary may persist because of the emphasis they receive. In his eagerness to effect a change in his child, an overanxious father may resort to punishment and ridicule, and produce in the child an unconscious need to punish him in return by acting in an effeminate manner.

In some instances neurotic parents who have an unconscious

need for an effeminate boy nurture feminine interests and behavior without being aware of it. When their unconscious need for an effeminate boy stems from hostile destructive wishes involving castration, the adjustment of the child is seriously threatened.

Mothers who badly wanted a daughter instead of a son may treat the boy like a girl. They dress him in girls' clothes and let his hair grow long. The boy's reaction to such maneuvers will depend to some extent on his constitutional make-up. Some boys tolerate being treated as a girl during their early years and accept this role. Others protest violently when they are denied the kind of toys and activity they want.

On rare occasions an effeminate boy may have a girl's constitutional body structure although he has male genitals. The writer studied a nine-year-old boy who had a very delicate frame, small feet, hands with tapering fingers, a small waist, and a slight increase of fatty distribution on the abdomen and hips. This boy walked, talked, and acted like a girl and had no masculine interests. The endocrinologist who examined him attributed the developmental anomaly to chromosomal factors rather than endocrine dysfunction. There was no opportunity for a follow-up study of this boy.

Occasionally effeminate boys enjoy dressing themselves in girls' clothes. Their unconscious need to be girls forces them into this behavior, and they resist attempts to change it. When such a child does not respond to the usual therapeutic measures, intensive analytic therapy is indicated. This direct therapy will include educational measures to encourage active aggressive play. Intensive treatment of both parents will be necessary to uncover what they are doing unconsciously to nurture the boy's wish to be a girl. Treating the parents also may reveal other factors in the child's life which encourage him to try to be a girl rather than a boy. Favoritism for a girl by the parents or other close relatives may be a decisive factor in producing a need to be a girl.

The unconscious wish to be a girl, referred to in the discussion of obsessionally neurotic children, is present in many neurotic boys who do not evidence effeminate behavior. Occasionally they indulge in play with dolls, but they are ashamed of it and do it secretly.

Many boys have feminine interests without in any way wanting to be girls and without displaying effeminate mannerisms. They are gentle and afraid of aggression; they select relatively passive boys for companions or prefer to play with young children. If they are encouraged to join their peers in aggressive play, they may do so and in time lose their fear of aggression. Their behavior in this respect is similar to that of the child with ego restriction. These boys probably always will be more gentle and less aggressive than the average male. Their choice of vocation or profession may be based on this quality in their personality.

Most of the effeminate children who have received therapy at the Wilder Child Guidance Clinic were referred during the period of latency when they were seven to ten years old, after problems of behavior had developed. Many, though not all, of these problems were reactions to the child's effeminacy. Occasionally a parent more sensitive to this problem may refer a child during his preschool years.

Glen's treatment began when he was eight years old. His school asked for help with him because he clowned a great deal, was restless, and was generally disliked by the children and teachers. His mother mentioned Glen's effeminacy early in her first interview with the caseworker. She explained that his feminine interests disturbed his father who had hoped for a strong paternal relationship with Glen. Glen had two older and two younger sisters who presented no problems of behavior, but although the father felt close to them, he had looked forward eagerly to having a son as a companion. The mother said that she too was disappointed with Glen's effeminacy, and felt that maybe she should only have had daughters. Glen at one time had dressed in girls' clothes, but he stopped this activity when his parents and relatives ridiculed him.

Glen seemed to have little respect for his parents, especially for his father who correctly sensed his son's rejection. Though Glen had feminine mannerisms, he was active, sometimes destructive about the house, and reading was his only quiet pastime at home.

His psychologic examination showed Glen to have average intelligence with better than average achievements in reading. On the Rorschach examination he was cautious in his responses; he showed no real identification with a father person. He showed warmth to the mother figure, though there was evidence of anxiety in this relationship.

In their early relationship Glen impressed the therapist as being a bright boy, gossipy and talkative, with no outstandingly effeminate mannerisms or gait. He tended to blame others for his difficult behavior at school. The caseworker reported that the mother seemed to be a neurotic, domineering woman, depreciative of men in general, and particularly her husband and Glen, who she felt resembled each other. Glen's father, who ran an unsuccessful electrical supply business, was unhappy. He had little self-confidence and was often depressed.

In the first three therapeutic sessions of play with two other children, Glen avoided any play involving aggression. The group therapist noticed that Glen appeared to act more effeminate when frightened by the aggression of other children. He seemed to use his effeminacy as a defense against attack. On such occasions he would put his hands on his hips and say, "Oh, dearie me," or "Heavens to Betsy."

The staff concluded at the initial conference that Glen was a neurotic, effeminate boy in sexual conflict. His destructive behavior was directed toward his mother whom he feared and loved, and toward his father whom he depreciated. He appeared to be identified with his more successful dominating mother and sisters who were making good social adjustments. Girls seemed to fare better than boys in his home. The treatment plans called for continued work with the parents and individual and group therapy with Glen.

In his weekly interviews with the therapist Glen rarely acted in an effeminate manner. He enjoyed talking and constructed elaborate fantasies of attack and destruction. He allowed the therapist little opportunity to understand his behavior through discussing his fantasies. He jumped from one activity to another and from one story and fantasy to another.

The caseworker tried to lessen the mother's fear of Glen's aggression. His mother was afraid that Glen would become seriously delinquent by the time he grew up, probably because she identified him with a relative who had terrorized her when they were children. The worker tried to encourage her to give her husband greater recognition, but she could do little until much later in treatment. The father in the meantime became increasingly discouraged about his failings. An occasional interview with the worker seemed to improve his spirits, but he soon grew depressed again.

During the next few months Glen continued to be passive and frightened of aggressive activity in the group. In spite of his fear, however, he provoked other children to attack him by brushing against them during their play. The addition of two passive boys to the group seemed to add to Glen's courage. At about the same time another aggressive boy entered the group and Glen was less threatened by him than by the other aggressive boys, since he was more kindly, tolerant, and deeply passive. After observing his behavior, Glen began to imitate him, started to attack the punching clown gently, and gradually became more aggressive in his attack. He plotted with the newcomer to attack the passive boys in the group. During this period much of his effeminate screaming disappeared, and his voice seemed to grow deeper and more masculine. Unfortunately, another aggressive, sadistic boy was added as a final member to the group. Glen feared this boy, and his appearance in the group precipitated a regression to more effeminate behavior. The group therapist noticed that during a period when Glen's mother was ill he was very disturbed and seemed more effeminate.

The individual therapist found that Glen, when left to his own devices, would spend most of his time telling bizarre, fantastic stories. When the therapist insisted that the fantasies no longer be brought into the interview Glen calmed down and they talked to each other. On one occasion the therapist succeeded in talking to Glen about his fear of aggression. He explained that Glen was afraid to be a boy because of danger connected with being a boy.

His mother reported that she had decided to permit Glen to listen to "Captain 11," a thrilling adventure serial on television. She had denied him this program for a long time because of its overstimulating effect on him. Immediately after each serial episode, however, Glen acted out the entire performance, screaming at the top of his voice. In spite of his mother's threat to forbid him the program again if he continued to reenact it, Glen was unable to stop. His extreme rage when the program was again denied him stirred up his mother's fear that he was capable of the most extreme violence.

Glen continued in therapy for a year and a half since he seemed to be responding and would become secure enough eventually to give up the effeminacy which was his defense against anxiety. The unconscious danger he was avoiding in this way was castration. Glen's identification with his mother symbolically castrated him. When he turned from his mother to his father he was again castrated, since his father was passive, dominated, and neurotically castrated. Glen's identification with his mother offered him some security since the mother was the strong parent in the family. He defended himself by identifying with the aggressor.

Glen's mother was slowly beginning to realize that her husband must play a more active role with Glen. The individual therapist was attacking Glen's view of himself as a helpless child, helping him to discover why he was afraid to become more masculine. The make-up of the play group was changed to meet Glen's needs.

Glen's fantasies of aggression and bloodshed and his need to reenact dangerous adventures suggested that he was trying, at least in fantasy, to deny the effeminacy which threatened him. It supplied him with an outlet for externalizing the danger that threatened him internally.

When Glen's case was closed his mother felt that Glen was getting along better; he was less excitable and more tolerable in school. However, a year later the school social worker came in for a follow-up conference and reported that Glen was still acting up and was a problem in school. We felt that little would be gained by seeing him again at the time.

*When his therapist asked the mother for an evaluation toward the end of 1960, she reported that Glen was presenting many problems that disturbed them and that they had planned to call the clinic for further help. She also reported that his interest in violent episodes had continued. Glen was composing stories, hoping to have them published, and although the mother believed he had real talent, she was threatened by the intensely morbid nature of these stories. She felt he still showed signs of effeminacy.

Glen's relationship to his father had not improved. His mother blamed herself for it, aware that she had done little to better the situation. The therapist felt, as he had before, that the mother had a need, symbolically, to castrate the father as well as Glen. The mother's relationship to her husband continued to be poor, but she planned to continue living with him. She was planning to reinstitute treatment for Glen and was looking forward to helpful interviews with the caseworker. Glen was eager to come in again to see his therapist and to show him the stories he was writing.

It appears that Glen's character problems are deeply anchored and will not respond readily to therapy. He will be given another opportunity, in the hope that he has matured sufficiently during the interval to be more amenable to treatment. The caseworker hopes that the mother will respond, but is not hopeful about changing her deeply hostile feelings toward men.

Dr. Martha Macdonald [1] reported several passive effeminate boys who externalized their aggression in uncontrolled attacks of rage. She felt that they were attempting through their aggression to deny their effeminacy. These boys, like Glen, all had dominating mothers and passive ineffectual fathers with whom they were unable to develop a positive relationship. During their rages they were capable of the most serious type of sadistic, aggressive, antisocial behavior.

Much of Glen's behavior warrants concern that he, too, unless helped, may become more desperate as he grows older and act out some of his hostility now confined to fantasy.

Effeminacy is not synonymous with homosexuality, though many homosexuals are effeminate. One of the underlying fears of parents of effeminate boys is that their sons will become homosexual. They are relieved to learn that this is not inevitable, even when the effeminate child does not receive therapy.

[1] Macdonald, Martha Wilson, Criminal Aggressive Behavior in Passive Effeminate Boys, *Amer. Journ. Orthopsychiat.*, vol. VIII, January, 1938, p. 70.

CHAPTER 15

The Narcissistic Child

The child conditioned by early traumatic experiences to withdraw the libido onto his own ego and become narcissistic illustrates the difficulty in classifying children into personality groups. While we can differentiate a child who is markedly narcissistic from one who is not, narcissism may characterize children with vastly different histories. A delinquent child's narcissism keeps him from considering the effects of his dissocial behavior on others. A neurotic child's narcissism makes him seek excessive amounts of interest and concern for his own personal emotional needs. The autistic child does not dare invest his libido in others and remains narcissistic. As in the case of the other qualities discussed in this section, the narcissistic child will be considered as a separate entity because the treatment methods required to modify narcissism are often different from those used to treat other clinical conditions.

Freud's article on narcissism [1] continues to be the clearest exposition of this subject. He describes the self-preservative aspect of narcissism which protectively limits the susceptibility of the individual to outside influence. This may block the child's ability to relate himself to others, and so interfere with his development,

[1] Freud, Sigmund, On Narcissism—An Introduction, in "Collected Papers," vol. IV, London, Hogarth Press, Ltd., 1925, p. 30.

but the child's personality requires this mechanism to remain intact.

The infant gives up his primary narcissism when he invests his mother or mother substitute with libido in return for her affection, tender care, and protection. When he is frustrated in the process of socialization he temporarily withdraws the libido from his mother and applies it to his own ego. The free exchange of libido from the object to the ego, and back to the object, is a measuring rod of the child's accessibility to influence, and a reflection of his state of well-being. The seriously neurotic child who is fixated to a neurotic parent may be unable to withdraw libido from that parent.

The rejected, unloved child must withdraw his libido from the objects which traumatize him. Children vary considerably in the ease with which they withdraw libido from others onto their own ego, and this has been considered by many authorities to be due to constitutional differences. Excessive withdrawal of libido surcharges the child's own ego with libido, and produces chronic tension and a hypersensitivity to any criticism in the child. He tends to be selfish and demanding, and overreacts to prohibitions. He tries hard to find objects in whom to invest libido, and in his search he may select not only persons, but animals and inanimate objects. His hypersensitivity and distrust make it difficult for him to develop significant ties to persons.

Few children are so narcissistic that they cannot develop any libidinous relationship to other persons. This fact is often overlooked in attempts to explain behavior by theoretical mechanisms. That a child cannot effect a tie to many people does not mean that he cannot develop a relationship to anyone.

One of the most inaccessible children known to the clinic, who had been rejected from the time of his birth, had been completely unable to relate himself to a succession of foster parents. He had moved from one foster home to another because the foster parents could not or would not accept him without receiving some warmth or acceptance from him in return. He was cruel, tormenting, and inconsiderate; he regarded all adults as intolerant and punishing. Each move from a foster home intensified his narcissistic behavior so that when he was nine years old the child-placing agency decided they could do little for him. They tried one more foster home, to all appearances little different from the other homes in which he had lived. The foster mother was kind, firm, and understanding, but so had been several of the others. From the outset the boy found it easier to like this foster mother and her seventeen-year-old son. Before long he was enjoying the home, was making an effort to be liked, and by degrees developed a strong tie to the family. His behavior problems greatly lessened.

Whatever methods were used by these people, they established that a strongly narcissistic child can form a strong emotional tie when the conditions are right. Such a child usually relates himself to an object. He finds something narcissistic in the object with which he can identify and proceeds to love himself in the object. In time, if the person he has chosen remains consistently warm and friendly to him, the narcissistic libido changes to object libido and an object relationship results.

An infant deprived of a warm, close relationship during the early months of life loses an opportunity of learning to give and accept affection. Spitz [2] conducted a series of research studies involving the mother-child relationship during the first year of the infant's life and demonstrated the destructive effect on the infant's development when he has been deprived of an early intensive relationship to his mother. Under these conditions the infant retains his primal narcissism.

Many studies have shown that children who remain in an institution for the first two to three years of their lives invariably

[2] Spitz, Rene, The Psychogenic Diseases in Infancy, in "The Psychoanalytic Study of the Child," vol. VI, 1951. New York, International Universities Press, Inc., p. 255, and, Relevancy of Direct Infant Observation, *ibid.*, in vol. V, 1950, p. 66.

become markedly narcissistic. Beres and Obers [3] made follow-up studies on thirty-eight children who had spent their first three years of life in an institution and then were placed in foster homes. Their studies showed that these children were very difficult to control. They were unable to tolerate frustration, were insistent on immediate gratification, and failed to respond with warmth when attempts were made to give them affection. They craved demonstrable affection and could not be satisfied with the amount they received. They were irritable and subject to violent temper outbursts. They learned poorly at school, behaved badly, and showed little consideration of others.

According to Beres and Obers, all the observers but Lowrey [4] felt that the characters of these children were irreversible. Seven of the children in Beres and Obers' study developed satisfactory emotional adjustments by the time they reached adolescence. Beres and Obers attributed the improvement they found largely to the children's opportunities for developing close, stable relationships to adults, either through a placement situation, a casework relationship, or psychotherapy.

Lowrey found that providing for these deprived children the cushioning experience of living in a small group, cared for by adults who were genuinely interested in them, helped the children to develop in all ways within a year, so that foster-home placement was possible and worked out successfully.

The therapist must keep in mind that the narcissistic child will welcome the opportunity to develop a real object tie to the therapist, for only in this way can the child rid himself of emotional tension. The therapist must direct his effort toward convincing the child that unless he can learn to trust adults and give them affection, he will have a difficult time in life. The narcissistic child may need a good deal of urging to continue coming in for interviews, espe-

[3] Beres, David, and Samuel Obers, The Effects of Extreme Deprivation in Infancy on Psychic Structures in Adolescence—A Study in Ego Development, in "The Psychoanalytic Study of the Child," vol. V, 1950, p. 212.

[4] Lowrey, Lawson, Personality Distortion and Early Institutional Care, Amer. Journ. Orthopsychiat., vol. X, no. 4. October, 1940.

cially when he feels that he does not have a problem. The goal of therapy is to help the child realize that it is safe to love another person.

Arny was nine years old when he first came to the clinic. His parents and teachers felt that Arny needed help in learning to be more considerate of others. He was sadistic to his siblings and to younger children in the neighborhood. No one seemed to like him, but this did not bother him much. He read a great deal, was interested in science, and had a vast fund of information about scientific matters.

Lack of consideration for others was his outstanding trait. He told the therapist that he hated both parents and both sisters. He was convinced that his parents preferred his sisters to him and announced that someday he would get even. He had his secret way of killing them and no one would suspect he was the one who had done it. He planned to pierce a thin metal object into their hearts and hoped the therapist would say nothing about this to anyone. He felt no remorse about almost killing a visiting relative who had denied him something he wanted. He had purposely thrown a knife which would have struck her had she not moved quickly. She deserved to be killed, he said, because she always blamed him for things he did not do.

Arny looked hard and cold and often sneered when he talked about stupid adults and children whom he met. He boasted about his ambitions, which were justifiably high since he was very bright. No one was close to him and he felt close to no one. In spite of his coldness and frank hostility toward his family and contemporaries, Arny seemed lonely and yearned to be close to someone.

Both his parents were concerned about Arny. Neither seemed to be warm or particularly attached to the other. Both found it easier to feel close to their daughters who accepted affection. Arny had never wanted affection, they said, and even when a year old he had managed to keep them from holding him on their laps. He grew more cuddly later, but they felt this was to compete with his sisters rather than because he really enjoyed it.

His mother was an energetic, attractive young woman who formed quick, warm, superficial relationships with others. She had a great many friends, none of whom were very close to her. She was attracted to men and enjoyed their company, preferring them to women. She tried very hard, she said, to love Arny but he had always fought her. He was closer to his father, but she did not think he really loved his father either. She reported nursing Arny for several months. She said she had looked forward to his birth and had wanted several children, but had grown less enthusiastic after her experience with Arny. She felt he had become hostile toward her when his first sister was born and had never forgiven her.

The caseworker felt that the mother had really never had affection for Arny; she was eager for help but would need analysis to achieve a real capacity for relationships to others. She had a very poor relationship to her own mother and described incidents in her life as a child which were extremely traumatic. Apparently her mother was an unusually vain, narcissistic, cruel woman who had resented her child and always fought with her. The mother had been unable to forgive her mother, but had also been unable to lessen a neurotic attachment to her.

When Arny's mother found that he could not feel close to her, she began to reject him and then grew bored with him, much as she reacted to grownups whom she did not like. From time to time, however, she made frantic efforts to get Arny to like her by buying him expensive gifts and taking him with her on trips. She felt that these efforts had failed to improve their relationship.

In the group-therapy sessions Arny was cold and distant with the other boys. He showed little interest in what they were doing and only occasionally extended himself to become friendly with any of them. For the most part he was selfish, hostile, and provoking. He seemed to enjoy getting the boys to fight each other, while he stood by and laughed.

The group therapist sensed times when Arny wanted to feel close to her but these periods never lasted long. Whenever an occasion arose, she pointed out to Arny how his behavior was making him disliked by the group, but although he listened to her attentively and seemed interested in what she was saying, he was unable or unwilling to change his behavior toward the other children.

In contrast, he slowly developed a positive tie to his individual therapist. At first he said that he enjoyed coming for interviews to get out of school. Later he admitted that he enjoyed talking to the therapist, and his parents reported that he looked forward to his interviews. The therapist frankly discussed with Arny any unfavorable reports which the school made about him. He scolded Arny for making so little effort to get along with his sisters and his mother. The therapist pointed out to him that he wanted everything done for him without in any way attempting to do for others. Specific instances of quarrels with his friends and members of the therapy group were taken up in detail to show him the part he played in producing problems. The therapist told Arny that he suspected that underneath his hostility to his mother, he felt a good deal of affection for her, but he resented having to share her with his father and his sisters. The therapist explained that his mother had loved him at one time and would love him again if he gave her a chance.

After two years of treatment Arny was quite friendly with his therapist, enjoyed talking to him, and even missed him during his vacation. He apparently realized it was safe to trust the therapist. Complaints from the school lessened, and his mother reported that he was playing with several friends in the neighborhood. Although Arny was beginning to relate to others, a much longer period of treatment would be needed to make him a comfortable youngster.

*Arny moved from the city and did not receive further therapy. After the clinic study, Arny spent two years in a private school for boys; he made a slow start, but then began to make friends. In his last year at the school he led his class in grades. He is now in a public school and is doing well. He has many friends—boys and girls—and seems to be getting along well socially. The family has remained intact.

Deeply established narcissism responds very slowly to treatment. A child who withdraws from relationships with others to defend himself must have a severe anxiety problem. He is denied the opportunity of turning to others for solace and release of tension when reality frustrations mount. He has no one who is significant to him, to whom he can turn. The importance of recognizing early that a child is reacting in a narcissistic manner cannot be overestimated. Help must be instituted before the tendency to isolate himself emotionally becomes established.

A child who cannot attach his libido to a love object is in a dangerous position. We are justified in being concerned about such a child and exerting considerable effort to effect the change in him that will make a positive relationship to another person possible.

CHAPTER 16

The Child with Neurotic Character

Neurotic character is defined differently by authorities who have written on this subject. In general the term includes a neurotic individual who has internalized his conflicts, but expresses them in general personality traits rather than neurotic symptoms. The neurotic character, for example, may show evidence of unconscious guilt feelings and a deep need to be punished, but he does not have such neurotic symptoms as paralysis of the extremities, loss of vision, or the rituals of the obsessional neurotic. He may be as sick or sicker than the neurotic patient and more difficult to treat; the difference lies in the way the conflict expresses itself.

Glover's discussion [1] of the term *character neurosis* in psychoanalytic terminology clarifies much of the confusion which still surrounds pathologic character. Glover found that in the course of analytic treatment neurotic characters often produce transitory neurotic symptoms. The appearance of these symptoms demon-

[1] Glover, Edward, Pathological Character Formation, in "Psychoanalysis Today," Sandor Lorand (editor), New York, International Universities Press, Inc., 1944, p. 218.

strates that the neurotic character is formed by the same kinds of instinctual drives which produce neurotic symptoms. In the case of the neurotic character, the ego has modified the instincts so that they are acceptable as character traits. When the same instinctual drives are rejected by the ego, they are repressed and produce neurotic symptoms. These same instinctual drives, when distributed over all the waking thoughts and activities, may pass unnoticed, since they are acceptable to the social order in this manner. Most normal individuals in this way find lesser outlets for their instinctual drives in their daily life experiences. When these drives are excessive, however, they are rejected by the social order and then appear as neurotic character traits or neurotic symptoms.

The same processes very likely occur in children also. The amount of effort required in therapy to modify character problems in children seems related to the extent to which neurotic conflict has been absorbed by the character. The inhibited child, who suffers little neurotic conflict, usually will be much easier to treat than the child whose character is extensively infiltrated by neurotic conflict, as in hysterical or obsessive character neurosis. The number of cases of severe neurotic character manifestations treated in the Wilder Child Guidance Clinic is small. The number of children with mild or moderate neurotic character involvement is much larger.

The Child with Hysterical Character

The child with a hysterical character tends to be infantile, over-emotional, flighty, impulsive, self-deceptive, histrionic, and dishonest. Hysterical characters are superficial in their love relationships, passionate in their likes and dislikes, and overdemanding of affection. They fantasy excessively.[2]

Arthur, a markedly unstable and flighty adolescent boy, was

[2] Spurgeon, O. English, and Gerald Pearson, "Common Neuroses of Children and Adults," New York, W. W. Norton & Company, Inc., 1937, p. 223.

sexually preoccupied and fantasied excessively.[3] He had great difficulty in concentrating on his schoolwork and had few close friends. Children liked him but found him bizarre because of the unbelievable stories he told. He frequently stared into space during an interview and was startled when the therapist called him by name. He was afraid of the dark, suffered from anxiety dreams, and felt guilty about his frank sexual fantasies. He was subject to violent tantrums and overreacted to minor frustrations. He occasionally stole from stores and had been in sexual difficulties with younger children, though these difficulties were never serious.

Arthur's parents were in a continual state of friction. Threats of divorce, much drinking, quarreling, and accusations of infidelity were common. Arthur was exposed to sexual scenes which overstimulated him and made him feel anxious and guilty. When most upset, Arthur would fantasy that a tunnel led to his home under an open field, which he feared to cross at night. This tunnel was populated with animals who were ready to protect him whenever he was in serious danger.

The therapist succeeded in getting Arthur to speak frankly about his many anxieties and guilt feelings. He was particularly disturbed by his sexual thoughts and wishes about his mother and his hostility toward his mother and father. He was tortured by sexual fantasies related to religious characters in his church, and was convinced that he would have to pay a tremendous penalty for these wishes in the hereafter. The therapist's attempts to get at underlying conflicts failed, and he discontinued them when it became obvious that Arthur was threatened by any stimulation of unconscious material. After he was assured over and over again that there was no danger of his carrying out in real life any of his violent wishes, Arthur lost much of his anxiety. When his anxiety lessened materially, his protective fantasies

[3] Lippman, Hyman S., The Case of Arthur Laplante, in "Psychiatric Interviews with Children," Helen Witmer (editor), New York, The Commonwealth Fund, 1946, p. 378.

stopped. Attempts by the therapist to stimulate the fantasies at such times failed.

Arthur's sexual fantasies diminished and his masturbation became less frequent as he became more secure. A follow-up study several years later indicated that he had retained his improvement in spite of many upheavals in his family during the intervening period.

Children with hysterical characters are no more consistent in their efforts to work with their emotional problems than they are with their life situations. Their statements to the therapist will be unreliable for a long time in therapy and he must repeatedly point out inconsistencies. Their enthusiasm about therapy seldom persists long enough to permit the development of insight. They are most likely to respond to a consistent, warm relationship that helps to neutralize the emotional tensions in their homes.

The Child with Obsessional Character

Many gradations lie between the normal child who has an occasional compulsive trait and the so-called "obsessive character" who has personality characteristics which make life difficult for him and those with whom he associates. Many of these character traits have already been mentioned in the discussion of the obsessionally neurotic child. The obsessive child tends to be stubborn and defiant, since obsessional characters, like obsessionally neurotic children, are fixated at the anal stage of libido development.

The number of such children in the Wilder Child Guidance Clinic case load is small, and the few children treated as severe obsessional characters were very resistant to change. Their outstanding characteristic was marked stubbornness and inability to accept opinions different from their own. They were industrious and perfectionistic in their schoolwork. They tended to mix poorly with children, not because of a narcissistic withdrawal, but because they did not seem interested in relating to others. One sensed the presence in these children of many fixed inelastic character traits which they used to prevent the *irruption* of underlying anxiety. They distrusted therapy since it might disturb the rather rigid set of defenses that kept them free from danger.

One child with many of these obsessive character traits had conceived a country of his own with mountains, rivers, and farm lands well distributed. The cities were divided by streets and avenues named after famous people or members of his own family. The city contained all of the important public buildings any large community would have, and each of these also had a special name commemorating some important character. The child could repeat every one of the hundreds of details which he had laboriously worked out on a map, and the amount of detail in his creation must have required concentrated effort over many months. This boy controlled what the therapist could discuss with him, and the therapist abided by his rules because an occasional infraction precipitated marked anxiety.

Children with obsessional neurotic characters usually have parents with similar character make-ups. The child either has an inherited tendency to become fixated at the same level of libido development as his parents or he is conditioned by the neurotic atmosphere in the home to become fixated. Identification probably plays the important part in the child's taking on personality characteristics of obsessional parents; imitation could not effect such a character change.

An interesting example of this condition in reverse occurred in a fifteen-year-old boy whose mother was a severe obsessional neurotic. She tried very hard to make her son carry out the rituals that enslaved her. She punished him when he stubbornly refused to cooperate, and she pleaded with him to do such things as wash his hands frequently after touching objects that were in any way soiled. She would ask him to wash his hands before he turned on the water faucet and then again after he had turned it off, and to try turning off the faucet with his elbow rather than touching it with his hands. She failed in her attempt because her son obviously did not identify with her. When he was fifteen years old he ran away from home and succeeded in locating his father from whom his mother had been divorced for many years.

Most of the lesser obsessional disturbances studied at the Wilder Child Guidance Clinic showed as many positive as negative qualities derived from their characters. These children were persistent in their efforts to tackle a difficult assignment, had great powers of organization, were reliable and thorough. Whenever the dominance was in favor of such positive characteristics, therapy to modify perfectionistic drives or excessive orderliness was not attempted.

Many factors produce definite personality characteristics in the individual which remain with him through life. Such factors as deviations in body build, illness, especially severe illness, and particularly illness which affects the central nervous system causing brain damage, and deviations in intelligence may profoundly affect the development of the child. The extent to which parents can continue to love a child who is a deviate largely determines whether the deviation will produce character disturbances. A great difference in the capacity for self-acceptance, for working up to intellectual ability, as well as relating positively to others exists between a mentally retarded child who is loved and accepted by his parents and one who is rejected. Traumatic incidents in the life of a child, especially during the early developmental years, may seriously affect his character structure. The loss of a father through hospitalization, imprisonment, or death may mean not only the loss of a loved object but also the loss of a masculine identification figure.

One other factor of significance is the effect on the personality of accidental influences which cannot be determined or recognized. The slow change in a child from being passive to becoming more aggressive is almost imperceptible, and yet, after a few months or a year, one notes in some children a rather marked character change that could not have been predicted. One could continue with the subject of personality problems to include others, since there are many that merit the consideration given the ones described. Descriptions of personality problems are not confined to this chapter; the subject has already been discussed in the section on neurosis and will be discussed again in the section on acting-out behavior.

Character structure can be modified by reaching the early determinants of character formation. Negative influences which shape the character adversely must be recognized early and eliminated. This is prevention at its best.

Section 6 |

THE CHILD WHO
ACTS OUT

The term *acting out* denotes aggressive behavior which expresses
an unconscious fantasy or wish. Since his action symbolizes an
unconscious wish, the person who acts out does not know what his
behavior means.

The term was used originally by psychoanalysts to denote the
patient who acted out his deeper feelings instead of discussing
them, dissipating the unconscious wish or fantasy in activity rather
than trying to understand it. Acting out in such situations is discouraged in favor of the patient's talking about his feelings.

In therapeutic work with emotionally conflicted children, play
therapy represents a form of the child's acting out his unconscious
thoughts and feelings through the play characters. By translating
this play activity back into the thoughts which the child is expressing, the therapist learns to understand the child better and
explain his feelings.

More recently, *acting out* has been used to denote aggressive antisocial behavior which expresses underlying conflict. The child who acts out aggressive impulses is attempting to resolve his emotional tension. The delinquent child acts out frequently because he is in a chronic state of tension and unrest. Despite the pleasure he seems to obtain from acting out his dissocial wishes, the delinquent is unhappy and insecure. Acting out satisfies him no more than neurotic symptoms satisfy the neurotic child. Both forms of behavior are unsuccessful attempts to gratify deep needs.

Acting-out behavior is hard to change because it is a form of defense best suited to the particular child's needs. Having been denied love, he lives on the pleasure principle, unwilling and unable to accept frustration. The emotionally healthy child, secure in his love and acceptance, is content to accept prohibitions because he is loved. The unloved child has little to gain from conforming; moreover, he feels like punishing his parents.

The most seriously rejected children, continuously deprived of affection, fail to develop social controls. Aggression, to be of service to the child in his development and social adjustment, must be neutralized by libidinous components. Freud, in his revised theory of aggression, postulated that aggression is a primary instinct seeking constant expression and gratification. When unneutralized by the love of the parents, the aggression drive assumes the most brutal, wanton character, destroying objects and life with no consideration of the suffering it causes.

Only when aggression and the sexual drive (libido) are fused can aggression serve the ego in a socially acceptable manner as an important component of normal behavior. Anna Freud [1] has defined the many ways the child needs aggression in his development and described the pathology that occurs when aggression is deficient. She mentions the tendency of the young child to direct aggression against himself when an external outlet is unavailable

---

[1] Freud, Anna, Aggression in Relation to Emotional Development: Normal and Pathological, in "The Psychoanalytic Study of the Child," vols. III and IV, 1950, p. 37.

and differentiates such aggression against the child's own body from masochism, which occurs later when the superego has developed. Aichhorn [2] considered that every child tries first to be aggressive toward an external object. He reacts against himself only when all external opportunities for aggression are blocked. He applied this principle to a plan of therapy for dissocial behavior which will be discussed in the cases of acting out to be presented.

Aggression is the child's normal reaction to frustration; it is his means of letting his environment know when his basic needs are not gratified. The child who exhibits an excessive amount of aggression is not in emotional equilibrium. Study of children who are excessively aggressive demonstrates that they are denied their normal needs for aggression, that their other instinctual needs are not being gratified, especially their need for affection, or that physical or physiologic pathology is present. Malnutrition, lack of rest and sleep, overstimulation, or infection frequently make a child unable to tolerate frustration.

The most common underlying factor in a lowered frustration tolerance is ego weakness. A weak ego cannot control aggression, especially early in life when it cannot rely on the superego for support. The significance of the early affectionate tie between the infant and his mother has been already emphasized. The absence of this close relationship is particularly significant in a child's becoming excessively aggressive and unable to tolerate frustration. Child-guidance-clinic studies demonstrate pathology in the parent-child relationship in almost all cases of serious delinquency in children.

Rejection of the pregnancy and the infant at birth occurs frequently in the families known to social agencies. Because rejection jeopardizes the future life adjustment of the child, it is important to discover as early as possible whether or not a child is rejected and unloved. When no effort in treatment succeeds in changing the parents' rejecting attitude toward the child, particularly in the

[2] Aichhorn, August, seminar, Vienna, 1930.

case of a mother with a young child, radical steps must be taken, otherwise the cost in suffering to the child and the community may be tremendous. A mother who is immature and inconsiderate, who has not learned to assume responsibility and cannot give her child genuine affection, must be helped to give up her child as early as possible. Her contribution to her child's welfare can only be destructive, since her clinging to him prevents his finding someone else to give him the love he needs. Many mothers may reject their children for understandable reasons, but they are still capable of accepting them emotionally. When the factors which interfere with a mother's accepting her child without reservation are eliminated, the rejection may disappear. With assistance from a social agency or other help, such a mother may be able to provide the emotional climate her child requires.

When a neurotic mother is unable to develop a consistent positive relationship to her child, she may periodically reject him, as Anna Freud has recently reported.[3] Behavior in the developing child may stir up dormant conflicts in the mother, and she may react by rejecting the child. She may, however, be rejecting his behavior rather than the child himself. Under such conditions it is important for the child's welfare that the mother be helped to understand why she reacts as she does to her child. Kate Friedlander[4] in a recent study demonstrated that intensive therapy helped such mothers to accept children whom they had rejected previously.

Beatrice Reiner and Irving Kaufman recently published a study on the character disorders of parents of delinquent children.[5] All the parents who were studied were fixated at pregenital levels of development, and their arrested development con-

---

[3] Freud, Anna, Safeguarding the Emotional Health of Our Children—An Inquiry into the Concept of the Rejecting Mother, Child Welfare League of America, 1955.

[4] Friedlander, Kate, Neurosis and Home Background, in "The Psychoanalytic Study of the Child," vols. III and IV, 1950, p. 423.

[5] Reiner, Beatrice Simcox, and Irving Kaufman, Character Disorders in Parents of Delinquents, Family Service Association of America, 1959.

tributed to the delinquent, acting-out behavior of their children. The underlying problem of the parents was anxiety, stemming from unresolved depression. The authors found that therapy for these parents required long periods of time, often extending over several years. They divided the treatment into stages of establishing a relationship with the therapist, of building the parent's ego through identification, of helping the parent to establish a separate identity, and finally of helping him to gain self-understanding.

Those who have worked with impulse-ridden, adult, character problems are aware of the difficulty in establishing a positive relationship, the danger of countertransference, and the frustration induced by the patient's acting out. Those who undertake such therapy must have infinite patience, much intuitive skill, and thorough knowledge of the dynamics of behavior.

CHAPTER 17

The Unsocialized Child

Rejected children in a delinquency-producing setting may be aware many times every day that they are not wanted or needed in their home. Unless the parents are brutal, however, most of these rejected children prefer to remain with their parents. Their distrust of adults convinces them that they will receive similar treatment in any other home. They are correct in expecting little acceptance in other homes, since they have no intention of changing their behavior.

Emil, at eight years of age, was running away from home and stealing from his home, his school, and neighborhood stores. He had an explosive temper and when angry he became obscene and uncontrollable.

Emil's father was a brutal alcoholic. At the time of the study he was in prison, having been charged with the crime of carnal knowledge, but he had been in the home until Emil was four years old. Emil's mother much preferred his half brother who was three years old. Her own mother was convinced that her grandson would end up as his father had, and she advised Emil's mother to get him out of the home before he disgraced the family further. The mother also identified Emil with his father. She had remarried and her husband was a kindly, warm man whom Emil much preferred to his own father. He remembered his father as a cruel man who quarreled with his mother and often beat her, and him too. His mother felt guilty because she could not love Emil, and apparently had tried hard to learn to love him. She felt, however, that little would be gained by placing Emil in another home and opposed any plan for his removal from his own home.

Emil was difficult to control in his interviews with the therapist, who unfortunately began treatment by being very permissive with him. He ran around the building interrupting other interviews, leaned out the window to yell at passers-by, and even physically attacked the therapist. The therapist, a strongly built, kindly man whom most of the children dearly loved, had felt he could eventually win over Emil as he had other aggressive boys, but he realized his mistake too late. When he tried to set limits, Emil became even more difficult and in a scuffle broke a chair by throwing it against the wall in a manic-like rage.

In conference the clinic team decided that Emil was a consciously rejected boy who was identified with a criminal father, an identification strengthened by his mother's and grandmother's attitudes. He had succeeded in controlling his mother, who dared not deny him because of her guilt at rejecting him, and his stepfather, who felt sorry for an unloved boy. He, therefore, had acquired a false sense of power which, if unmodified, would cause him and others suffering. Behind his aggression he undoubtedly felt considerable anxiety. This reaction was manifested in his Rorschach test, his occasional soiling, and his panic reaction when the therapist attempted to control him. His poor relationship with teachers, neighbors, and other children and his lack of real friends stamped him as narcissistic. This completed the picture of an antisocial character.

The group felt that Emil needed to be socialized, to be domesticated. He had learned to deal with reality in his own way, with brutal force, and he suffered no noticeable guilt through his behavior. He had a typical antisocial character and needed a setting that could bridle his aggression without antagonizing him. It was postulated that this would require at least two years away from his present home.

The team did not consider trying to deal with the emotional conflicts which complicated Emil's reality adjustment. These conflicts resulted directly from his being rejected, and they would disappear only in a setting where he would receive acceptance and love. Before Emil could be placed in a substitute family, he needed to live in a small institution where he could learn to accept social standards. He was placed in such a center where he stayed for a year; in the following year he was placed in a foster home.

The family situation in Emil's case was easily recognized as a pathologic one. Most of the delinquents who are studied in the child-guidance clinic live in homes where the pathologic circumstances can be recognized only after prolonged study of the parents. Neurotic conflicts in the parents, their ambivalence toward the delinquent child, shame and guilt related to failure with the child, emotional dependency on the child, and many other factors complicate the picture immeasurably. Removal of the delinquent child from the home is usually recommended only as a final measure because of the resistance of the parents and the delinquent child to such a procedure. Experience has shown that a delinquent youngster who does not accept the idea of foster-home placement rarely benefits from such a move. Separated from his home, his grievances rapidly fall into the background and in his loneliness for his home, the positive aspects of it are all that he remembers. In all cases, therefore, the staff makes serious attempts to work with the emotional problems of the child through improving the parent-child relationship. These efforts, however, are often unsuccessful.

*Emil, at fourteen years of age, is in an excellent foster home on a farm, where he has made good gains during the past three years. However, in the last few months he has been unhappy at school and did some acting out. With another boy he stole a gun, got some shells, and threatened to fire the gun in the schoolyard. He also stole twenty dollars from a relative of his foster parents. The caseworker has worked closely with the foster parents, who feel crushed by his recent delinquency after Emil had been doing so well. The caseworker has been interviewing Emil and thinks that his recent acting out is, in part, due to an adolescent increase in aggression. Emil has not seen members of his family and has been eager to visit his mother and sisters, but he continues to feel hostile to his father. The caseworker feels justified in asking our clinic to work with Emil again, if his acting-out behavior continues.

A parent's rejection of a child is often initiated by the child's refusal or inability to love that parent. The reasons for the child's rejection may be difficult to discover; in most instances the child probably senses his parent's ambivalence. A child does not reject a parent without good cause, since every child prefers to love rather than to hate.

Edith, a nine-year-old girl, was referred because of chronic stealing and lying. She showed no affection for either of her adopted parents nor for her adopted grandparents who lived in the home. She was impudent and rude at home and at school. She denied stealing in the face of indisputable evidence. There was nothing to suggest the slightest guilt in connection with her dissocial behavior.

Edith's adoptive father was an accountant who had been previously married. His first wife had been killed in an automobile accident shortly after they adopted Edith. His present wife had married the adoptive father because she wanted a child, having been unable to conceive in a previous marriage. She was deeply hurt when Edith, four years old at the time of the remarriage, refused to return her new adoptive mother's affection. The adoptive mother tried to break down the child's rejection of her but did not succeed, and when Edith became unruly and defiant she began to reject her. Her rejection increased until the time of the referral when she was demanding that Edith be placed away from the home. She was unable to concede defeat, however, for at the same time she suggested that her marriage be dissolved and she be allowed to have Edith live with her.

Edith was contemptuous of her new adoptive mother, had little noticeable affection for her adoptive father, and failed to develop an affectionate tie to her therapist, a young woman who tried hard to be pleasant and helpful. Edith resisted efforts to understand why she acted out. She failed to show the slightest concern about the dangerous consequences of continued stealing. Ten months of individual interviews and group-therapy sessions failed to change Edith's behavior or attitude. The group therapist felt that she was beginning to develop a relationship with her, but Edith had none with the children in the group when the clinic study was stopped by the parents.

The parents had initiated the study with mixed feelings. The adoptive mother had taken courses in child behavior and felt threatened by her failure to socialize Edith. In her interviews with her caseworker she refused to see that she played any part in producing Edith's behavior. She felt she had offered Edith her home and her love, but Edith had refused to be friendly. She blamed the delinquency to traits Edith had inherited from a sexually promiscuous mother who had given birth to this child illegitimately. She admitted fearing that illegitimate children turned out badly and said that Edith was already showing sexual preoccupation by masturbating and decidedly preferring boys and men who visited their home. The adoptive mother became annoyed when the worker tried to help her understand her reaction to illegitimacy and sexual conflict. Such discussion implied that her attitude had a bearing on Edith's behavior. The mother wanted no more of such an investigation.

Edith was rejected because she refused or was unable to accept affection offered to her by her adoptive mother. Her behavior apparently stemmed from a strong attachment to her adoptive father, following the death of his first wife. Unfortunately, the therapist was unable to determine how Edith had reacted to her first adoptive mother and why she had never been able to love her present adoptive mother. Edith's only comment was that she had been unable to get along with her present adoptive mother as long as she could remember.

The behavior of the adoptive mother reflects her instability and deep sense of inferiority and failure. A more stable, secure woman might have reacted more slowly when rejected by an unhappy four-year-old girl. She would have been able to tolerate aggressive attacks directed against her until these proved to be no longer necessary.

One of the serious problems related to the therapy of the child with an antisocial character disturbance is the difficulty in determining when the ego has gained sufficient strength to master instinctual drives.

Trudy, a sixteen-year-old adolescent girl, was referred to the clinic by an intern who felt that, during her stay in the hospital for treatment of gonorrhea, she seemed somewhat out of touch with reality. At the time of the study, she was living in a school for delinquent girls because of her sexual promiscuity, running away from home, and drinking to excess. On first coming to the school, she stole clothes and other possessions of some of the girls, but otherwise she seemed to get along well with the girls and the staff. She was permitted to attend a high school in the company of several other girls and got along well at school although she was not a bright girl or a good student.

Trudy's father was an ineffectual man in his sixties, who did manual work and was a poor provider. Her mother, who worked also, was younger than her husband, had little affection for him, and was reported to be sexually promiscuous. An older brother had been delinquent and had already spent time in an institution. The agency which worked with this family recommended that Trudy not return to her home when she was ready to leave the institution.

Trudy did not cooperate in the psychological examination and projection tests, apparently threatened by them. She was most cooperative in her interviews with the therapist, with whom she left an impression of sincerity and a determination to lead a different life when she returned home. She refused to consider any other placement than her own home, denied the accusations made about her home, and insisted she would find after-school jobs to help in the support of her family if allowed to return home. She had decided to become a Catholic, and during her stay in the institution she took instructions. In a series of interviews Trudy persisted in her intention of living at home and was convinced she could make a successful adjustment there.

Trudy had shown a tendency to act out when she was denied permission to do things in her own way. She had satisfied the institution staff, however, that she was capable of living in a socially acceptable manner. She came unescorted to the clinic, a privilege denied most of the girls, because of her proved trustworthiness. Her religious interests were sincere and profound. In spite of the bad reports about her home, therefore, Trudy was allowed to return there to continue with her school work and with therapy at the clinic.

After her return home Trudy began missing appointments with her therapist, and the reasons she gave were poor. Another adolescent who had known Trudy at the institution reported that she had seen her on a recent visit; Trudy had looked tired and explained she had been out very late on the preceding night, a school night. Trudy also missed appointments with her probation officer, who kept in touch with the therapist and acknowledged that Trudy had slipped back rapidly to her previous pattern of behavior. Trudy had told her probation officer that she was still certain she could fight off her drive for pleasure and make good.

The conclusion reached in conference was that once again a delinquent's ego strength had been overestimated. Trudy required much more therapy and institutional experience than she had received. The Borstal Institution staff [1] developed a three-year program for their delinquent adolescents, having learned through long experience that character change in acting-out youngsters requires at least three years time. Other therapists who have attempted to

[1] Personal interview on visit to Borstal Institution outside of London, 1935.

provide intensive treatment for children with antisocial characters have found the same length of time is needed before the delinquent can accept the reality principle.

It is understandable to permit a delinquent to return home when he insists he cannot be happy anywhere else. Unless considerable casework treatment has been provided in the home during his absence, however, it is unrealistic to believe that he will not return to much the same psychological factors which produced his delinquency. Only occasionally may a long period of therapy strengthen the delinquent's ego sufficiently to enable him to return to a delinquency-producing setting without succumbing to its influences.

*Shortly after the last time we saw Trudy in 1955, she was brought into court and committed to a school for delinquent girls, where she remained for two years. She completed high school and took some nurse's training. Part of her training was in a nursing home for old people, a good choice, since Trudy is a very pleasant, warm person who has much to give to needful older people. Trudy is now married, has no children, and plans to work in an old people's rest home.

Thus far in the section on acting-out behavior the discussion has dealt with the behavior of the unsocialized child. We come now to a discussion of the manner in which the acting-out behavior expresses the neurotic conflict of the child. This may occur in two ways: first, neurotic character; and second, neurotic delinquency.

CHAPTER 18

The Neurotic Character

Since the term *character neurosis* has already been referred to in the previous chapter dealing with character problems, the reader should not confuse the present discussion regarding the acting-out behavior of the neurotic character with the previous material. Alexander [1] describes the neurotic character as externalizing neurotic conflict to neutralize an underlying passivity and dependency craving. The aggressive person who needs to dominate often is deeply searching for someone to give him the protective care he enjoyed in infancy. Hampered by inner condemnation from meeting such demands, he becomes overbearing and chooses aggressive outlets. The daredevil, the gambler, the auto racer are people who risk their fortunes and lives by acting out in a deeply neurotic manner.

Children may manifest the behavior of the neurotic character by living active, aggressive lives which keep them just outside of danger but continually expose them to situations of danger. Their hostility is not related primarily to others; others are hurt by their actions more by accident than design.

Murray, a twelve-year-old boy who looked fourteen, was referred to the clinic by a family agency. After a delinquent escapade with

[1] Alexander, Franz, The Neurotic Character, *Int. Journ. Psychoanal.*, vol. XI, 1930, p. 292.

another boy, he had been removed from his home and placed in an institution for delinquents. Later, he had moved to a farm where he was to remain throughout the summer. He had become acutely upset, had severe spells of crying and panic, and begged to be returned to his home. The court refused his request although they were interested in the clinic's evaluation of the problem for which the agency had asked help. In conference after the clinic study, the court, the family agency, and the clinic decided that Murray would benefit by continuing to remain away from home, where he had been rather markedly indulged.

Murray was an active, aggressive, outgoing, attractive youngster who had joined a large group of fun-loving adolescents. They were bored with school and work, spent little time at home except to eat and sleep, and were frequently involved in mischief. One or two of the leaders of the group were delinquents and occasionally they had succeeded in influencing some of the more socially minded boys who either sought favor or feared opposing the leaders. Murray, a rather gentle youngster with little sadistic drive, joined in such acts occasionally. His removal from home followed his acting as a lookout for a house burglary and accepting a small part of the loot.

After the clinic study Murray declared that he would stay away from the group. Later, however, because he was lonely and could find no other outlets which offered so much pleasure, he began again to associate with the most socialized members of the group. It was not long before he started truanting occasionally, falling behind in his schoolwork, and missing appointments with his clinic therapist and probation officer. The pull toward acting out conflict was stronger than the motivation to accept the reality principle more fully. Although the danger of continuing along this path had been fully explained to him, Murray seemed satisfied with the direction in which his behavior was pointing, certain that he would not become dissocial.

Murray's certainty that he would not become dissocial was warranted. He stopped violating probation rules and began coming in regularly for clinic interviews. Murray seemed to need to violate rules just enough to receive scoldings from his therapist and warnings from his probation officer. Hacker and Geleerd [2] have described the need of some adolescents for an authoritative atmosphere to decrease their feelings of insecurity and anxiety. Bromberg and Rodgers [3] came to a similar conclusion in working with the more rebellious type of young prison inmate. According to these authors, the psychologic basis for the immature delinquent adolescent's antagonism toward authority lies in his need to deny a basic unconscious dependence on the very authority figure against whom he rebels.

The therapist who recognizes this need can react with less emotion to the adolescent who continues to rebel, and he will be able to keep the benevolent authority which the rebellious acting-out adolescent needs from adults.[4]

*Murray continued to contact his therapist by calling him every few months and, occasionally, by dropping in for an interview, but he remained out of trouble. At one time he asked for a series of interviews to relieve his anxiety and was referred to an agency for the treatment of young adults. He reported recently that he had lost his girl friend because he was too possessive and insisted on seeing her every day, but he was sure he would find another. It would appear that the acting-out phase has stopped and that the neurotic aspect of his conflict has become stronger. He should respond well to therapy.

The term *neurotic character* as used here refers only to such acting out as gives the person an opportunity to reduce emotional tension without hurting others. The term *aggressive character*, which is sometimes used in the literature to denote such a picture, is also

---

[2] Hacker, J. Frederick, and Elizabeth Geleerd, Freedom and Authority in Adolescence, *Amer. Journ. Orthopsychiat.*, vol. XV, no. 4, 1945, p. 621.

[3] Bromberg, Walter, and Terry Rodgers, Authority in the Treatment of Delinquents, *Amer. Journ. Orthopsychiat.*, vol. XVI, no. 4, 1946, p. 672.

[4] Szurek, Stanley, Emotional Aspects in the Use of Authority, in "Public Health Is People," Ethel L. Ginsburg (editor), New York, The Commonwealth Fund, 1950, p. 206.

used to describe acting-out behavior of which the main object is to destroy or injure. A person exhibiting such behavior is entirely distinct from adolescents like Murray.

A large number of adolescents in rebellion against society's restrictions are deeply resentful of their position in life. They resort to vandalism and sadistic attacks on people without selection, in a vain effort to lessen their accumulated guilt and tension. They destroy property or attack people to act out fantasied attacks on the authority figures in their homes.

The child-guidance clinic rarely sees vandals unless their acting out has been serious or repeated. When such children are studied, they seldom fail to disclose deep feelings of inferiority and frustration, with a long-standing wish to punish others for real or fancied offenses against them. During World War II, Anna Freud declared that it was difficult for children to repress their sadistic drives, a normal process in their development, when they knew the world about them was filled with sadistic destruction. Our culture and society tolerate much which aids in stimulating vandalism. Wars with wanton destruction of property and life, racketeering which receives much publicity, disillusionment in important figures in society who are dishonest, disregard for speed laws, and fatal accidents due to drunken driving all make it difficult to check the hostile aggression of those who seek excuses to act out.

Since they are aware of all the acting out in society, it is little wonder that unhappy, dissatisfied adolescents, many of whom have felt unloved and unwanted, inadequate and weak, welcome an opportunity to express their hate in a comparatively safe manner. The problem of vandalism will be solved only when the total mental-hygiene needs of the community are solved.

A child with neurotic character may act out his neurotic conflict aggressively also by teasing and annoying other children or quarreling with them. When such behavior becomes excessive, both the child and the parents need therapy. An unhappy child defends himself by denying and projecting guilt in order to relieve his anxiety. Parents become justifiably concerned when their child's behavior loses him friends or provokes many quarrels in the home. The extreme of quarrelsome behavior appears in the so-called "querulent individual" who acts out neurotic conflict by totally overlooking the arguments of his opponent no matter how sound they are. They are most difficult patients because they are inaccessible to reason.

A fifteen-year-old adolescent girl who felt displaced by a younger brother was vitriolic in her verbal attacks on her mother. As long as the therapist sided with her, she continued with her interviews. On one occasion, however, when she blamed her mother in a very unrealistic manner, the therapist pointed out how unreasonable she was. The girl then became angry, stalked out of the room, and refused to return. The disagreement of the therapist created an unendurable tension in her.

CHAPTER **19**

The Neurotic Delinquent

The essential feature of neurotic delinquency is that it represents behavior directed against society to express a neurotic conflict. Research in this aspect of neurotic illness was stimulated by Freud's study, Criminality from a Sense of Guilt.[1] Freud demonstrated that people with deep unconscious guilt derived from incestuous conflict commit delinquent acts with the intention—unknown to them—of being apprehended for punishment. The suffering from their delinquent act satisfies their need to be punished.

In children who act out dissocially the need to be punished may assert itself in several ways. Stupid errors in attempting to conceal guilt, the repetition of the act in the same manner, and references which establish the child as guilty all indicate a need for punishment. In some instances the child continues such incriminating behavior until he is recognized as the guilty party. This mechanism helps to explain the "naughtiness" of many young children who feel guilty about their hostile fantasies and wishes and grow more comfortable after they are punished for their naughtiness. An adolescent who has been in trouble repeatedly told his therapist that he had broken into the same store four times on four successive

---

[1] Freud, Sigmund, Some Character Types Met with in Psychoanalytic Work, in "Collected Papers," vol. IV, London, Hogarth Press, Ltd., 1925, p. 318.

nights. On the fourth night he had watched the movements of a police car driving back and forth in front of the store, and he had tried to break in while the police car was not directly in front of the store. He had not counted on there being someone in the store waiting for him, however, though he realized that he should have expected it. He admitted being relieved after he was caught and added, "It could have been worse, they could have shot at me."

A bright adolescent girl in serious conflict with a rejecting mother had been in an institution for delinquent girls for several months. She had mixed feelings about leaving the institution, fearing that she had not developed sufficient control to resist the temptation to act out away from the institution. In her next interview she felt she had been needlessly concerned about her lack of self-control and was really ready to leave. The night before she was to go to court to be discharged, however, she ran away from the institution and was easily apprehended. Her unconscious mind had made the decision for her. Several instances of boys in institutions for delinquents behaving similarly appear in the clinic records.

Alexander [2] has described the mechanism of the ego's bribing the superego by inflicting punishment on itself. A delinquent child, for example, may act out in such a way that he is punished, and his punishment justifies his committing further delinquency. Much recidivism may be explained in this manner, and it is important to consider this factor in cases of repeated delinquency.

Gerald, a brilliant adolescent boy, was referred to the clinic by the judge of the juvenile court who felt that Gerald might be insane. He had been found intoxicated and stuporous near his home after buying liquor with money obtained through a forged check. The check was cashed by a merchant who had known Gerald for several years. Gerald was warned by the judge and placed on probation, but two weeks later he repeated the offense in the same manner. Each time he had forged the name of a neighbor who had been a close friend of Gerald's family and had planned to help

[2] Alexander, Franz, "The Medical Value of Psychoanalysis," New York, W. W. Norton & Company, Inc., 1932, p. 109.

Gerald finance a university education. The judge questioned the intelligence of an adolescent who would expose himself so stupidly to apprehension, and when the psychologist reported an IQ of 170, he decided that Gerald must be in serious conflict.

After committing the same offense three times Gerald was placed in jail, and he came to the clinic for his interviews accompanied by a sheriff. A nice-appearing, undersized, rather delicate youngster who seemed anxious to talk, Gerald felt that he had sinned grossly and needed a severe penalty to check his delinquency. He was markedly dependent and insecure, with a very strong dependency attachment to his aggressive mother. Like the other members of the family, Gerald had little respect for his father, who was twenty-five years older than the mother, a poor provider who accepted his passive position in the family. The father and mother had been incompatible as long as Gerald could remember. In his interviews with the therapist Gerald said he hoped he would never marry and leave his mother because they needed each other. He felt very comfortable in the county jail, and when the time arrived for his release he volunteered to tend the elevator so that he could live in the jail where he felt secure.

A few weeks later Gerald repeated his offense and was sent to a reformatory where he remained for three years. He had no opportunity for therapy at the reformatory, though it was apparent that he was seriously conflicted and needed intensive therapy. A thorough psychoanalysis during this period might well have restored Gerald to the possibility of a brilliant career.

Gerald called his therapist, shortly after leaving the reformatory, to say he was planning to get married. He was intoxicated at the time. A few days later his mother reported that Gerald and his wife had had an auto accident shortly after they left the wedding celebration. Gerald was driving and was deeply intoxicated at the time.

Gerald's case is a classical picture of a deep unconscious need to be punished because of underlying conflict. The tension produced by this conflict and the guilt related to it made it impossible for Gerald to use his brilliant mind toward making a successful life adjustment. Whenever he saw an opportunity to be successful, he indulged in the excessive drinking which brought him to disaster. Nothing short of intensive insight therapy could resolve this kind of conflict.

In the light of the above statement regarding Gerald, the follow-up report on him is of special interest. It demonstrates once more that therapeutic results may be achieved through many different kinds of treatment and that it may be unsafe to predict the results of therapy on the basis of unsuccessful treatment by the methods known to us.

*Gerald came in to visit me in 1958, twenty-five years after we had worked with him. He wanted me to know how well he was doing. He had remained married and had three healthy children who were all doing well in school. They were eager to have a good education, and Gerald was determined that they would have it. He talked about his earlier experiences, when he was in treatment with us, and was certain that his chief problem had been alcoholism. He had begun to drink while in high school, which had seriously affected his schoolwork, and later he had been in a series of automobile accidents and had been institutionalized on several occasions. In 1943, when his family was destitute and falling apart, he joined Alcoholics Anonymous. As a result he stopped his drinking and began to do well. He has been a hard, conscientious worker in Alcoholics Anonymous and spoke with pride of the people he had helped.

At the time of this interview he was working with an architectural firm and was earning a good living, although his success was not commensurate with his very high intelligence. As he spoke I had the feeling that he was totally unaware of how high he had tested intellectually. He said he was glad to be able to tell me these things about himself because we had been kind to him. When I thanked him for dropping in to see me, he asked me to keep in touch with him, as a good friend.

This to me is a remarkable recovery in a seriously conflicted

young man whose prognosis was extremely poor. Perhaps his superior intelligence played a part in his being able to respond so
well to the treatment provided by Alcoholics Anonymous. As I
spoke to him he sensed my surprise at seeing how well adjusted
and mature he looked and sounded. He told me that there were
many people he had helped to join Alcoholics Anonymous, who
had done as well as he. I had occasion to call him a year later, and
he sounded as happy and strong as he had when he visited me.

The case of Gerald throws further light on the frequently remarkable results achieved by the efforts and program of Alcoholics
Anonymous. It would be to our advantage to know much more
of the dynamic factors involved in this program. In Gerald's case,
we are probably dealing with repression made possible by strong,
massive ego-strengthening devices.

Many children are referred to the child-guidance clinic because
of chronic repeated stealing, which is the expression of neurotic
conflict. Many different kinds of gratification are sought through
the act of stealing, although a need for affection is the most common cause. Rejected children often resort to taking objects which
do not belong to them, in a symbolic attempt to replace love that
is denied them. Often they steal money with which they buy
sweets or food; the loss of love expresses itself in an oral craving
which is partially met by food. Stealing in such children also grati-
fies their need to punish those who have denied them affection
but still demand that they accept social standards. Violating these
standards serves as a form of revenge.

Chronic stealing often occurs in children whose parents have
disillusioned them. A father who deserts them, or a mother who
has been disloyal or alcoholic, shatters a child's ego ideal and the
child feels free to give up the standards which he accepted during
the process of socialization.

When he was seven years old Oliver had come to America with
his father, leaving his hopelessly crippled mother in Europe. Many
years later his father remarried, although Oliver's mother was still

alive. Soon after the remarriage Oliver began to steal and when several excellent foster-home placements did not improve his behavior, he was placed in an institution for delinquents.

Since Oliver had always been close to his father who loved him, the placement agency had searched for warm, maternal foster mothers who could give him the affection he missed from a mother. Oliver's emotional problem, however, did not result from losing his mother's love. The remarriage of his father while Oliver's mother was still alive was a serious blow to him; he became disillusioned in a father who would stoop to such behavior. The social standards he had accepted from his father no longer exerted their former influence, and he lost respect for all authority figures. What Oliver needed most was treatment from a male therapist who could have helped him understand his father's motives and needs. By identifying with the therapist's ego ideal he might have reestablished his earlier social standards. Oliver's previously strong attachment to his father might have made such an identification relatively easy. It was because of his deep attachment to his father that the disillusionment was so traumatic. Unfortunately, individual therapy had not been available to Oliver.

Stealing of a compulsive nature most clearly reflects the presence of a neurotic component. In some instances a child who has great difficulty in controlling the urge to steal can make a superhuman effort to desist from stealing for a few days, only to find that he becomes acutely depressed. The mechanism in such a case is similar to that of obsessional neurosis in which the symptom appears in the form of rituals. An obsessional neurotic who has a hand-washing compulsion will report that when he overcomes the urgent internal demand to wash his hands he becomes emotionally tense and very uncomfortable. The stealing, like the ritual, represents a defense against anxiety.

Compulsive stealing characterizes the kleptomanic child who symbolically tries to replace something which he unconsciously fantasies was taken away from him. This is not infrequent in children suffering from castration anxiety. Kleptomania as seen in adults, when the emotional gratification comes from the act of stealing regardless of the object taken, has rarely been observed in children seen at the Wilder Child Guidance Clinic.

The fact that a child steals a large number of objects does not make him a compulsive delinquent even when he has no use for the objects taken. The child may intend to use such stolen articles as barter for articles which he can use and wants.

One seven-year-old child was referred to the clinic because the child-placing agency diagnosed him as a compulsive stealer. This child forged a list of groceries, and after receiving the various articles from the grocer threw them away before he returned home. During the interviews he disclosed that on every list there was one object which the child wanted for himself—a small pie, a box of Cracker Jack, or an ice-cream cone. He ate what he relished, after leaving the grocery store, and then discarded the objects which were useless to him. He explained that had he brought in an order from the foster mother requesting only the sweets, the clerk would have suspected that he had written the order.

A child who finds that he is successful in stealing objects may steal in order to satisfy himself that he can do something well. Such a motivation is more likely to influence a child who has never been successful in his schoolwork in spite of a real effort to succeed. He is driven to stealing by his feelings of inferiority and failure.

Interest in the unconscious role of parents in producing delinquency in their children has grown in recent years. Drs. Adelaide Johnson and Stanislaus Szurek have been particularly interested in this subject and with Dr. Falstein published their first paper in 1942.[3] Since that time, Dr. Johnson has continued in her work in collaborative therapy and has published several papers with other analysts who have worked with her.[4, 5, 6] The principle underlying

[3] Szurek, S. A., A. Johnson, and E. I. Falstein, Collaborative Psychiatric Treatment of Parent-Child Problems, *Amer. Journ. Orthopsychiat.*, vol. XII, July, 1942, p. 511.
[4] Johnson, Adelaide, Sanctions for Superego Lacunae of Adolescence, in

their theory is that antisocial acting out in a child is initiated and fostered by the parents. These parents failed to integrate, successfully, forbidden impulses and seek gratification of these impulses through their child. The antisocial acting out of the child is unconsciously sanctioned by the parents and they receive a vicarious gratification in this way. By means of this mechanism the parents unconsciously live out their hostility to the child whom they reject.

Drs. Johnson, Szurek, and Falstein devised a plan of collaborative therapy in which the child, the mother, and often the father, too, are in analysis. At frequent intervals each analyst discusses with the others the material he obtains. These discussions may occur daily and provide an excellent opportunity for each therapist to come under the observation of the others. In this way the therapist can reduce the extent to which he unconsciously permits the patient to control the therapy.

Brian Bird,[7] in discussing collaborative therapy, explains the mother's influence on the child's antisocial acting out as being due to a defect in her own personality which does not allow the ego of her child to act independently. Her ego continues to act for him and maintains direct contact with his id, and in turn his ego is directly influenced by her id. The child therefore remains in a state in which his ego continues to be susceptible to stimulation by the id of the mother. As a result, the id impulses of the mother are freely though unconsciously brought to bear on the child's ego, and he carries out her id impulses because of his immature, dependent relationship to her.

Bird also cautions the therapist working with the delinquent

"Searchlights on Delinquency," K. R. Eissler (editor), New York, International Universities Press, Inc., 1949, p. 225.

[5] Johnson, Adelaide, and S. A. Szurek, The Genesis of Anti-social Acting Out in Children and Adults, Psychoanal. Quart., vol. XXI, 1952, p. 323.

[6] Giffen, Mary E., Adelaide M. Johnson, and Edward M. Litin, Specific Factors Determining Anti-social Acting Out, Amer. Journ. Orthopsychiat., vol. XXIV, 1954, pp. 668–696.

[7] Bird, Brian, discussion of paper by Giffin, Johnson, and Litin, ibid., p. 685.

against becoming embroiled in the acting out of his patient, so that he acts out with him. This occurs more often in the case of the unanalyzed therapist, who reacts to the uncanny capacity of the delinquent to stimulate the id impulses of the therapist.

Since such therapy discussed by Dr. Johnson and her associates is intensive, these studies have been limited to small numbers of patients, and are still in the research stage. As other therapists undertake similar research, the number of children whose acting-out behavior can be traced to unconscious demands from their mothers may be determined. Many such mother-child combinations have come to the Wilder Child Guidance Clinic for treatment. The results of therapy usually have been unsatisfactory since a mother and child can rarely be seen more often than once a week in a child-guidance clinic. On rare occasions a mother who is unconsciously forcing her child to be delinquent can respond to casework therapy which helps her to see her destructive influence on her child. She may change her behavior toward her child, even though unconvinced of the need for it, and this in turn may influence the child's behavior. More often, the unconscious marked rejection of the child makes it impossible to modify the mother's behavior by casework therapy.

Sally was referred when she was ten years old because her mother could not discipline her. Her mother reported that Sally stole money or articles frequently, defied her mother, and often embarrassed her in front of others. Sally was a bright, likable child who reported to her therapist that her mother nagged her all the time. She was happy and popular away from home, got along well with her sister and brother, and appeared to be very fond of her father. The study suggested that Sally was reacting normally to pressures from a very neurotic, masochistic mother.

Casework interviews with the mother indicated that she had had a similar problem with her own mother, who had rejected her in favor of a more attractive, brighter brother. She had never forgiven her mother for this favoritism, and she blamed her chronic unhappiness on her mother's attitude toward her. She had been very much attached to an adolescent boy when she was sixteen, but her mother refused to let her see the boy. She resented this interference and said frankly that she hated her mother. The staff felt that the problem could not be solved at a child-guidance clinic, since Sally was a normal child, while her mother needed intensive psychotherapy.

When Sally was seventeen she was again referred for treatment because of stealing, insolence to her mother, and staying out late at night. Sally refused to come to the clinic, declaring that her mother was insane and was creating problems in her and her sister. An interview with the father corroborated Sally's impression that the mother was producing difficult situations by exaggerating lesser problems.

Shortly after this, the mother referred Sally's sister, a bright fourteen-year-old who, like Sally, acted out by stealing and staying out late. The school staff reported that the child presented no problems, but that they had never seen a mother so determined to convince them that her child was delinquent and needed help. They felt that the mother would eventually force her daughter into delinquent behavior.

Sally later telephoned her former therapist to warn him that her mother would continue her behavior until she or her sister got into real trouble. She stated that she hated her mother and had felt unloved by her all her life.

The caseworker tried to point out to the mother what might happen if she continued to keep her family stirred up, but the mother, concerned about her own emotional needs, could not accept the clinic's evaluation of the problem. The mother was again referred to a psychiatrist in private practice for intensive psychotherapy, and the father was advised to do what he could to neutralize the mother's pressures.

*Sally, who was married and divorced twice, is now living with her parents. She has a son four years old, who is not doing very well. She has often talked about getting in touch with her therapist because she is unhappy. She has grown into an attractive young lady and is working in a department store, but she is concerned about her child and is afraid that he will have some of the problems she has had. She has been referred to a family agency and advised to stay in treatment long enough to resolve her serious conflict with her mother, who still feels that the clinic was wrong in attributing Sally's difficulties to her.

Sally's younger sister is graduating from high school. She is a hard worker and has saved eight hundred dollars to take nurse's training. Her mother reports that she is "honest as the day is long. The only time she ever stole was just before that time when she came in to see you."

Since a mother chooses a child she unconsciously rejects as the one through whom she will live out her dissocial needs, an adopted child is often the victim of such a situation. Frequently in such cases the mother was not eager for the adoption but complied in it because her husband seemed eager to have a child in the family. To the neurotic woman this may mean that she has disappointed her husband and that he is seeking to remedy an unhappy relationship by adopting a child.

Adelle and her sister were adopted when Adelle was a year old and her sister was about four years old. Adelle's own mother drank excessively and deserted Adelle's father and the two children. Little was known about Adelle's father. The adoptive parents had wanted to adopt but one child, but the agency told them their one opportunity to adopt a child was to take the two children. They preferred the older of the two children but they adopted Adelle in order to be able to have the older child.

Adelle was referred to the clinic when she was sixteen years old because she had run away from home on two occasions. She had run away when she was fourteen years old and been gone for about three days until she was apprehended in a city several hundred miles from her home. When she ran away the second time, at sixteen, she was gone for a longer period and there was some question of her having had sexual relations with a young man she met on the trip. Both parents were upset by the second running away and were eager for a study at the clinic.

It became obvious early in the study that the adoptive mother was a very vindictive person who had never really been able to accept Adelle. She spoke with a good deal of hostility about Adelle's unruly behavior and extreme stubbornness from early childhood to the present time. The adoptive mother felt that Adelle had been doing everything she could to make life difficult for the mother. In contrast, her older sister was a friendly, pleasant child who caused the family very little trouble. The adoptive mother related numerous instances to prove that Adelle had inherited a dissocial character from her own dissolute mother. She was convinced Adelle was going to end up badly, as her mother had. In describing her interviews with this mother the caseworker said that she had never spoken to a woman who had so much deep hate for a child; she actually hissed at times as she spoke about Adelle, trying to get the worker to agree that Adelle had not only behaved badly but was going to end up badly.

The therapist, in talking to Adelle, was impressed with the fact that she had been continuously struggling to get her adoptive mother to love her. She had succeeded in winning the love of her adoptive father and she got along very well with her older sister, but she felt that she was fighting a losing battle in trying to get her mother to think of her as a decent person. She realized that her behavior all along had disturbed the family. She was sorry that she had caused them so much unhappiness, but she felt that she was behaving no differently from other adolescent girls she knew. Although she liked boys, they would stop seeing her as soon as they realized that her mother was hostile to them and didn't want them around. She knew that if her mother's attitude continued she would run away again. From her point of view there was little to be gained in staying on at home. She knew that she would miss her father and sister terribly, but in the end she thought she would be happier away from home. She was finding it impossible to tolerate the excessive restrictions her adoptive mother placed on her. All her friends had told her that she was foolish for listening to her mother and that it was about time she began to behave like a grownup.

Therapy with the adoptive mother was very difficult. The caseworker was convinced that Adelle's mother had no insight regarding the part she played in producing the delinquent behavior in Adelle. She thought that Adelle was ruining her life and was going to continue in this way. When the caseworker questioned whether the mother's discipline had provoked Adelle to rebel, the mother became indignant and refused even to consider such a possibility. Such an attitude is common in mothers who unconsciously need to destroy a child whom they deeply reject. The associated guilt makes it difficult for them to see the part that they are playing.

*Adelle, now twenty years old, has had several brief trials at therapy, to which she did not respond. Treatment, according to her mother, was useless. Adelle went to two schools, but after short stays she "ran wild" and did poorly in her schoolwork. She ran away from school to marry a young man "no better than she" and has a child who is very difficult. Adelle's mother is convinced that the child is going to develop into the same kind of person as Adelle. When Adelle was a very young child her mother was convinced that she would develop into a delinquent youngster, and she sees the same qualities in her grandchild.

Adelle has decided to leave her husband, but the mother has little hope for her. The mother's attitude toward Adelle has not changed. She is just as sure of herself as she was six years previously.

Adelle and Sally have continued to act out without much change since they were studied at the clinic. This behavior is understandable, for there was little we could do to interfere with their mothers' plans to foster, unconsciously, the acting-out behavior of their children. As yet Adelle has shown no real wish to obtain psychiatric help, but Sally has.

Dr. Adelaide Johnson, in her intensive analytic work with parents, emphasizes the need to speak very frankly to such mothers, explaining in no uncertain terms that their behavior is an important factor in the child's delinquency and that the delinquency will continue until the parents can understand what they are doing. In most instances the parents are angry at such an explanation, but in the end they submit to the kind of study which helps them modify their attitude and behavior toward their child.

The results reported by Dr. Johnson and her coworkers were obtained through psychoanalytic treatment. In time, their findings may find application in forms of therapy available to the child-guidance clinic team and to therapists in other agencies. Meanwhile, one must be cautious about ascribing to mothers the responsibility for their children's acting-out behavior. The assumption may be erroneous and might create additional anxiety in a mother already overburdened with anxiety.

The treatment of neurotic delinquency has its brighter side. Technics have been devised for treating successfully many neurotic acting-out forms of behavior which formerly were considered to be untreatable. Technics used for neurotic illness in children also are effective to a degree in controlling neurotic delinquency. Even severe forms of acting-out behavior may respond well, when the therapist is able to effect a quick positive transference relationship to the child.

Several therapists in child-guidance clinics report successful results from frankly confronting parents with the behavior which encourages their child to believe that acting-out will be permitted. Without trying to explain the unconscious causes for their permissiveness, the therapist insists that the child's acting-out behavior must be controlled. He presents the parents with repeated evidence from their statements, attitudes, and behavior to show them how they support dissocial behavior in their child and continues until the parents become aware of what they are doing. This is often facilitated through a discussion of the preconscious factors that have conditioned the parents to be permissive. Some parents whose need for outlets through their child is less demanding or less rigid respond to this approach and may not require the intensive effort demanded in the collaborative therapy described by Adelaide Johnson and her coworkers. This process may be supplemented by joint interviews between therapist, parents, and child. Ackerman [8] believes that many emotional problems of children are best handled when several or all the important members of the family discuss the problems together in the presence of the therapist. We have been experimenting with varying forms of family therapy during the past year and have been encouraged by the results we have observed.

Contrary to the opinion of many therapists who are pessimistic about the treatment of emotionally disturbed children of adolescent age, experience in our clinic has demonstrated that adolescents in neurotic conflict can respond well to therapeutic efforts. Most adolescents referred to a child-guidance clinic are overburdened by threatening instinctual demands. Those who can act out their demands are relieved of pressure, but their environment reacts against them, and the parents or school ask for a study. After their first violent protests at coming to the clinic these acting-out adolescents usually try to be friendly and, finding that the therapist is pleasant and understands the problems youngsters meet, are willing to talk about themselves. With most of these adolescents the interviews are directed toward treating ego inadequacy, and not the infantile conflicts which are the underlying cause of the difficulty. Similarly, in his counseling work with college students, Blos [9] avoids psychoanalytic procedures to resolve infantile conflicts and deals instead with the derivatives of these conflicts as they appear in ego reactions. He limits his interpretations to the defensive maneuvers of the ego—contradictions, denials, and forgetfulness—and relies mainly on the transference relationship between the adolescent and himself. He does not, however, allow the adolescent to develop a transference neurosis.

Therapy in a child-guidance clinic with adolescents is not limited

[8] Ackerman, Nathan A., in "The Psychodynamics of Family Life," New York, Basic Books, Inc., 1958.

[9] Blos, Peter, Psychological Counseling of College Students, Amer. Journ. Orthopsychiat., vol. XVI, no. 4, October, 1946, p. 57.

to treating ego inadequacy. Many adolescents have sufficient ego strength to tolerate interpretation of their unconscious conflicts which press close to the surface. The therapist can help such adolescents understand, for example, that hostility to a parent may be a defense against a threatening incestuous wish. He can help them recognize that their acting out represents a struggle against a continuing infantile dependence on their parents. Before such interpretations are possible, however, the therapist must know the early life history of the adolescent. He uses the same technics to learn about the adolescent's childhood as he uses with preadolescent children.

According to Gitelson,[10] the therapeutic task with adolescents is character synthesis rather than psychic analysis. He feels that the therapist must provide the child with a dependable relationship and emotional freedom, with dependent security through his authority and developmental stimulation through his kindly encouragement. The therapist's manner must swing with the adolescent's to encompass the many contradictory impulses to which the adolescent reacts.

All types of adolescents and adolescent problems are seen in a child-guidance clinic, and therapists vary in their ability to develop a working relationship with them. Some therapists are at ease with neurotic adolescents, but not with those who act out; some work well with withdrawn, neurotic, and acting-out adolescents, but not with younger children; some are more successful in therapy with girls than with boys. The therapist working with an adolescent will serve him best by considering the adolescent's own individual conflicts, problems, and defenses.

The case of Martha illustrates how therapy with adolescents in a child-guidance clinic need not limit itself to ego inadequacy.

Martha, a bright, attractive sixteen-year-old girl, was referred by her mother who tearfully reported that she had intercepted a letter

[10] Gitelson, Maxwell, Character Synthesis: The Psychotherapeutic Problem of Adolescence, Amer. Journ. Orthopsychiat., vol. XVII, no. 3, July, 1948, p. 422.

to Martha from a boy who said he hoped she was not pregnant. The letter confirmed the mother's suspicion that Martha was keeping company with boys who would get her into trouble. Both parents were acutely shocked to learn that Martha was engaging in sexual intercourse. Martha denied affairs with any other boys. She told her parents she would be glad to talk to a psychiatrist about her problem when they insisted that she do this. She also submitted to a physical examination to rule out the possibility of pregnancy and venereal disease.

Martha seemed to enjoy her interviews with her therapist, in spite of the manner in which she had been referred. She had studied some psychology and planned someday to be a teacher or a social worker. She spoke freely, asked intelligent questions, and early in her interviews reported confidential material. She was the third of four children, having two older sisters and a younger brother. She felt rejected by her mother and had never been close to her. She resented her mother's overanxiousness and unhappiness, and she envied her friends' happier homes. She had been dating boys since she was thirteen years old, and began being sexually promiscuous when fourteen. She was often ashamed of her sexual behavior, realizing that the boys who knew her talked about her promiscuity.

Her therapist agreed that her behavior could interfere with her future happiness and make her immediate life at home very unpleasant. He told Martha he would be glad to help her develop some awareness of her need to jeopardize her reputation and future welfare. He added that Martha could only succeed in gaining this insight if she could control her sexual acting out. She understood this restriction and accepted it; actually she welcomed this help in controlling her sexual behavior.

Martha was not strong enough to check her sexual acting out entirely, and violated the rule she had accepted on two occasions. When her transgressions interfered with her therapy because of the guilt they precipitated, the therapist told Martha that further behavior of this kind would be taken as indication that she did not wish further treatment. Martha did not violate this rule again, and after she overcame her resentment at the restriction, her treatment progressed rapidly.

During the first part of treatment dream material was used extensively, and this helped Martha to recognize a strong attachment to her father and hostility to her mother. A repeated theme in her dreams of being alone and lost initiated a discussion of her feeling alone in her family. Her father paid little attention to anyone in the family, and her mother was preoccupied with her own problems. She realized that she had never felt close to her parents, who had longed for a son when she was born. She was convinced as a child that had she been a boy, she would have received a warmer welcome. Her belief was substantiated by the birth of her brother. Martha felt that her parents didn't understand her and didn't seem to try.

She concluded that her chronic feeling of unhappiness was her own fault, and she didn't care if she hurt herself through her sexual behavior. Strangely, she did not mention reaching out for libidinous gratifications and a feeling of being needed through her sexual affairs. When asked if she did not have a wish to punish her parents by violating principles which they held sacred, Martha answered that such a thought had not occurred to her. She had always been most eager to keep her behavior from her parents, aware of how they would react.

Martha felt that her mother contributed to her sexual behavior by never trusting her. She always warned Martha against allowing boys any liberties and did so in a way that infuriated her.

After a year of therapy Martha felt she no longer needed help. She had made an excellent life adjustment; her work was better in school than during her first two years, and she had found a young man who seemed to be in love with her. She was aware of a capacity for real affection which she had never felt with any of her previous male companions. Casework with Martha's parents was sporadic because of their unwillingness to participate. The caseworker succeeded in helping the parents to have more confidence in Martha. Since Martha was so cooperative in her treatment interviews, the staff made no special effort to work more intensively with her parents.

*Martha has continued to get along very well and recently wrote her therapist to let him know that she is now happily married.

Neurotic acting out of children occasionally is expressed through abnormal sexual practices. Because of the great concern of parents and the concern which society in general displays in connection with sexual acting out, these sexual problems often appear to be more serious than they really are. Window-peeping, exhibitionism, sexual activity with young children, and homosexuality are the most frequent offenses coming to the clinic's attention. With few exceptions, these youngsters are inhibited, insecure, and suffer from marked feelings of inadequacy. They come from families where there is considerable emotional conflict, tension, and unhappiness. Conflicts around sex in the family may manifest themselves by disloyalty, promiscuity, and lurid sexual scenes, or by excessive suppression and exaggerated concern about sexual matters. Few of the parents in these homes have taken the time to discuss sexual subjects objectively with their children or are capable of doing so.

Specific reasons govern a child's acting out sexually instead of or in addition to other kinds of antisocial behavior. Early sexual experiences with other children, frank sexual seduction by adults, unconscious seduction by parents, taboos against sexual activity, physical maturation anomalies all determine the extent to which sexual acting out occurs and even what form of sexual expression the child selects.

Parents today are much less concerned about the usual forms of childhood sexual activity than they were when child-guidance clinics were first developed. The public has learned that much of a child's sexual experimentation is simply a preparation for later normal sexual activity, and parents have become more tolerant of it. Fewer children are referred today than formerly because they enjoy running around naked, or stimulate their genitals. Since the parents' anxiety is less, they can objectively seek activities and interests for their children to prevent early sexual acting out from becoming an established pattern of behavior.

Adolescents who experiment sexually with younger children seem to cooperate in therapy better than those who exhibit themselves or are homosexual. Perhaps they feel their behavior is less abnormal, and they are therefore less threatened by the study. They acknowledge that their action is reprehensible, and they feel shame and guilt, but they are not unwilling to accept treatment. They are usually children who have been sexually aroused for some time, and have been developing pubertal changes rapidly. Their egos are still too weak to master their instinctual demands, and when all defenses fail, they act out in a way they believe will be safe. Their guilt appears in their clumsiness in covering up their acting out, though such guilt may appear only in those who are detected. Few of the children treated for this problem over a period of months resort to such sexual attacks again.

In the course of therapy, sexual matters are discussed frankly with these children, since the therapist can assume that they know little about sex or are confused about what they know. They discuss sexual differences between boys and girls, boys and men, girls and women. The therapist hears their ideas of childbirth and impregnation before giving them the actual facts. The clinic obtains the parents' permission to discuss sexual matters early in the study. The worker explains to the parents that the therapist will discuss with the child all subjects to which children react emotionally.

In the clinic experience, boys who exhibit themselves rarely remain in treatment for long periods of time. The bizarre nature of their behavior threatens them, and they seriously question their own sanity. They are greatly alarmed to realize that a sudden irruption of sexual behavior may recur with serious consequences to themselves. The therapist generally attempts to take advantage of this anxiety by pointing out to them that the danger will be less if they learn why they exhibited themselves. The serious nature of this form of acting out calls for a strong attempt to lessen the child's resistance so that he can regard the therapist as his friend.

In spite of the attempts to win the exhibitionists over to therapy, their resistance grows and they finally drop out of treatment. In most instances the disgrace associated with being apprehended prevents the recurrence of the exhibitionism. The few who remain in treatment are helped to see that their behavior is an expression of anxiety and fear of the opposite sex. The problem of sex is discussed thoroughly with them, and they are encouraged to spend more time with children their age of both sexes. The caseworker helps the parents recognize that this form of sexual expression rarely persists and has little relationship to the more serious forms of sexual attack. When the mother's attitude toward the opposite sex is largely disparaging and rejecting, the caseworker attempts to modify her attitude.

The adolescent with a compulsive need to exhibit himself rarely responds to child-guidance-clinic treatment. His neurotic conflict and fear of castration are close to the surface and force him to exhibit repeatedly. Such an adolescent eventually is apprehended and institutionalized. Nothing short of psychoanalytic therapy will resolve his acting out.

Kim, a fourteen-year-old boy, submitted to a study because the court and his mother demanded it. His mother, typical of many mothers of youngsters who exhibit their genital organs, was a dominating, aggressive woman who controlled all the members of her household. She was divorced from her husband, who had left the home when he could no longer tolerate her scolding and nagging. She depreciated men in general, though she had made an effort to be kind to her son.

Kim lost his hostility to the clinic after a few interviews. However, he could not endure the discussion of his sexual problem. The therapist had suggested talking to Kim's mother and advising her to discontinue the interviews which were so painful to him. Kim begged the therapist not to do this, since his mother was convinced he would become a degenerate if he did not submit to therapy. Kim was certain he had been so traumatized by his stupid behavior that there was not the slightest possibility that he would repeat it. The interviews revealed that Kim felt considerable hostility to his mother and had no respect or love for his father, who had always neglected the family, including Kim. He shied away from any discussion of sex, and when it grew obvious that therapy could not lead to productive results, the caseworker explained to the mother that continued treatment was unwise and might prejudice Kim against future therapy if and when it was necessary. The mother accepted the clinic's judgment and treatment stopped.

The same results usually occur in the treatment of homosexual boys. Occasionally a homosexual boy or girl who has seriously suffered from anxiety and stigma will remain in treatment until anxiety lessens and he feels less stigmatized. Occasionally such a child will develop sufficient ego strength to avoid homosexual activity much as youngsters learn to control masturbation.

Homosexuality in adolescents is often only temporary; it represents an attempt of the ego to resolve sexual conflict. With a little support from the therapist, such adolescents gradually give up their homosexual behavior and become oriented heterosexually. Most homosexual adolescents who come to the clinic, however, have already been repeatedly in difficulties through attempting to seduce other boys sexually. By this time, therefore, their homosexual adjustment is fairly well established. Many of them accept this adjustment without any surface guilt or anxiety. They are not interested in therapy and come to the clinic because they have been ordered to do so by the court or by their anxious parents. The largest number of adolescent homosexuals are deeply conflicted and ashamed of their abnormality. They may have marked feelings of inferiority and may be seriously depressed. Through therapy such youngsters can learn to accept themselves as worthy individuals even though they continue to make a homosexual adjustment to life. Their anxiety and guilt can often be reduced through long-time therapy. Those youngsters who do not respond to child-guidance-clinic therapy and who remain unhappy and conflicted in their homosexuality require intensive psychotherapy.

The problem of sexual pathology has too many cultural, sociologic, psychologic, and pathologic aspects to justify brief discussion. Guttmacher's recent book [11] treats many significant aspects of these problems and, although written to describe adult offenders, applies as well to adolescents.

For many years the courts referred to the clinic children with sexual behavior of a benign character. They did not trust themselves to decide what forms of sexual practices were dangerous to the community and what were not. During recent years, as the staff of the probation office learned more about all forms of social pathology, the milder offenders have been treated by the probation officers themselves, leaving the services of the psychiatric team at the clinic free to treat those children who required intensive study and therapy.

The most serious forms of acting-out behavior occur when the child's sadism has not been neutralized by affection and remains close to its native state of savagery. The unloved child not only has the hostile aggression to destroy, but he is insecure, afraid, and distrustful. He has been hurt deeply many times. He feels that others are potential enemies, particularly anyone who deprives him. He is especially vulnerable to frustration and lacks the mechanisms which inhibit the socialized child from striking out. Bender [12] points out that deprived children, having learned that adults can satisfy the child's basic needs, consider those who do not satisfy these needs as acting aggressively toward them, and strike out defensively.

The child who feels deeply unloved may attack those who are responsible for his suffering directly or indirectly or both. Lilly, a twelve-year-old girl, placed a fatal amount of sedative medication in a glass of milk she knew her sister Ruth was going to drink. Only the quickness of her parents' actions prevented a tragedy.

[11] Guttmacher, Manfred, "Sex Offenders—The Problem, Causes and Prevention," New York, W. W. Norton & Company, Inc., 1951.

[12] Bender, Lauretta, The Genesis of Hostility in Children, *Amer. Journ. Psychiat.*, vol. 105, 1948, p. 241.

Ruth was rushed to the hospital when she complained that the milk tasted very bitter. Her stomach was lavaged. Lilly was suspected because she had frequently shown that she hated Ruth, but the parents said nothing about their suspicion. Lilly then poisoned the food of a baby cousin whom she was visiting. Fortunately, the baby's mother detected a strong odor in the food and so it was not served. Lilly was the only one who could have been responsible for the poisoning, and when confronted with this fact, she admitted what she had done. Declaring that she hated her aunt, who made unreasonable demands on her and had insulted her in front of her friends, she denied any wish to kill the cousin whom she dearly loved. She had poisoned him only to hurt her aunt. In confessing her guilt about her cousin she admitted the previous attempted poisoning of her sister.

Her parents were shocked by these incidents, fearing that Lilly was insane, and they wondered if they dared trust her with the sister whom she had harmed, a younger brother, and an older brother. Lilly had not shown the hostility to her brothers which she had expressed toward Ruth, but neither had she shown any hostility toward her cousin. The parents were particularly concerned that Lilly showed so little anxiety and guilt about what she had done. She said she was afraid something terrible might have happened and she might have gone to prison, but she told this to them with little feeling.

Lilly had gotten along badly with Ruth since her birth, and they quarreled a great deal. The parents had never been able to feel close to Lilly, but her sister Ruth was cuddly and was close to them. Lilly avoided any display of affection and rejected her parents' attempts to be demonstrative; they kissed the other children good night, but Lilly would not permit them to kiss her.

The parents were worried about disciplining or denying Lilly in any way, and they were relieved when the staff advised them to be kind and affectionate to her and to treat her as they always had, keeping the two girls apart whenever there was friction between them. The caseworker told the parents that if their anxiety mounted and they found they could not stand the tension, Ruth should be moved to relatives for a visit. Removal was not necessary, however, and the two girls became friendly within a few weeks, though, according to the mother, Lilly often teased her sister unmercifully.

Interviews with Lilly by the therapist were not revealing. Lilly talked about the poisonings before being asked, aware that they were the cause of her being in therapy. She spoke of her dislike for her sister who, though younger, tried to push Lilly around and boss her. She made the same statement about her aunt. She declared that she had often talked to her aunt about sexual matters and suggested that her aunt was preoccupied with sexual subjects. The parents told the caseworker that they also felt that the aunt dwelt on sexual matters too much. They even suspected she might have had a covert homosexual attachment to Lilly.

In discussing the poisonings with the therapist, Lilly showed little emotion. The therapist encouraged her to talk about friends and relatives she liked and pointed out to her the many ways in which she had helped children be happy. He supported her belief that she would never resort to hostile attacks again. She continued to make hostile remarks about Ruth for several months, but stopped them eventually. She became friendly with Ruth, and after seven months, they were closer to each other than ever before.

The therapist's attempts to discuss dream material with Lilly were unsuccessful, though she reported occasional dreams. The interviews produced little new material, although Lilly repeatedly mentioned feeling rejected by both parents, especially her father.

Casework with both parents was very productive. Lilly's mother was an agitated, tense woman who was frequently depressed and unable to enjoy her friends or family. She had been unhappy as a girl and had felt eager to be married to get away from her parents. She resented her husband's lack of real feeling for her or the children, especially Lilly, and hungered for an expression of genuine love from him. She was almost totally unable to express aggression or hate for anyone, having learned from her father, a rigid and compulsive man, that to hate was both sinful and reprehensible.

The caseworker gradually helped the mother to discuss her deep feelings frankly, and the mother marvelled at the amount of deep hate she had always had and was now able to admit. She had resented her father all her life and blamed him for making her whole family miserable. She hated her husband for withholding affection, and she stopped catering to him until he showed some consideration for her and the children. (Her husband had in the meantime been changing in his behavior through his interviews with the caseworker.) She had always felt sorry for Lilly and had tried hard to love her, but Lilly had been difficult, provocative, and cold.

By degrees the mother became more assertive, more active socially, and she took up some committee work. She recognized that she had suppressed her children's aggression and began to help them express aggression in their play. She encouraged Lilly to hold her own in a quarrel with a neighbor's child and not worry about possible criticism. Within a year she was free of her anxiety, less concerned about her children and, as she stated, "ready to live for the first time."

The father, too, came regularly for interviews with the same caseworker who was treating the mother. He was cold and distant during the first few visits and said he was afraid that Lilly might someday become a murderess. Ever since she was a little girl he had felt that he would never feel close to her because she was as emotionally cold as he was. The other children were outgoing and he could not help feeling warm toward them. He was quite certain he had tried several times to be demonstrative with Lilly when she was a young child, but he had given up when his overtures were not met. He admitted that he had frequently lost his patience and spanked Lilly when she was young. She had defied him, and when punished, clenched her fists and would not cry.

The caseworker soon induced the father to think of Lilly's feelings as ambivalent, not just hostile. This distinction seemed to please him, since he could apply this reasoning to himself too. The caseworker helped the father to see that many of Lilly's, his, and his wife's feelings had been influenced by the insecurity from which they all had suffered for many years. The father acknowledged that he had been an unhappy and insecure little boy and had remained unsure of himself all along. He spoke of his difficulty in feeling close to his wife, though he was sure he loved her and needed her. Within a few weeks he was speaking about his wife with more understanding and announced one day that he had brought his wife a gift for the first time in years, except on her birthday. He seemed proud of himself when he told the worker this, and she assured him that she had recognized much earlier that he had a real capacity for warmth.

In a significant interview several months after treatment began, the father reported his intense anger at Lilly for expressing an early hatred of her baby sister. He had been so angry that he had spanked her in a fury, feeling that Lilly was mean and abnormal. She had not cried at the time, and the father had finally stopped spanking her, but he remained furious for a long time. The worker did not try to discuss the possible causes for the father's overreaction to Lilly's rejection of her sister. He described taking Lilly to nursery school every day, without saying one word to her, but waiting longingly for her to talk to him, though she never did.

The caseworker discussed sibling rivalry with the father and he was amazed that it was a normal occurrence. The father accepted the worker's suggestion that Lilly's hatred for her sister would have lessened materially if her parents had recognized and understood why Lilly behaved as she did. Instead, she had had to fight back to meet her father's aggression toward her, and their incompatibility developed. Before long, Lilly had objected to any limits set by her father, and he had become more resentful and rejecting.

The father reacted acutely to this interview. He was grateful to the worker for pointing out what had happened, was ashamed for having behaved so stupidly, and was determined to get Lilly to love him. He agreed with the worker that he would have to make the overtures. She warned him not to expect a quick response and not to overdo, and he assured the worker he would deal with the problem diplomatically. At the close of the interview he said, laughing, that he hoped Lilly could stand the shock.

A few weeks later the father reported success. Lilly had been overjoyed at his friendliness and thanked him again and again for the little gifts he had brought to her. He had always been certain that she would have rejected any gift from him. On one occasion Lilly had actually kissed him. He hoped very much that he would learn to love Lilly as deeply as he did his other children, but he did not expect it to be easy. The worker told the father she would rely on his maturity to deal with that problem. She was sure he could succeed.

After a year of treatment the number of interviews with both parents and Lilly decreased, and six months later when the parents moved from the city the case was closed. During the last few months of therapy the father and mother had grown much closer to each other. They had more quarrels with each other because the mother was now more outspoken and insisted that her wishes be respected. The father learned to be closer not only to Lilly but to his other children as well.

A letter from the mother four years later reported that their family life was continuing to be comparatively happy. Lilly was getting along well in school and had a normal social life. The other brother was soon to be married. For about a year after their occurrence, Lilly occasionally mentioned the poisoning incidents, and the parents did not discourage these references.

About three years after the incidents, on hearing some reference to poisoning, Lilly remarked to her parents that she had practically forgotten what had taken place.

*Lilly is now married and is getting along very well, according to a report from the mother. She has a lovely daughter who is well and happy. She was married after she finished high school, lived for a time in Germany, and then returned to her home state.

There has never been any recurrence of the emotional problems she had as an adolescent. On two occasions while in high school Lilly suddenly blacked out, once while she was at a basketball game and again while she was running up stairs. Her doctor arranged for a complete neurologic examination which turned out to be entirely negative. In the absence of any other attacks during the next few years, it may be safe to assume that these episodes were due to current tensions or conflicts. Lilly and her parents get along very well together, see each other frequently, and have taken trips together. Two more children have been born to the mother's family and are developing nicely.

On one occasion when I was talking about a problem similar to Lilly's with Dr. Helena Deutsch, she told me that, over the years, she had seen several girls who, during their early adolescence, developed stormy emotional reactions which subsided without aftereffects. It was as though unconscious conflict suddenly erupted into consciousness and then, as the ego became stronger, returned to a state of repression.

Children rarely attempt to take the lives of other children. Such attempts occur most often in adolescent children in fits of rage. Over a period of several years only three cases of adolescent children attempting murder have been handled at the Wilder Child Guidance Clinic. One, a twelve-year-old boy, killed his alcoholic stepfather. A thirteen-year-old boy, when intoxicated, slugged a taxi driver and stole his cab; this boy suffered from organic brain damage. The third was Lilly. Serious attempts to kill another child by very young children are extremely rare.[13]

A five-year-old girl, who had been living in a foster home for about a year, became jealous when a baby was placed in the same home. One day, soon after the baby arrived, the foster mother heard the baby coughing as though he were choking. She ran to his room to find it filled with vapors of talcum powder and the little girl forcing the powder down the baby's throat. There was

[13] Bender, Lauretta, and Frank J. Curran, Children and Adolescents Who Kill, *Journ. Crim. Psychopath.*, vol. I, no. 4, 1940, p. 297.

little doubt that the girl was trying to injure the baby seriously.

Lauretta Bender and Curran reviewed a large number of cases of children studied at Bellevue Hospital and found very few young children who attempted to kill. Apparently, then, the great hostility in sibling rivalry, and the frequent death wishes which children express in interviews, are not usually carried beyond the fantasy stage. On the other hand, many attacks made on younger children by older siblings at the height of their sibling rivalry may miscarry through the parents' intervention. Moreover, the parents may not recognize the nature of the attacks or perhaps do not allow themselves to consider them murder attempts.

A young child probably never attacks another young child with the idea of killing; his goal is rather to hurt the rival or get him out of the way. Less aggressive young children often suggest that the parents return the baby to the hospital or give him away.

During the latency and prepubertal periods, aggressive, sadistic children have often attempted vicious attacks which might have been fatal had not another child witnessing the act become terrified and reported it. Many instances of serious attacks by such children occur in the clinic records. One boy, nine years old, tied a slightly younger boy to a tree on a cold wintry night and left him. The younger boy had insulted and taunted the older boy who, in a fit of rage, beat him and tied him. When the younger child did not appear for supper, his mother questioned several children and finally discovered someone who had seen her son and his attacker together. She found her son almost frozen and in terror. When the older boy was interviewed a few weeks later, he reported the incident without any guilt; he felt that the younger boy deserved all he had got.

CHAPTER 20

The "Psychopath"

The most pathololgic kind of acting-out behavior has been described in the so-called "psychopath." For a period of three years, the author and several other child psychiatrists particularly interested in delinquent behavior of children met in round-table discussions on the subject of psychopathic behavior in children.[1] The group was never unanimous on what psychopathic behavior was or whether or not such a clinical condition could appear in a child.

Cleckley's[2] effort to establish a differential diagnosis of this condition in adults has helped to establish a symptom complex which appears to be more of a clinical entity than anything previously described. The symptoms he notes are chronic aggressive, uninhibited behavior which fails to respond to the most intensive therapies, failure to benefit from previous experience, inability to form stable affection ties, and the absence of recognizable feelings of guilt. One important additional characteristic is a general superficiality

---

[1] Karpman, Benjamin (chairman), The Psychopathic Delinquent Child, Round Table, *Amer. Journ. Orthopsychiat.*, vol. XX, no. 2, April, 1950, p. 223.

Karpman, Benjamin (chairman), Psychopathic Behavior in Infants and Children, Round Table, *Amer. Journ. Orthopsychiat.*, vol. XXI, no. 2, April, 1951, p. 223.

[2] Cleckley, Hervey, "The Mask of Sanity," St. Louis, The C. V. Mosby Company, 1941.

in thinking and judgment. The psychopath lives for the moment, disregards the future, constantly seeks gratification, and refuses to tolerate frustration.

He lacks the loyalty to friends or codelinquents which other serious delinquents seem to possess, and he cannot plan his delinquency well; he is too superficial and lacks the judgment such criminal behavior demands. He often suffers from acute anxiety, but only in relation to the possibility of apprehension and punishment. He occasionally suffers from some neurotic symptoms, but unlike the neurotic delinquent he is not basically neurotic; he does not suffer from guilt consciously or unconsciously.

Cleckley has not tried to determine the etiological factors responsible for this pathologic character development. His interest was to establish the psychopathic personality as a clinical entity. The psychiatric team, however, is primarily interested in etiology. The round-table group searched for early life situations which produce psychopathic behavior, hoping that early recognition might prevent further abnormal character development.

Most of the participants of the round table and most clinicians who have studied this problem in children are extremely cautious in diagnosing a child a psychopath. They are justified in doing so, for the term is coming more and more to mean serious acting out which rarely responds to therapy. The therapist has little justification for predicting that a child will continue to remain impervious to therapy, since so many significant changes occur as a result of maturation alone.

Clinicians generally agree that early emotional rejection is an important factor in producing behavior in the child which resembles what Cleckley describes in the adult with a psychopathic personality. They agree also that such a child is instinct-driven because his ego and superego, the two mechanisms which normally check instinctual drives, are weak. They disagree on what constitutional factors determine the greater strength of these drives. Some authors attempt to explain psychopathic behavior as the result of exposing a child during his developmental periods to inconsistent discipline from his parents. Greenacre [3] describes a configuration in which the father is a respected member of the community, compulsive, stern, remote, preoccupied, and fear-inspiring. The mother is an indulgent, pretty, frivolous woman. The parents' ideals and attitudes toward the child's experiences conflict. Both parents are markedly narcissistic and have a poor relationship to the child. They demonstrate an excess of solicitude and indulgence, but have little love for the child. Both parents are interested in external appearances and are eager that the child reflect favorably on them. The mother has a strong narcissistic investment in the child, and the child struggles to break the dependency tie. The result is marked exhibitionism and narcissism in the child. Greenacre feels that the child runs from one parent to the other to escape reality and in the end rebels against both.

This clinical picture is not an uncommon one in our cases. The resulting disorganization in the child's emotional character make-up is responsible for uninhibited aggressive behavior, impulsive delinquency, and superficial relationships to others. Greenacre does not believe that there is an absence of superego structure in these individuals. Although they behave as if they did not have consciences, she feels they must have or they would be overwhelmed by the force of their own aggression.

Greenacre's description of the psychopath is much the same as that Aichhorn gave for the *Hochstapler*. No adequate translation exists in English; perhaps the closest term is fourflusher or confidence man. Basically the *Hochstapler* is a deeply neurotic individual (those he described were adolescents), highly exhibitionistic, living for pleasure only, very charming, cunning, and able to exploit his charm like the fourflusher in our society. Aichhorn emphasized that the therapist must recognize such a character at once and expose his deceitfulness, for otherwise he has little chance to win him over to therapy. When Aichhorn could gain the respect of such an adolescent and a narcissistic transference developed, he

---

[3] Greenacre, Phyllis, Conscience in the Psychopath, *Amer. Journ. Orthopsychiat.*, vol. XV, no. 3, July, 1945, p. 495.

discovered that beneath the aggression was a marked obsessional neurotic character structure, a strong dependency tie to the mother, and a predisposition to homosexuality.

The types of individuals described by Aichhorn and Greenacre closely resemble those described by Cleckley, except for the presence of neurotic conflict not deeply concealed. The presence of this neurotic component suggests a greater degree of earlier socialization than Cleckley and others imply. Zulliger,[4] in discussing this type of character pathology in adolescents, finds them inaccessible to therapy because they do not develop affective identifications or transferences. He believes that their superego is only a shell with no real depth or nucleus.

Aichhorn held that some people may have little or no superego development, but he differentiated these from his *Hochstapler* adolescents. Patients without a superego are not deeply neurotic; they cannot be reached through therapy. He believed that such patients as children had never been loved by anyone who was significant in their lives. They had failed early in life to effect a deep emotional tie. Aichhorn felt that therapy never succeeded with a child unless the therapist could reawaken in him a relationship that had previously existed. The prognosis was very poor if the child had never been loved. He added that fortunately there are few such children.

Treating the so-called "psychopathic child" is no different from treating any child whose acting out is extreme and who is forced by his strong instinctual drives to behave in an impulsive, delinquent manner. One may assume that such a child has a defective ego and superego, and that the main goal of therapy is to provide him with a strong, healthy ego and a superego that will assist the ego in controlling instinctual drives.

Schmideberg,[5] who has made important contributions to the

[4] Zulliger, Hans, Berichte und Gedanken zur Erörterung des narzisstisch-triebhaften Charakters, *Z. f. Psychoanalit. Pädagog.*, vol. IX, heft 3, Mai–Juni, 1935, p. 149.

[5] Schmideberg, Melitta, Psychodynamics of Child Delinquency, Round Table, *Amer. Journ. Orthopsychiat.*, vol. XXV, no. 2, April, 1955, p. 261.

understanding of the intrapsychic factors which produce delinquent behavior, has recently emphasized once again the importance of the child's environment. She has not attempted to minimize the intrapsychic pathology. Many other clinicians working with delinquent youngsters have found that the emotional climate in which a child lives, the opportunities he has for pleasure, recognition, affection, and the satisfaction of material needs, largely determine whether or not he can become or remain socialized. A child finds it easier to steal when he is deprived of things he needs, easier to become truant when he has little supervision in his home or neighborhood, easier to misbehave sexually in a crowded home with alcoholic parents. Chronic deprivation and subjection to the emotionally traumatic scenes which characterize disorganized families furnish the soil in which delinquency thrives.

Such homes do not merely precipitate delinquency, they produce it. Chronic tension and the denial of love create ego weakness; poor models of behavior in the home, dissatisfied, embittered parents engender poor ego-ideal and superego development. Repeated frustration and disillusionment increase hostile aggression.

Whenever possible, treatment of the delinquent child begins while he is in his home. He is accustomed to this setting, where he has developed the defenses which are important to him, even though they may be unacceptable to others. He has an emotional stake in his home where he feels protected, and he may be far more amenable to therapeutic influences if allowed to remain there, especially when the therapist has been instrumental in helping to keep him there. How long a delinquent child can benefit from remaining in his own home and neighborhood depends on the balance between positive and negative features in the home, and this can only be learned through careful study. In those instances in which the home is directly responsible for the hostile acting-out behavior of the child, removal is necessary. Often the child will request removal after he has discussed his home with his therapist and discovered for the first time that there are foster homes where he can be much happier. He learns that he may visit these foster homes, talk to the foster parents, and decide for himself if he would like to live with them.

Communities, hampered by the high cost of maintaining an adequate program, have moved slowly in developing resources for delinquent youngsters. Communities have neglected to provide adequate intensive casework for families which breed delinquency, since most of the parents in such families cannot be reached. The number of families suffering social breakdown has increased with a corresponding increase in the number of anti-social acting-out children. Here and there a family agency, a child-placing agency, or a child-guidance clinic has spent a long time with such "unreachable" parents and discovered that they could be helped to appreciate good casework and were eager for this support. The parents' distrust of society and social agencies had to be overcome by a determined social worker who could convince the parents of her sincerity.

Many interesting and important research projects in juvenile delinquency have been in progress during the past few years in the fields of social science, social work, psychology, and psychiatry. The studies relate to prevention, diagnosis, and treatment and involve the individual, the family, and the community. Special attention has been given to the cultural factors that play a role in the development and control of juvenile delinquency. A recent report submitted by the National Institute of Mental Health entitled "An Assessment of Current Mental Health and Social Science Knowledge Concerning Juvenile Delinquency," written by Donald A. Cook and Seymour Rosenfeld, contains a valuable bibliography of the important research studies. The publication will probably appear in book form during the next year and will be a valuable source of information.

Recent studies by the New York City Youth Board [6] and a report by Alice Overton demonstrate that disturbed and resistive fam-

[6] Ortoff, Murray, Reaching the Unreached—Meeting the Unmet Needs, New York, New York City Youth Board, 1952.

ilies can be influenced to cooperate with social agencies.[7] One of the important steps in securing the good will of these families was to demonstrate the agency's interest in the welfare of every member of the family. Since each person in the family interacts with each of the others—parents, siblings, and anyone else living in the home—all the members of the family reacted to the problems of the others. The family had to be treated as a unit, with the father and the mother as key members. Problems of physical illness, emotional conflict, economics, and delinquency were dealt with carefully. Emotional problems between the parents, employment problems of the father, school problems of the children, and the problems of the mother's work in the home responded to the caseworker's effort. In the end, families previously considered unreachable were helped to meet their difficult reality and sustain their improved social adjustment.

To homes like these many delinquents return after being in institutions, and such environments produce much of the recidivism of these children. The fact that these families, when approached correctly, will often accept good casework, increases the responsibilities of the parole worker who must assume this function himself or enlist the service of a family agency.

The rehabilitation of a disorganized family is a complex, difficult task. A well-trained, devoted caseworker can effectively treat twenty such families, if methods of communication are good. As far as possible, the same worker handles most of the problems in the family, calling for consultation as she needs it and using all the resources in the community. The family-centered approach to families in breakdown is comparatively new, and the devotion of the people who have performed the demonstration work has produced encouraging results.

Most disorganized families that receive good casework for all the members of the family can provide more constructive homes for

[7] Overton, Alice, et al., Serving Families Who Don't Want Help, *Social Case Work*, vol. XXXIV, no. 7, July, 1953, p. 304.

their growing children, reducing the delinquency of the children in the family. This factor alone should more than offset the added cost to the community of providing intensive casework services.

Most families with a child who has been adjudicated delinquent will benefit from casework services. Some will need very little service, but this decision can be made only after a caseworker has evaluated the family. Many families which give a surface impression of emotional adequacy will be found on study to be seriously in need of casework help. The philosophy back of family-centered casework does not apply only to disorganized families in the lower economic strata. Considerable juvenile delinquency has been found in the families of the middle and upper economic classes.

Often a disorganized family is kept from functioning adequately because of the constant friction and tension over the delinquency of one of the children. Child-placing agencies have had difficulty in finding foster homes to deal with the hostile aggression of these youngsters, especially when the children are adolescents, and most of them eventually end up in institutions for delinquent children. Some communities have made successful use of aggregate foster homes where from six to eight children are cared for by foster parents experienced in dealing with acting-out youngsters.

The younger child who has not been socialized may make a good adjustment in a carefully selected foster home where the foster parents and the placement agency can work closely together. Foster homes adequate to deal with a child with special problems are discovered through the arduous task of finding homes with characteristics that appear to meet the delinquent's needs. Young, vigorous foster parents who like activities, sports, and fun will usually tolerate the aggressive delinquent more than less active foster parents. The foster parents must be able to tolerate delinquency and expect that it will continue for a time at least. They must have a clear picture of the child's past behavior to avoid surprise and shock. They must be encouraged to speak freely about any intolerance they may have for a particular kind of acting out, like stealing, fire setting or sexual activity, before the child is placed with them. They must be able to accept the parents of the child in their care, frequently a difficult task. When the delinquent child living in a foster home is receiving therapy, the foster parents must accept the treatment plan, because without their cooperation therapy may fail. Foster parents, like a child's own parents, may appreciate a chance to talk with the child's therapist about the child, and when they regularly accompany the child to the clinic, arrangements are made with the placement agency for the clinic caseworker to have interviews with them.

The fact that a hostile, delinquent child fails to adjust in a good foster home does not rule out the usefulness of foster-home placement for any given child. Often several homes may have to be tried before one is found that meets a child's needs, a fact previously mentioned in the discussion of the narcissistic child. Usually the child who has decided that he will not accept any foster home is quickly recognized by the skilled child-placement worker and experienced foster parents. Such a child may be suffering from neurotic conflict requiring direct treatment, or from brain damage. He needs more than foster-home placement.

Several references have been made to neurotic delinquents. Walter (pp. 96 ff), who suffered from acute neurotic anxiety, was also involved in dissocial acting-out behavior, though not during the period when he suffered from anxiety. Gerald (pp. 251 ff), who had a deep neurotic need to be punished, acted out to such a marked extent that institutionalization was necessary. Martha (pp. 266 ff), acted out sexually in a promiscuous manner to express her neurotic conflict, and Lilly (pp. 273 ff) attempted to poison her sister because of extreme neurotic jealousy. These children demonstrate a few of the many ways in which neurotic symptoms and antisocial behavior combine to express instinctual drives and emotional conflicts.

The healthy, well-adjusted child manages to live out his hostile aggression without offending society. The socialized side of his personality neutralizes the antisocial drives. The neurotic delinquent has been unable to achieve such a balance, with the result

that he acts out against society. The strength of the neurotic component determines the nature of the therapy required to lessen the
acting-out behavior. When the dissocial component is strong and
the neurotic component weak, the problem is largely one of socialization. When the neurotic component is the strong one, psychotherapy is the treatment of choice.

Sometimes the ego has been so traumatized that one cannot
determine what has taken place dynamically. The children Redl
and Wineman [8] described were so seriously conflicted and unsocialized and so difficult to reach by means of the usual interviewing
technics, that attempts to get at underlying conflicts were out of
the question. The problem with these sick children was to get them
to trust another person. The amount of effort used to win over
these boys even partially was as great as that used to gain the confidence of a psychotic patient. The analogy to the psychotic is not
inappropriate, since the boys described by Redl and Wineman
suffered from ego pathology almost as extreme.

Alexander and Healy [9] have attempted to use psychoanalytic
treatment for several young serious delinquents in prison, to demonstrate the value of intensive treatment of neurotic delinquents in
institutions. Others [10, 11] have reported using therapy for serious
acting-out behavior in youngsters in institutions, applying the technic used by Aichhorn with a group of hostile, aggressive boys
treated in an institution.[12] Aichhorn allowed these youngsters to
act out to the utmost for a period of several months in the institution, so long as they did not inflict bodily harm on each other or

[8] Redl, Fritz, and David Wineman, "Children Who Hate," Glencoe, Ill.,
Free Press, 1951.

[9] Alexander, Franz, and William Healy, "Roots of Crime," New York,
Alfred A. Knopf, Inc., 1935.

[10] Schulman, Irving, Modifications in the Treatment of Anti-social Behavior, read at annual meeting of American Orthopsychiatric Association, 1955.

[11] Noshpitz, Joseph, Problems in the Psychotherapy of Adolescent Character
Disorders on a Closed Ward, read at annual meeting of American Orthopsychiatric Association, 1955.

[12] Aichhorn, August, "Wayward Youth," New York, The Viking Press,
Inc., 1935.

the staff. When they reached a stage where they no longer had any reason to act out, when further acting out yielded them nothing since no adults interfered with their hostile aggression or punished them, they started to react against themselves in a neurotic manner. Aichhorn then proceeded to analyze their conflicts.

The value of long-term therapy with a severely disturbed neurotic delinquent child is described in detail by Bettelheim.[13] The child, Harry, seven years old, repeatedly ran away from home and school, stole, exposed himself to serious danger from accidents, barely escaping being killed. The patience of his favorite counselor, and the judgment used in the many difficult situations that arose within the institution and outside during Harry's runaways, testify to the need of talent and skill in dealing with uncontrolled aggression in children. The study of Harry reflects the extreme terror and anxiety that lie concealed beneath violent acting-out behavior. The violence of his behavior and the terrifying situations to which he exposed himself and others more closely resemble nightmares than reality experiences. One gets the impression of an almost naked id expressing itself against the outside world. Bettelheim's description of hostile, sadistic aggression plus the panic associated with the ego's fear of being overwhelmed makes the reader marvel that this boy eventually was tamed and socialized.

Therapy as described in the case of Harry is possible only in a highly specialized residential treatment center like the Orthogenic School. Such institutions, now available largely for teaching and research, may someday provide all communities with the means for therapy of children who suffer from serious emotional conflicts.

Reference was made in Harry's case to the anxiety of the ego when the instinctual drives became extreme. Anna Freud [14] describes the panic that develops in the hostile, aggressive child when the ego feels it has lost control and is in danger of being over-

[13] Bettelheim, Bruno, Harry—A Study in Rehabilitation, *Journ. Abnor. Social Psychol.*, vol. 44, no. 2, April, 1949, p. 231.

[14] Freud, Anna, "The Ego and the Mechanisms of Defense," London, Hogarth Press, Ltd., 1937.

whelmed. It is difficult to conceive of a specific anxiety emanating from the id itself, since it is the ego which suffers anxiety regarding the way the outside world will react to excessive drives from the id. Clinical experience with hostile, aggressive children makes it possible to differentiate children who will welcome a therapist's strength and firmness in keeping them from expressing their excessive drives. Such children, with the pressure of their instinctual demands unmitigated by the superego or the ego, become panicky when someone does not use force or pressure to control their impulses. Heirens, the youthful murderer, wrote on the mirror in the room where he had committed a murder, pleading that someone stop him from continuing his brutal murders. The fact that he did not sign his name suggests that only part of his ego sought restraint.

Bert, an eleven-year-old boy, was referred by a child-placing agency because of uncontrolled, hostile, destructive behavior. Bert had been diagnosed as suffering from postencephalitic brain damage, although his history did not suggest encephalitis and the neurologic findings were negative. The examiner, however, said he had never encountered a child who had been so destructive and uncontrolled, and he could think of nothing but brain damage that could produce such a picture. Bert's life history of rejection by both parents, excessive cruelty in a home which was disorganized during all the time that he lived there, and an almost total lack of supervision explained his behavior.

Bert was placed in an excellent foster home where the foster parents were determined to have him accept them by putting themselves at his disposal at all times and making his reality very pleasant. Bert's destructive behavior lessened somewhat, but he continued to be very demanding, smashed dishes on the floor if the food was not to his liking, and was defiant and disobedient. The foster mother described the following two incidents which led the staff to believe that Bert was suffering from the anxiety of being overwhelmed:

First, each time that the foster mother went to the telephone to answer a call, Bert let out a bloodcurdling yell of terror and appeared to be apprehensive during the telephone interview. This seemed to be related in some way to something terrifying that happened to him following a telephone call, but this was not verified. Second, the foster mother reported that Bert screamed in his sleep and had severe night terrors which were so marked that she had to remake the bed, often several times each night.

Knowing that the foster mother was a warm, kindly person, it was suggested that she stop allowing Bert to act out in this manner in her home, and to insist on obedience. If he broke another dish, he was to know that the cost of this was to come out of his allowance; if he was aggressive or destructive in any way, he was to be isolated; and if he screamed when the telephone rang, he would be punished. The explanation of the mechanism which the therapist thought was operating in Bert's case helped the foster mother to accept the procedure, since she realized that she had made no progress with him through the use of her own methods. The foster mother reported within a few days that the change in Bert's behavior was quite remarkable, and he was a much more comfortable boy to live with.

This fragment of a long, involved case history is a dramatic example of the effect of pressure when the weakened ego demands support from the outside world. One wonders why the ego did not accept the many demands and punishments which the outside world had made previously. The case suggests that the pressure which a child like Bert needs must come from someone he has learned to love.

In a modified form this mechanism probably operates in the schoolroom when healthy, active youngsters overreact to a teacher who is a poor disciplinarian. Such children tell the therapist that they are greatly relieved when a good disciplinarian comes to the room and quickly puts an end to their stupid aggression.

Treatment of neurotic, delinquent youngsters can be effectively carried out in child-guidance clinics, when the hostile aggression is not too uncontrolled. Treatment consists of developing a close, warm tie, a positive transference relationship to the delinquent, and then analyzing the neurotic component of the conflict, some-what like the method used in analyzing a neurotic illness. Many psychiatrists in child-guidance clinics have applied psychoanalytic methods in their psychotherapy of neurotic delinquents and feel that such therapy is applicable to those youngsters whose acting out decreases as they develop a positive tie to the therapist.[15, 16]

Aichhorn's [17] experience with hostile, aggressive youngsters in an institution taught him technics which, with modification, he used with less seriously disturbed acting-out adolescents in his private practice and child-guidance clinics. He devised several methods to accelerate the development of a strong positive emotional tie. He used these methods largely with adolescents whom he diagnosed as *Hochstaplers*, and they might well be effective in the treatment of any narcissistic, hostile, aggressive youngster. Aware of the marked narcissism of these delinquents, Aichhorn did not attempt to foster an object relationship or transference to him but depended upon a narcissistic relationship. He demonstrated to the delinquent that he, Aichhorn, was the cleverer and the more cunning of the two; that he knew more than the delinquent about delinquency and methods of outwitting law-enforcing agencies.

He proceeded in some instances to point out to the delinquent his stupidity in permitting himself to get into a situation which could only end in disaster. In this way, Aichhorn hoped to win the admiration of the delinquent who could find an adult worth knowing only if he was entertaining and perhaps even useful to him. At the same time Aichhorn considered that his method included some socialization, since the delinquent must have recognized that although the therapist knew all about delinquency, he still remained socialized.

[15] Gardner, George E., The Pseudo-psychotic Nucleus in the Behavior Disorders, *Amer. Journ. Orthopsychiat.*, vol. XVIII, no. 2, April, 1948, p. 309.

[16] Lippman, Hyman S., and Sylvia Reisman, A Neurotic Adolescent Struggling against a Deep Need for a Criminal Career, in "Case Studies in Childhood Emotional Disabilities," vol. I, George Gardner (editor), New York, American Orthopsychiatric Association, 1953.

[17] Aichhorn, August, seminar, Vienna, 1930–1931.

Aichhorn frequently startled or shocked the delinquent by suddenly sending him on an errand involving the spending of Aichhorn's money just after the parents had reported to Aichhorn in the boy's presence that he was not to be trusted. Sometimes, when little progress was being made in effecting a relationship, he provoked the delinquent into an argument, believing that it was important to get the adolescent to react emotionally. One adolescent felt proud of having traveled from another country for treatment because his delinquency was so serious. While the father was presenting his complaint about his boy's defiance and uncontrolled behavior, Aichhorn noticed that the boy was bored and annoyed. He advised the father in the boy's presence to stop spending money on further therapy; he had already spent enough money without results and had done all that a father could do to save his son from spending the rest of his life in prison or from becoming insane; it was up to the boy to decide whether he wanted to make a real effort to get over an extreme illness. When the boy came in the next day, furious at Aichhorn, he was told that he had a right to be angry but that he was also terribly afraid. The boy broke into sobs, and Aichhorn told him that he was ready for treatment.

Eissler [18] describes other technics of Aichhorn's, which he found useful in his own work. Eissler lays special stress on helping the delinquent feel that the therapist is omnipotent.

All these methods have but one object in view: to develop a strong positive relationship necessary for the beginning of therapy. What follows later in the treatment is similar to the analytic methods used in treating neurotic character disturbances. Aichhorn once remarked in a personal interview that many of the methods he used came from an intuitive grasp of situations. It was difficult to explain theoretically why certain treatment methods were effective with particular delinquents. It was obvious after watching him at work that his warm, friendly, accepting manner and his deep recognition

[18] Eissler, Kurt R., Ego Psychological Implications of the Psychoanalytic Treatment of Delinquents, in "The Psychoanalytic Study of the Child," vol. V, 1950, p. 97.

that the delinquent could not be blamed for anything he did were quickly sensed by the youngsters he treated. His ready grasp of the total situation and his ability to get to the heart of a problem quickly enabled him to apply methods which others may be unable to use.

Probably many talented therapists have been successful in socializing instinct-driven, acting-out youngsters, but have never published their results. Doctors hesitate to describe an occasional success when there are so many failures with this type of adolescent. Dr. Stanley King, one of the staff psychiatrists at the Institute for Child Guidance in New York City, has successfully treated many severely disturbed, hostile, aggressive youngsters whom he took into his own home for foster care. Dr. and Mrs. King had a series of these boys in their home for many years; when one improved and left, they accepted another.

One such youngster [19] was a destructive, cruel, defiant, and hostile adolescent who particularly hated all adults in positions of authority. He had been rejected by sadistic, alcoholic parents and had been delinquent most of his life. He showed little guilt about his delinquency and seemed disinterested in changing his behavior. The Kings welcomed him to their home and told him they would try to make him happy there. They explained that the laws of the state demanded that he be in the house every night by 10:00 P.M., that he attend school, and that they would have to insist that these laws be respected. The Kings told him he could eat with them if he wished, or by himself if he preferred. For a long time Fred ate alone and devoured his food; like most delinquents he had a voracious appetite. He was secretive, sarcastic, and unfriendly in spite of the Kings' friendly overtures. He regularly stole any small sums of money that happened to be left around, and he was aware that these thefts were known to the Kings.

At no time did the Kings punish Fred, and his difficult behavior

19 Lippman, Hyman S., Difficulties Encountered in the Psychiatric Treatment of Chronic Juvenile Delinquents, in "Searchlights on Delinquency," New York, International Universities Press, Inc., 1949, p. 156.

was overlooked whenever possible. One evening, some time after Fred had been with them, Dr. King heard Fred tell some other adolescents in front of the house that Dr. King was cruel and enjoyed ordering him around and beating him. Dr. King, however, said nothing to Fred about this conversation.

After several months, Fred began to join the Kings at their table for meals, although he rarely spoke and continued to act unfriendly. The Kings did not report the exact steps in his slow improvement, but about a year after Fred had come to the King home, he surprised Dr. King by asking him for a ride downtown. During the ride Dr. King did not try to talk to Fred; he knew that Fred would soon start talking spontaneously. After that, Fred began trying rather clumsily to help Dr. King in his work around the home, and before long, every time the doctor looked up from what he was doing, Fred was there. One day, Fred began telling Dr. King about some of his early life experiences, and then he showed a great eagerness to talk. (Dr. King remarked to the author that one has to talk to severely traumatized youngsters to realize how acutely they suffer.)

Fred brought out his hostility against his family, schools, social agencies, the police, and others who had hurt him. Dr. King was able to explain to Fred that though much of his resentment was understandable, a good deal of his suffering was due to his own attitude and behavior. Fred's delinquency stopped. He continued to live with the Kings throughout his high school and college years.

The outstanding feature of this treatment was the Kings' extreme patience, their confidence in their ability to get Fred to accept them, and the absence of retaliatory aggression. They were highly permissive without being indulgent. The Kings were firm when firmness was needed, but they never attacked. They tried to be helpful at all times, expecting nothing in return. During his stay in their home, Fred had thousands of little opportunities to test the Kings; finally he convinced himself that they were really safe.

Dr. King and Aichhorn had similar personalities. They were

warm, cheerful, kindly men with infinite patience. They saw the consistency of the delinquent child's behavior and that he was acting in the only way possible for him in the light of his life experiences. Neither therapist had much hostility in his make-up, and they shared a great love for children.

Van Ophuijsen [20] was particularly interested in therapeutic work with seriously disturbed acting-out youngsters. He originated the term *primary behavior disorders* for describing children who begin to react with hostile aggression very early in life. The narcissistic acting-out behavior was invariably associated with early rejection by the parents. Having discovered that these children did respond to him after they developed a positive tie, he concluded that treating such children was a particularly good field for psychiatric social workers trained to perform direct therapy with children. He supervised a group of psychiatric social workers, each of whom was working intensively with such children. They were allowed as much time as they needed, and they could be very permissive with the children. After several months, the younger children of the group of delinquents grew less aloof and allowed the workers to join them in play. This was the first step in breaking down the delinquent's narcissism. In the case of the adolescent delinquents, the workers realized they had made the grade when the adolescents displayed a real interest in them for the first time. Van Ophuijsen cautioned the workers to be most careful with the delinquents as they moved into the object relationship, which in its early stages was very tenuous. The delinquent at this time was hypersensitive, not sure that he was doing the safe thing. A few angry remarks, a brief inattention to their needs, could destroy the hard-won gains. In the end, the workers succeeded in socializing these children. Van Ophuijsen was convinced that only the development of object love made treatment possible with these delinquents.

The demonstration that a child this far from accepting social standards can be brought back to society has tremendous implica-

---

[20] Van Ophuijsen, J. W. H., Primary Conduct Disorder, in "Modern Trends in Child Psychiatry," Nolan Lewis and Bernard Pacella (editors), New York, International Universities Press, Inc., 1945, p. 35.

tions in a program of therapy. If these children can be helped, then the large bulk of serious delinquents can surely be helped.

Susan Isaacs [21] once searched for a delinquent who was so callous and cold-blooded that he could commit any type of crime without the slightest evidence of remorse or guilt. The probation officers and prison workers finally located a young woman in prison who had committed every crime except murder, and she had attempted murder on several occasions. The prison officials accompanied this woman to Mrs. Isaacs' home daily for psychotherapy. In describing the case, Mrs. Isaacs remarked that she was amazed at how many different articles in her interviewing room disappeared without her being aware of it until later. After several months of persistent effort, the delinquent slowly began to recognize Mrs. Isaacs as a person. Toward the end of the first year, she began to talk about her home and early life and revealed a background of emotionally traumatic experiences which were unbelievably vicious. She had been a rejected, unwanted child. She had been beaten mercilessly by a sadistic, epileptic mother. She broke into sobs as she described looking at her mother, unconscious in an epileptic attack. Over and over again she had wished that her mother would die in an attack, and she had found it difficult to keep herself from killing her mother at such times. She could vividly recall her terror each time she realized her mother was about to have another convulsion.

During the next year of treatment, this delinquent woman described more and more of her early life experiences which had led her into juvenile delinquency and then serious crime. At the time Mrs. Isaacs told this story, the patient had been in analysis for several years and was still in treatment. She was coming to Mrs. Isaacs' home unaccompanied, and in all respects was a comparatively normal, healthy woman.

While those therapists who have demonstrated that severely hostile, delinquent youngsters can be socialized are all psychoanalysts, their therapy included little interpretation of unconscious material. Therapy depended almost entirely on the patient's developing a

[21] Isaacs, Susan, personal interview in London, 1935.

positive transference. The analysts' understanding of neurotic anxiety, defense mechanisms, unconscious resistance, helped them to
be patient. The absence of superego development and the history
of severe early rejection in these delinquents pointed the direction
therapy would have to take in order to succeed. The analysts were
convinced that, following the development of a positive transference, the delinquent would find it possible to identify with the
social standards of the analyst, and this is what happened in each
successful case.

Section 7

THE CHILD WITH
A TENUOUS HOLD
ON REALITY

The Psychotic Child

An extreme form of ego disturbance appears in childhood psychosis. This condition varies considerably in onset and in the age when it appears. In some children the onset is sudden, with a noticeable change in the child's personality and appearance. In others, the onset is insidious, and the child gradually withdraws and refuses to eat or play.

Anxiety is a prominent symptom, and the child's dependency may be so extreme that he cannot tolerate any separation from his mother. The child may prefer to be alone and to play in a stereotyped manner, tearing paper into small bits or twirling objects without appearing to enjoy himself. Frequently the psychotic child has a waxy complexion; his eyes, which may not focus, look through rather than at one. He often looks into space and, as he walks around aimlessly, claps his hands together, or holds his arms up as if to strike. Such children have an extremely weak hold on reality; the outer world seems to mean little to them except as a possible source of great danger.

Since Leo Kanner first described infantile autism in 1943, this condition, sometimes called atypical development and infantile schizophrenia, has received increasing attention. In a later article in 1949 [1] Kanner differentiated infantile autism from organic dis-

[1] Kanner, Leo, see references at end of this chapter.

eases involving the brain. Kanner found he could recognize this condition in the second half of the first year of life by the infant's apathy, lack of eagerness to be picked up, failure to react to the approach of people, and the absence of adjustment of posture to people who picked him up.

An early diagnosis of this condition is important, since therapy should be initiated as soon as possible. Deafness, blindness, and feeblemindedness, which present a somewhat similar picture, must be ruled out first. One must be very cautious about making a diagnosis of childhood psychosis in the first year of life, however, and exclude all other conditions, since the very mention of the term psychosis is terrifying to parents. Pediatricians or general practitioners are most likely to see such children. Should the possibility of psychosis be present, the doctor should refer the child to a psychiatric team for diagnosis based not only on the behavior of the child but on the steps in his development and the relationship between him and his mother.

The chief etiologic factor in early childhood psychosis seems to be the lack of an early affection tie between the mother and infant. Apparently the mother cannot give her child the intense, continuous, warm mothering which favors the development of a healthy ego, making identification possible. Without the warm, close contact with the mother, the ego cannot carry on the important function of synthesis which helps the child differentiate between self and nonself.

A special research project has been in progress for several years at the James Jackson Putnam Center in Boston, where Beata Rank and her coworkers have been developing a specific type of therapy for these severely regressed children and their mothers. Mrs. Rank feels that emotional illness in the mothers is primarily responsible for the children's pathology. Manic-depressive psychosis, deep depression, or extreme immaturity make these mothers incapable of mature emotional relationships, even to their own babies.

It is often difficult to find any evidence of early rejection of the autistic child through interviews with the parents. The parents may say honestly that they have always loved their child; their devotion cannot be questioned. Only when the parents have been in treatment to give them some insight into their underlying fantasies, fears, and wishes can their real relationship to their sick child be uncovered. The relationship between the worker and such a mother, who frequently has unsatisfied infantile dependency needs, requires the most sensitive handling in order to support the positive elements in the relationship. Focusing the treatment on the mother-child relationship gradually reveals the mother's involvement with her child, and her trust in the worker will help her accept her feelings without excessive guilt. By degrees, the mother can recognize her deep rejection of her child and slowly begin to tolerate and accept him. As the mother gradually identifies herself with the worker and learns that she has rejected the child, she may be able to make restitution and recognize the child's need for love.[2]

Most of the studies of childhood psychosis reported in the literature deal with very seriously disturbed children. Few references are made to those children who are autistic to a lesser degree, who are occasionally treated in a child-guidance clinic, and who respond to less heroic measures than those used with markedly regressed children. Many disturbed children who are markedly withdrawn or overexcitable, who show some degree of mutism, wave their hands in the air, jump up and down, or pay little or no attention to those about them are seen at the Wilder Child Guidance Clinic. In some cases these children will respond to treatment even when the parents are not available for therapy.

William was referred when he was five years old, because the kindergarten teacher found she could not control his behavior. He made no contacts with the other children, did not enter into their group activities, and wandered around in a trancelike state. His only companion was a sister two years older than he. William made no spontaneous remarks, but repeated in parrot fashion statements made by the therapist. He made such remarks as,

---

[2] Pavenstedt, Eleanor, and Irene Anderson, see references at end of this chapter.

"Don't you spill that paint, you fool," as he spilled the paint; "Now you are going to build the blocks," as he began to build; and reversed pronouns in remarks such as, "Give me those pencils," handing them to the worker. Many of his remarks describing current play activity were obviously the kinds of statements his mother made to him frequently. At times it was as though his mother was in the room, angrily insisting that he do things in a certain way, or complaining about things he had done.

He often darted away from the therapist and ran into other rooms, unmindful of what was going on. He enjoyed being chased and showed remarkable skill in getting out of sight quickly and into remote corners of the building. This behavior was not only a game; he seemed compelled to break away and run, though nothing observable in the play interview had annoyed or frightened him. He showed little anxiety during his clinic visits.

He seemed to enjoy his sessions with the therapist, whom he saw two or three times each week, though he expressed fondness for her only once, when, unfortunately, she was obliged to turn his treatment over to another therapist. She explained to him that she had to leave, that she loved him dearly, and that someone else would play with him. He said little and continued to play, but later went over to her and put his arms around her neck. He said nothing to indicate that he felt the loss. Two months later, when playing with his next therapist, he said, "Miss Jackson is not going to be here any more."

On occasions when Miss Jackson had worn different shoes from those she had worn daily for some time, William, looking at her feet as he always did when she entered the waiting room, said, "This isn't Miss Jackson." Soon, however, he would recognize her, and run ahead of her to her room. After several months of treatment by his first therapist, he was somewhat more tractable and occasionally used the correct pronoun "I" in referring to himself. He had not improved sufficiently to be acceptable to the kindergarten and was excluded after a few days' trial.

His mother entered William in a day nursery because of her

great difficulty in dealing with him at home all day. The second therapist saw him for short play interviews daily. His relationship with this therapist was not so strong as that to his first, largely because he had developed a strong, warm dependency tie to one of the workers in the day nursery. This worker devoted a good share of her time to helping William. She became very fond of him and felt she could have done more for him if his mother had been more considerate of William's needs, more kindly and accepting. She noticed that on days when William was withdrawn and markedly distracted, he had been severely reprimanded or punished by his mother. On certain days the therapist at the clinic had noted that William was more easy to manage and more in contact with his immediate activity. The staff's infrequent contacts with the mother had made it difficult to verify her influence.

The mother did not involve herself in therapy. William's first therapist, who also worked with his mother, had succeeded in getting her to discuss some of her early traumatic life experiences, including the early death of her mother. When this therapist left, however, the mother, who had originally resisted treatment, lost all interest in discussing her own life any further.

At the time William left the day nursery he had improved considerably, according to the worker there. By degrees he had dropped many of the mannerisms which made him appear bizarre. The worker felt that William was taking on behavior which more resembled that of the other children, at least part of the time. He was still unable to develop real ties to the other children of his age in the day nursery, but to some degree at least he was playing with other children and entering into conversation with them. At other times, however, he still withdrew from the group to play by himself and stare into space.

Occasional contacts with the mother by telephone indicated that William, at nine years of age, was making progress in school and was up to his grade placement. He had found one particular friend with whom he played a great deal, and he seemed to enjoy himself. According to his mother he always was an affectionate child. The school has not been contacted for a report of his behavior, but his continued advancement and the fact that his parents have not sought help for William during the past three years suggest that he was doing well.

*In a follow-up interview with William's parents ten years later, they reported that he was a junior in a parochial school and was doing very well scholastically. Although he had one or two close friends who enjoyed his company, he continued to find it difficult to make friends because of his sensitivity. Remarks made by his friends bothered him and made him feel they did not like him. His parents tried hard to convince him that these remarks were typical of growing youngsters, but he continued to overreact. He was seldom invited to parties and felt hurt that his classmates (and teachers) did not make a greater effort to include him in their activities. The parents wondered whether to do more in getting him to associate with others, even though they understood that too much urging would irritate William and could have the opposite effect.

The mother appeared to have forgotten how disturbed William had been when he was five years old. She remembered that he had been restless and difficult, but did not recall her own worry about him. When the therapist remarked that Bill had made considerable progress and would very likely continue to do well, she wondered if the clinic staff had been unduly concerned about him.

In marked contrast to William was Leroy who, at three years of age, after what appeared to be normal development, suddenly became lethargic and withdrawn after an acute fright when an older child attacked him. He was awake most of the night following the attack and screamed in fear if his parents left him. During the next few days he stopped talking, sat in a corner sucking his thumb, and did not respond to attempts to play with him.

By the time a therapist saw him at five years of age, he was markedly deteriorated and mute, ran around the room clapping his hands, rolled on the floor, and laughed loudly for no apparent reason. He had been thoroughly examined at a children's hospital where organic findings were negative. A child psychiatrist at the hospital had made a diagnosis of early childhood schizophrenia.

Leroy's mother was an immature, hysterical woman who suffered repeated depressions. She quarreled almost continuously with her husband whom she did not love but had married to escape from an intolerable home situation. He was dull, coarse, hard-working, and very fond of Leroy.

When Leroy failed to respond to therapy at the clinic, he was moved to an excellent foster home, where a very warm, solicitous foster mother accepted and loved him. He failed to respond to her affection, however, and during the next two years went rapidly downhill, withdrawing more and more within himself.

Schizophrenic illness occurring in the prepubertal and adolescent years differs little from that of later adolescence and early adult life. Schizophrenic illness during latency and before the onset of puberty is rarely seen in child-guidance-clinic work. When such a child is referred, as intensive therapy as possible is instituted with the child and his parents. Every effort is made to encourage the child to hold onto reality, while the therapist tries to understand his anxiety and panic. In most instances residential treatment care is required if the illness has a strong hold on the child and causes serious regression. The most highly specialized services are required in a residential treatment center for psychotic children, and this includes the resident staff and household assistants as well as the professional visiting staff.

There is much difference of opinion regarding the etiology of early childhood psychosis, and a state of confusion remains concerning its nature. Treatment has been attempted through a variety of physical, educational, analytical, and nonanalytical methods.[3] We are not as yet in a position to state which of the therapies

[3] Friedman, Seymour, Diagnostic Criteria in Childhood Schizophrenia, *Bull. Menninger Clin.*, vol. XVIII, no. 2, March, 1954, pp. 41–51.

provides the best or the most lasting results. The fact that so many thoroughly grounded and well-trained psychotherapists are devoting themselves to this problem offers hope that helpful methods of therapy will be forthcoming.

Parents of psychotic children suffer greatly, particularly those whose children offer very little hope of getting well or even improving. Parents know the very poor prognosis of psychotic illness. In general, parents tend to blame themselves for the problems and illness of their children and vainly try to determine what mistakes they have made which may have produced the difficulties. These parents must learn the difference between unconscious conflicts which may favor psychosis in a child and conscious feelings or wishes which harm the child and which can be modified. The mother must be assured that she has behaved in the only way possible to her and that her attitudes result from a myriad of situations over which she has had absolutely no control. Her burden is heavy enough without adding to her tension and guilt.

Since many authorities who have worked with psychotic children are convinced that unconscious fantasies in the parents play an important role in the development of childhood psychosis, it is advisable that all parents of psychotic children have psychoanalytic therapy or be analyzed. When this is not possible, the parents—especially the mother—should receive intensive casework treatment from an experienced social worker supervised by a psychiatrist who has been analytically trained or oriented.

Emphasis in this discussion has been given to the role of the mother, since she is the child's first important source of affection. Research may disclose that the father plays a very significant role through his attitude and treatment of the child and through the effect his attitude or feelings have upon the mother.

Parents who cannot feel close to their psychotic child should be encouraged to have the child placed in a treatment center or in a foster home. In both instances, the child must be assured of warm, motherly care.

Several important articles on childhood psychosis are listed below.

References

Bender, Lauretta, Paper delivered in the discussion at meeting of the International Association for Child Psychiatry, Toronto, Canada, Aug. 13, 1954.

The prognosis of childhood psychosis depends on the child's capacity to develop defense mechanisms; when the psychotic child begins to develop more neurotic symptoms, he is showing signs of progress.

Infantile autism is due to a constitutional factor, a maturation lag, and is determined before birth by heredity.

Benedek, Therese, Adaptation to Reality in Early Infancy, *Psychoanalyt. Quart.*, vol. VII, no. 2, April, 1938, p. 200.

Emphasizes that the warm contact between the mother and child allows the infant to establish a confident anticipation of gratifying his needs, forming an early identification. Without the close tie to the mother, the object world remains strange, distant, and incomprehensible.

Ekstein, Rudolf, Keith Bryant, and Seymour W. Friedman, Childhood Schizophrenia and Allied Conditions, in Leopold Bellak (ed.), "Schizophrenia," New York, Logos Press, Inc., 1958.

An excellent detailed discussion of schizophrenia in childhood. All clinical aspects are discussed, including etiology, diagnosis, differential diagnosis, treatment, and prognosis. Treatment includes somatic treatment, psychotherapy, and residential treatment. The authors point out that the years 1936 to 1946 were characterized by an emphasis on diagnosis and therapeutic pessimism and that the phase 1946 to 1956 was one of therapeutic experimentation and optimism. They feel that there is a great need for further experimentation and treatment techniques, which may result in an increased probability of recovery.

Fabian, Abraham A., Some Familial Considerations in Childhood Schizophrenia, *Amer. Journ. Orthopsychiat.*, vol. XXIV, no. 3, July, 1954, p. 513.

Describes the difficulty in obtaining significant data from parents of psychotic children. He differentiates facts held back consciously by reticence from the unconscious factors referred to by Rank and MacNaughton.

Fabian, Abraham A., and Marjorie Holden, Treatment of Childhood

Schizophrenia in a Child Guidance Clinic, *Amer. Journ. Orthopsychiat.*, vol. XXI, no. 3, July, 1951, p. 571.

Disturbances in the other members of the family caused by a psychotic child, as seen in child-guidance-clinic work.

Ferenczi, Sandor, The Unwelcome Child and His Death Instinct, *Int. Journ. Psychoanal.*, vol. X, part I, January, 1929, p. 125.

In discussing Freud's theory of the life and death instinct, Ferenczi states, "I only wish to point to the probability that children who are received in a harsh and disagreeable way die easily and willingly. Either they use one of many proffered organic possibilities, or if they escape this fate they keep a streak of pessimism and of aversion to life. . . . The life force which rears itself against the difficulties of life has therefore not really any great innate strength, and becomes established only when tactful treatment and upbringing gradually give rise to progressive immunization against physical and psychical injuries."

Friedman, Seymour, Diagnostic Criteria in Childhood Schizophrenia, *Bull. Menninger Clin.*, vol. XVIII, no. 2, March, 1954, pp. 41–51.

Review of the recent important literature on childhood schizophrenia.

Gerard, Margaret, and Helen Mary Overstreet, The Technical Modification in the Treatment of a Schizoid Boy within a Treatment Institution, *Amer. Journ. Orthopsychiat.*, vol. XXIII, no. 1, January, 1953, p. 171.

Treatment of an eleven-and-a-half-year-old boy in an institution. He is referred to as schizoid in the title of the article, but the description seems to be that of a schizophrenic child with delusions and disorientation. In addition to providing a detailed description of aggressive treatment of a seriously regressed child, the article provides the reader with the literature dealing with recent contributions to the treatment of schizophrenia.

Kanner, Leo, Problems of Nosology and Psychodynamics of Early Infantile Autism, *Amer. Journ. Orthopsychiat.*, vol. XIX, no. 3, July, 1949, p. 416.

Infantile autism differentiated from other clinical conditions.

Mahler, Margaret S., On Child Psychosis and Schizophrenia: Autistic and Symbiotic Infantile Psychoses, in "The Psychoanalytic Study of the Child," vol. VII, New York, International Universities Press, Inc., 1952, p. 286.

When the infant cannot receive warmth and affection from

his mother, he may react in one of two ways. He may withdraw into autistic behavior in which reality is essentially given up, or into a symbiotic relationship with his mother in which he loses his identity and remains as one with his mother.

Pavenstedt, Eleanor, and Irene Anderson, Complementary Treatment of Mother and Child with Atypical Development, *Amer. Journ. Orthopsychiat.*, vol. XXII, no. 3, July, 1952, p. 607.

Parents may be honest when they say they have never rejected their child. Only when they have been in treatment which gives them insight into their unconscious fantasies, fears, and wishes can their real relationship to their sick child be uncovered. The worker must be able to respond to the infantile dependency needs of these mothers, most of whom have not been or have not felt loved by their own mothers.

Annette Garrett, *discussant* of this article, makes important observations concerning the role of the caseworker in the treatment of disturbed children.

Putnam, Marion C., Draft of International Preparatory Commission's Report on Childhood Psychosis, meeting of International Association for Child Psychiatry, Toronto, Canada, Aug. 14, 1954.

Dr. Putnam summarizes treatment of atypical children at Putnam Center:

"We try during the *first phase* of therapy to make restitution to the child for the frustrations of his past, which may still be operating in varying degrees in his current environment. We meet the child's needs at whatever level he presents himself, avoiding frustrations whenever possible and providing a maximum of gratification. Through the contact with the more understanding parent substitute the child slowly reaches out to the world around him. While the child may still be unable to cope with the postponement of his immediate wishes, he learns during this first phase of therapy to establish some contact with the outside world, to relinquish to some degree the primary process, to decrease the primacy of the pleasure principle and to make some reality testing.

"In the *second phase* of therapy it is the therapist's task to help the child make the necessary steps toward socialization. In learning to adjust to reality the child must develop the capacity to postpone immediate gratifications and to establish tender relationships with people. This implies a transformation of his inordinate demands and his passionate attachments into tender love and generally more mitigated expressions of his libidinal and aggressive drives. Supportive and educational measures should play a prominent part in the therapy, to enable the child to modify his aggressive and libidinal drives by developing the capacity to play, to learn, and to be active. He learns, in short, to adopt the reality principle without completely relinquishing the pleasure principle."

Rabinowitch, Ralph, Paper read at meeting of International Association for Child Psychiatry, Toronto, Canada, Aug. 14, 1954.

A comprehensive report on a research project on the etiology of infantile psychosis.

Rank, Beata, and Dorothy MacNaughton, A Clinical Contribution to Early Ego Development, in "The Psychoanalytic Study of the Child," vol. V, 1950, p. 53.

Rocking movements, head-banging and clapping, pulling the ears and hair, and even verbalizations are attributed to the libido's remaining fixed on itself. The body zones become erotized and the child becomes hyperexcitable.

The mother's early disappointing relationship with her own mother produces forbidden unconscious fantasies regarding her child. The mother's projection of herself into the child, who is devaluated as her bad self, is evidence of the mother's precarious ego balance and lack of ego outline.

Sterba, Editha, An Abnormal Child, The *Psychoanalyt. Quart.*, vol. V, no. 3, July, 1936, p. 375; continued in no. 4, October, 1936, p. 560.

The psychoanalytic treatment of a psychotic young child.

Szurek, Stanislaus A., The Family and the Staff in Hospital Psychiatric Therapy of Children, *Amer. Journ. Orthopsychiat.*, vol. XXI, no. 3, July, 1951, p. 597.

The treatment of psychotic children in a residential treatment setting in a hospital.

CHAPTER 22

The Markedly Unstable Child

Many children studied in a child-guidance clinic exhibit a peculiar type of instability which is difficult to classify. These children have a poor hold on reality, though at no time is their contact with reality entirely lost. They are obviously not psychotic, nor do they appear to be particularly neurotic. They spend much more time on details of a drawing or a game than they do on trying to size up the total situation. They are slow in grasping cause and effect relationships. Diffused random activity characterizes their play. They have difficulty in achieving time concepts and may wander around the clinic building when they know they are expected home punctually.

William Goldfarb's studies in concept deficiency throw light on the problems of these children. Goldfarb [1] contrasted the adjustment of fifteen children who had spent their first three years in an institution followed by foster-home care with that of fifteen children who from early infancy lived in foster homes. He noted that the institution children were characterized by what he called a defective level of conceptualization. They showed difficulty in

[1] Goldfarb, William, Psychological Privation in Infancy and Subsequent Adjustment, *Amer. Journ. Orthopsychiat.*, vol. XV, no. 2, April, 1945, p. 247.

organizing a variety of stimuli, were unable to think abstractly or make generalizations, and were retarded in their learning ability. Goldfarb believed that he could differentiate those children who had suffered early deprivation through living in an institution from those who had been traumatized by early rejection. The differences, he thought, were due to the institution child's inability to identify with an adult while the rejected child has been able to relate himself to a person, even though negatively. This early identification is important for the development of psychic structure and provides the motivation for normal "maturation and differentiation of personality."

Goldfarb concluded that the institution child was undeveloped in contrast to the rejected child who was in conflict. The rejected child felt hostile because of his underlying tension and anxiety; his behavior was less diffuse and more goal-directed.

Observations at the clinic have not disclosed this sharp differentiation. The behavior of many rejected children closely approximates that described by Goldfarb in the child deprived through his institutional experience. Rejected children vary considerably in their behavior; the aggressive, hypersensitive, narcissistic, rejected child behaves quite differently from the passive, dependent, masochistic child who has been rejected. These differences must depend on which of the parents rejects the child, or if both do; on the age at which parent substitutes came into the child's life; on the child's constitutional make-up, health, and many other factors. The behavior Goldfarb describes results when the child has no chance to form an early identification. This produces an ego weakness with a resulting deficiency in his capacity to conceptualize. There are very likely other conditions which produce the same results, and perhaps for the same reason. Reasons other than the absence of an adult person may make it difficult for an infant to develop early identifications.

The rejected children whom Levy [2] described in his article ap-

[2] Levy, David, Primary Affect Hunger, *Amer. Journ. Psychiat.*, vol. 94, no. 3, November, 1937, p. 643.

peared to have the same tenuous hold on reality which characterized Goldfarb's cases. They, too, failed early to find adults with whom they could identify. Their basic problem was an inability to accept prospective adoptive parents. They failed to use their intelligence in learning.

Robert, ten years old, was referred to the clinic by his parents after he had been expelled from school. His teacher reported that he repeatedly left his desk without permission, walked about the room in an aimless fashion, and disturbed the other children in his class. The usual methods of discipline failed to change Robert's behavior. Before his referral to the clinic he had been tried in another school, but after one week he was expelled because the teacher could not control his restless wanderings. His parents were advised to get psychiatric help.

During his first interview at the clinic Robert wore a blank expression, was markedly withdrawn, and remained curled up on the couch. His conversation at times was disconnected, and he left the impression of being psychotic. In the next two or three interviews, however, his behavior was less extreme, and the staff attributed his earlier behavior to tension. He continued to be withdrawn and disinterested in the interviews, though he was not hostile.

The study revealed that Robert was a rejected child. The rejection was not due to his behavior, but helped to account for it. He had an attractive younger brother whom his parents preferred. Both parents gave the worker the impression of being rigid and demanding, the mother more so than the father. They were concerned because Robert was not making an effort to get along; they knew he was capable of doing better schoolwork. At one time they stated he was a peculiar child as long as they could remember. "He was never normal."

In the conference the staff decided that Robert might best respond to therapy from a woman, since his poorest relationship was with his mother. A caseworker was assigned to see Robert once a week for interviews. Another caseworker worked with the parents.

In play situations Robert jumped from one activity to another as though he had to respond to every stimulus. He asked questions unrelated to the current discussion. He demanded every moment of the worker's time and called attention to what he was doing when he thought she was not observing him. He referred to his poor schoolwork and to his parents' dissatisfaction with his achievements in school. He felt that he was dull, though he was not.

The worker felt that Robert's planning ability was unusually poor. He could not express feeling. He tended to begin one project and then another, ending up in a hodgepodge. He talked about an older brother in the army and then said he was in high school; actually, he had no older brother.

Robert was assigned to a therapy group which met once a week. One of the six boys in this group was an aggressive, fighting boy whom Robert feared. The group therapist's opening remark in discussing Robert was, "This boy seems to be out of touch with reality." He showed little interest in the other boys in the group or in their games. He seemed to disregard danger, and showed "no feeling." On one occasion when he seemed really interested in making a cake, he mixed Dutch Cleanser with the milk. The other boys in the group avoided him.

When Robert became too upset in this group the staff decided to place him in a group of more passive boys. Neither the group therapist nor his individual therapist was able to get him to accept another group; he felt that the first group was his, and he wanted to stay on with them, the first indication that he might have a feeling relationship to the group. He later consented to try a second group and slowly began to show some progress, making clumsy efforts to mix with the other children. In his first attempt at beanbag play he threw the beanbag at one of the boys and then ran away like a little child. Though his bizarre behavior diminished, he never really was accepted as one of the group. He complained at home that he was not happy with the group and told his therapist that he wanted to discontinue attending the group sessions. In conference the group therapist decided that

Robert had achieved his maximum from the group and that he needed more individual therapy before he could benefit from group participation.

Though his intelligence was within average limits Robert's school achievements remained poor, and he operated at a level so low as to make him eligible for special-class placement. The parents had difficulty in accepting this recommendation, feeling that Robert would become convinced in time that he was mentally retarded. They were right in feeling that Robert was too bright to have to attend a special class for retarded children, and only later could they accept the fact that since he was operating at a low level in spite of a better native ability, it would be difficult to have him back in school unless he could be given the special help he required.

After about a year of interviews Robert began to move into more meaningful behavior in his contacts with the therapist. He began to finish more projects; in his drawing he depicted themes with more coherent details. In contrast to the first months of interviews, when he seemed to lack all concept of time, he began to improve, though on one occasion in the last few months of therapy, he came to the clinic on Sunday looking for his therapist. During one brief period he made many drawings filled with themes of accidents, blood, destruction, and death. His play interviews at this time dealt with the same subjects, but by degrees he lost interest in discussing this kind of material. This period was the only one in which there was any real evidence of hostility on Robert's part in his two years of therapy at the clinic. The therapist did not discuss these hostile fantasies with Robert.

Robert became very fond of his therapist, brought her little gifts, and accompanied her for short distances if she left the clinic after his interviews. He asked personal questions about her family life and once suggested that he move into her home. On one occasion, when his mother forgot to send him for his appointment, he cried bitterly and wanted his interview made up at another time.

Meanwhile his work in the special class improved, though the other children in the class still considered him "different," and he showed no interest in joining their games. He later returned to the regular grade school and succeeded fairly well in his studies. Toward the close of his treatment interviews he surprised his therapist one day by thanking her for helping him to do better schoolwork. On another occasion he remarked, "I've got to keep my mind on my business so I won't have to ask the teacher the same thing about my lessons so many times." He appeared to have gained maturity in many ways, though at the time treatment stopped he was still recognizably different from other boys. His ability to relate himself to others increased and he was doing fairly well in school and at home. His mother's attitude did not change during these two years. She had not involved herself in therapy, nor had her husband; they could not see that they played any part in Robert's behavior manifestations. In the closing interview his mother remarked, "He never will really be normal."

Robert obviously was rejected, and we may assume from the material that he had been rejected early in life. The ego pathology he manifested is characteristic of children with little capacity for conceptualization. He could respond to prolonged therapy from an affectionate mother substitute with whom he could develop a safe relationship.

We cannot evaluate all the forces in Robert's complex life which contributed to his improvement. He is reported to have had an unusually sensitive and generous teacher at school during his second year at the clinic, and she was undoubtedly a strengthening ego influence. The worker who conducted his individual therapy, who consistently accepted him regardless of what he said or did (a situation possible only in therapy), finally gave Robert confidence in himself and a feeling that he could do things as well as others. Robert's parents could not have fostered his self-confidence, nor could his helpful teacher have contributed to Robert's security without the intensive therapy which allowed him to accept help.

*Robert was unable to maintain his improvement. He was referred to the clinic again four years later. He saw the caseworker who had treated him when he was younger. Although he was managing to stay on in school, there was evidence of some deterioration. Robert's family doctor was concerned because, occasionally, his actions were so bizarre as to suggest schizophrenic illness.

After a few interviews with the caseworker, Robert was transferred to a psychiatrist, who was unable to establish a close relationship to him. Robert continued to come in for interviews, but revealed very little about himself. He complained about boys at school who were teasing him, calling him names, and making false statements about his mother. The school reported that Robert was acting silly—he danced around in an effeminate manner and made a sorry spectacle of himself.

Robert again asked to see the caseworker, whom he called his friend. She called in the psychiatrist, as she was explaining to Robert that he needed special treatment in a hospital, where he would feel safe from those who tormented him. Because he had been making threats to kill his parents, the caseworker advised him to accept the help that would take him away from his many conflicts. He agreed that he would accompany his mother to a hospital and accept treatment. We confirmed his doctor's suspicion of schizophrenic illness.

One may speculate that, had Robert been able to continue receiving intensive support, his ability to hold onto reality without extensive regression might have been possible. Our treatment of Robert, which covered a period of two years, was stopped when we felt that he would be able to capitalize on his strengths.

It is unfortunate that few communities have the resources for prolonged therapy for such youngsters as Robert, to carry them through the trying period of adolescence. We now have a residential treatment center in our community, but we cannot provide long-time treatment in it. Only a psychiatric hospital for seriously disturbed children could meet the needs of children like Robert, and we are in the process of establishing one in Minnesota.

CHAPTER 23

The Child with Organic Brain Damage

Many instances of bizarre behavior in children cannot be explained by emotional problems. Training in psychiatry so conditions the physician to look for pathologic emotions that he may overlook the fact that the pathologic brain can initiate serious abnormal behavior. Organic brain damage may so affect the child's ego that his hold on reality is threatened or lost.

Much of Dale's difficult behavior, in the case cited (p. 204), was a direct result of his encephalitis. His bizarre behavior after his attack so disturbed his parents that they discontinued any attempts to discipline him. Parents become badly frightened when a child is delirious during an acute illness, has convulsions, or acts in an unusual manner. They suspect that the child's responses are due to brain damage and tend to overprotect him. Precautions are needed since a confused child may be unable to use his judgment or to do things he used to do, but much difficult behavior is due not to brain damage but to the parents' prolonged anxiety and overprotection.

The absence of neurologic findings does not completely rule out brain damage. Our present methods of testing for organic pathology of the brain are not developed to the point where we can say without question whether a child has had brain damage or not. Many children whose behavior cannot be explained by a medical history may have suffered from unrecognized organic brain pathology at one time.

The attitude of the parents toward the brain-damaged child is important in determining his attitude toward himself and his illness. When parents can remain optimistic about their child's future development and can think of his condition as a handicap that can be largely overcome, they can provide a constructive atmosphere for his future development. In some of our clinic cases parents were able to develop a favorable attitude toward their child's illness only after treatment disclosed that their child was capable of making a good adjustment in spite of his brain damage.

When a child responds well to clinic treatment but the parents nevertheless cannot change their attitude toward him, it is important that the reasons for their attitude be discovered. There may be deep conflict in the relationship between the parent and the child, or an inability in the parents to face the fact that their child is anything but perfect. Nothing short of intensive therapy will solve this problem of the parents.

Emotional factors superimposed on organic brain damage are often overlooked when the brain pathology seems to account for the whole picture.

A twelve-year-old boy, Val, was referred to the clinic by the county hospital from which he had tried to run away to a former foster home. Val's mother and father both had died from paresis in a state hospital, and Val and his fourteen-year-old brother had been placed by the county agency in a foster home where they had lived for a long period.

They had been happy in this home, and in spite of some erratic behavior Val had gotten along fairly well. On several occasions he had shown sexual curiosity and interest in the nine-year-old daughter of the foster parents. They had been tolerant of this behavior at first but had warned him that he would have to leave the home if his sexual behavior continued. When a few days later the foster parents found Val and the little girl playing under her bed, they requested that Val be placed in another foster home. Val protested violently, but he was removed.

A few days later the second foster parents reported that Val had stood in front of the house shouting obscenities at young women who passed on their way home from work. When the foster parents scolded him he had threatened to slit their throats during the night while they were asleep. He was immediately hospitalized and the examination disclosed that he, too, was suffering from juvenile paresis despite the fact that he had been receiving treatment for congenital syphilis over a period of years. The laboratory findings showed conclusively that Val was paretic, and his uncontrolled behavior and seeming loss of reality sense were further evidences of organic brain damage. The medical staff concluded that his behavior marked the beginning of progressive deterioration and suggested institutionalization.

The agency social worker, however, after several interviews with Val, suspected that emotional factors were contributing to Val's serious and bizarre behavior, and Val was referred to the clinic for study. At the clinic he seemed to be in close touch with reality; he did not exhibit bizarre behavior or disorientation. He cried a great deal when he described how upset he had been at leaving the foster home where his brother, to whom he was strongly attached, still lived. He said he had hoped that his obscene behavior and his threats would make it impossible for the new foster parents to keep him so that he would be returned to the first foster home. The clinic study and the observations of his behavior at the hospital suggested that it would be entirely safe to return him to the original foster home, especially after the foster parents, when interviewed, explained they were willing to give Val another trial. The foster mother said she had planned to have him return after he had discovered what it meant to live somewhere else.

Val was returned to his former foster home where he remained well for approximately a year. His behavior in the home and at school during this period was entirely acceptable. He had always been aggressive, somewhat of a bully, and somewhat obscene, having lived with his own emotionally sick parents over a period of years, but nothing suggested that he was a menace. A year after his return his adjustment began to deteriorate, however, and he is now in an institution.

Undoubtedly Val had organic brain involvement at the time of the clinic study, but this did not cause his emotional upset, though it may have influenced it. His year of relatively good social adjustment indicates that he had cortical control. Behavior like Val's in the second foster home often results from a neurotic need to express hostility to gain some needed satisfaction. Discouraging psychotherapy for children known to be suffering from organic pathology should not be countenanced, since evidence shows that some of the most disturbing behavior symptoms in these children may diminish as a result of psychotherapy.

CHAPTER 24

The Child Who Withdraws into Convulsive Seizures

The epileptic convulsion has been thought to represent a desperate attempt by the ego to escape from an unbearable traumatic situation.

In his article, The Unwelcome Child and His Death Instinct, Ferenczi says:

"We have become accustomed to look upon all phenomena of life, including those of mental life, as in the last resort a mixture of the forms of expression of the two fundamental instincts; the life and death instinct. On just one occasion Freud also mentioned the derivation of a pathological manifestation from the almost complete defusion of these two main instincts: he surmises that the symptoms of epilepsy express the frenzy of a tendency to self-destruction that is almost free from the inhibitions of the wish to live. . . . I know of cases in which the epileptic attack followed upon the painful experiences which made the patient feel that life was any longer hardly worth living." [1]

Children who react with hysterical convulsions to recognizable emotional crises may be attempting such an escape.

[1] Ferenczi, Sandor, The Unwelcome Child and His Death Instinct, *Int. Journ. Psychoanal.*, vol. X, 1929, p. 125.

Paula was referred to the clinic when she was three years old because of recurrent spells of unconsciousness accompanied by spastic contractions of the arms and legs and a marked rigidity of the body. These attacks sometimes occurred several times a day, invariably brought on by frustrations. She would cry in anger and hold her breath until she fell into an attack.

During her pregnancy with Paula her mother had lost both parents in a fire in their home. She had become acutely depressed and wanted to die, at the same time wishing that the baby inside of her would die. She showed little affection for her child when she was born and turned over most of her care to the father, a kindly, gentle person who welcomed the chance to do something for his girl. Paula's development was normal. She began to walk and talk at a very early age, and was demonstrative to both parents. The mother's health improved, she became less depressed, and began to feel very close to Paula.

Paula's convulsions began when she was about seven months old. She had failed to reach a household object she wanted, began to cry, held her breath until she became cyanotic, and went into a convulsion.

A history of organic involvement of the central nervous system appeared in the father's family, and the mother had always feared that their children might inherit this condition. Her own parents had shared her concern and advised her against the marriage. The mother considered Paula's spells to be a symptom of organic brain disease, though repeated complete neurologic examinations and encephalograms ruled out pathologic conditions of the brain.

When Paula was eighteen months old a son was born. The mother had not welcomed this pregnancy but she had not wanted the fetus to die. This child developed normally in every way and presented no problems. Paula was often jealous of her brother but this did not seem to affect the symptom.

With the persistence of Paula's convulsions, her mother became more and more disturbed and depressed and found it increasingly difficult to spend the time with Paula which she demanded. Paula had been jealous of her brother and often wanted to be treated like a baby. At first the mother indulged her whims, but Paula soon became too heavy to carry and she found herself less eager to please her and make her happy. She felt that Paula was having these spells to punish her, and her hatred of Paula increased. She frequently wished that Paula would die in one of her convulsive attacks.

Paula's father, an engineer, was often away from home for several days at a time, and her mother found it more difficult to control her anger at Paula during his absences. Finally, at the insistence of her doctor, she sent Paula to the home of a relative for a week to relieve her of her anxiety and tension and to see whether the attacks would continue when Paula was away from her. During the visit away from home and her mother, Paula's appetite was poor and she seemed unhappy and restless, but she was free from convulsions.

Relatives of Paula, who lived in another city, asked that she be brought there to see a neurologist who was particularly interested in children. Paula remained in a hospital for several days, during which time she had no convulsions. The neurologist was certain that the convulsions were not due to organic pathology. Another electroencephalogram was performed and this was negative, as were all the neurologic findings. In spite of the neurologist's assurance that nothing indicated organic brain pathology, the mother insisted on this explanation. The doctor felt it imperative that Paula live in a foster home for a long enough period of time to break her acute reaction to frustration, but her mother rejected this plan, maintaining that Paula needed her and her home.

She finally accepted her referral to the child-guidance clinic. The mother discovered that if Paula was not frustrated at all and was given everything she asked for, she had no convulsions. She tried indulging Paula for a period of two weeks, but she could not continue because it took so much time from her other work and from her other child. She feared too, that if she continued to comply with all of her demands Paula would be overindulged and poorly prepared for life. The doctor tried to point out to her that if Paula really suffered from brain pathology the convulsions would continue in spite of her indulgence. She did not accept this explanation, however, asserting that something inside of her convinced her that brain damage was the only cause for the convulsions.

The mother was interviewed once a week at the clinic. The worker told her that while it was important that Paula be given psychotherapy directly and in a group, it was imperative that she herself be psychoanalyzed. She needed intensive treatment to relieve her depression and marked emotional tension and to help her understand the part her unconscious conflict played in Paula's convulsions. The mother became depressed at this, feeling that her problem was hopeless, but finally accepted referral to a psychoanalyst for help for herself.

Paula had never been seen at the clinic. Her mother had only wanted to come in to discuss the problem with the therapist, and this had been permitted. After the mother had been advised to go to a psychoanalyst for herself, she withdrew from treatment at the clinic and agreed to have Paula seen by her pediatrician, who was very much interested in behavior problems. He had arranged to have Paula placed in a day nursery school after talking to the clinic therapist about her.

Paula's mother was a conflicted, neurotic woman. Her relationship to her own parents, though only briefly discussed with her, revealed considerable conflict. Her death wishes toward Paula before she was born were intimately related to the death of her parents. She said that at the time she had felt that "if my parents are not going to be able to see my child, I don't want to see my baby, either." Her anxiety that her children might suffer from organic brain involvement had appeared before she was married and was very likely related to a feeling that she did not deserve to have healthy children, because of her hostile relationship to her own parents.

In spite of her dislike of having Paula live away from home, the worker urged that this be done until the mother's attitude was less disturbed and more deeply accepting. Paula's presence in the home continuously stirred up her mother's hostility toward her and intensified her feelings of anxiety and guilt.

*Paula's mother went to an analyst, who kept her in treatment for over a year, seeing her twice a week for a while and then, because of the expense, seeing her once a week. A few months after her mother started therapy, Paula's attacks began to lessen, and by the time she was five, they had disappeared and have never recurred. Her mother reports that Paula, now twelve-years-old, is a lovely girl, has many friends, and is happy, bright, and a joy to the family; her father agrees wholeheartedly.

Paula's mother had been sure that therapy could not help her, since she was convinced that Paula's problem was organic and had little to do with her own conflicts. However, the mother found that her great anxiety did play a large role, and only when she learned why she was so anxious, was she able to relax. Her relationship with Paula gradually improved, and she is grateful not only for the disappearance of Paula's attacks, but for her beautiful relationship to her daughter and for the lifting of her severe depression.

The follow-up study of Paula illustrates an aspect of emotional behavior too seldom described. Paula's mother was eager to have children, but her neurotic relationship to her own mother filled her with apprehension long before her marriage. Her fear that her children would inherit the father's slight organic defect was based on her parental conflict. The death of her parents precipitated an acute emotional depression which stirred up hostility, a feeling of unworthiness, and a death wish for her unborn child. The earlier love for her mother, whom she preferred to her father, was not strong enough to neutralize her powerful, hostile feelings. Her masochistic need to suffer was too great for her to see what the therapists she consulted saw as neurotic anxiety and panic, which produced similar reactions in Paula. Paula's insecurity and confusion increased as she sensed her mother's ambivalent feelings. When the mother's growing, open hatred for her was unendurable, Paula resorted to a method of escaping from reality by withdrawing into a loss of consciousness. This symptom established in the mother's mind the fear that Paula was organically damaged and offered to Paula a means of punishing her mother for not consistently providing the affection she needed.

The mother's psychotherapy, which she rejected for a long time, finally made it possible for her to recognize her deep emotional need to destroy Paula and herself. Improvement came as she was able to see that along with her hatred for, and rivalry with, her own mother was love and acceptance. And underneath her sadistic, hostile feeling toward Paula was a strong need to love and protect her.

It is difficult to understand why some children react to rejection by continuous withdrawal while others withdraw only temporarily. Children like Paula, who have temporary periods of loss of consciousness, often are otherwise comparatively free from disturbances. The tension seems to increase until it reaches a certain strength when an explosive outbreak must occur.

For the child, withdrawal may lessen an unbearable tension from which he must escape. Like other defense mechanisms, withdrawal from reality represents an attempt to solve a problem which often cannot be solved. Withdrawal from reality is an extreme method for dealing with emotional tension, however, and we can assume that the situation which produces the tension must be extreme.

Many different clinical pictures appear among children whose hold on reality is slight. Other examples would have served as well as the ones given here. The so-called "psychopathic child" acts much of the time as if he had a poor hold on reality; the obsessionally neurotic child must obey an inner unconscious force to carry out rituals; the hysterical child runs away from home without knowing what he is running from; the suicidal child has an equally poor hold on reality. Whatever the cause for a child's wish or need to give up reality, even for temporary periods, the goal of therapy is to eliminate that need by making reality bearable.

Section 8

THE PROBLEM OF PREVENTION

The Problem of Prevention

Every social agency serving the welfare needs of people accepts prevention of social and emotional maladjustment as an integral part of its program. Knowing from experience how much work is necessary to cure children who have developed emotional conflicts and illnesses, the agency staff searches for means of preventing these conditions. During the early thirties, when the clinical branches of psychology, medicine, and even psychiatry still rejected the findings of psychoanalysis, social workers reached out eagerly for more knowledge of this new science. They welcomed a new body of information which offered hope that neurotic suffering of adults might be prevented by intelligent consideration of the emotional needs of children. Their interest in research studies from psychoanalysis has never lagged, so that many advances in their technics of dealing with children have come from this source.

Psychoanalysts have always been interested in preventing emotional illness. After discovering the emotional significance of the early years of a child's life, they sought to develop some method of child rearing that would prevent serious infantile conflict and later neurosis. Child analysts have been particularly interested in this problem, but in spite of their efforts no real program for preventing neurotic illness has been found.

Every conflicted child analyzed early has a better chance for an emotionally healthy life. Every child given successful therapy for emotional conflict has improved his future life adjustment. And since every emotionally conflicted adult and child radiates neurotic tension in many directions, therapy helps not only the patient but those with whom he has contact.

Two major methods of preventing emotional maladjustment have received attention. The first consists in rooting out the sociologic, cultural, psychologic, and economic factors which produce emotional tension and suffering. This is a project for the epidemiologist and sociologist who, together with experts from all fields dealing with human behavior, work toward developing a broad, global program of prevention. Edward Glover [1] described such a plan for the prevention of wars, recommending a thorough analysis of the conscious, preconscious, and unconscious factors which produce aggression and the defenses against aggression. The program called for a fifty-year study to be followed by a much longer period for the application of principles proved to be valuable.

Helen Witmer and Edith Tufts [2] have recently reviewed the many programs being carried on in this country for the prevention of delinquency. They conclude that we are only on the way toward learning what does and does not prevent delinquency and that practice and research will have to work closely together to achieve an effective program which is in its earliest beginnings.

The second type of prevention, which is the concern of this chapter, recommends the extension of already established methods of lessening emotional tension and conflict. If social agencies could make full use of all the procedures effective in the treatment of emotional illness, behavior problems, and learning diffi-

---

[1] Glover, Edward, "War, Sadism and Pacifism," London, George Allen & Unwin, Ltd., 1933.

[2] Witmer, Helen, and Edith Tufts, "The Effectiveness of Delinquency Prevention Programs," U.S. Department of Health, Education and Welfare, Children's Bureau, 1954.

culties of children, the unhappiness and suffering of these children and their families would diminish rapidly.

Steps in treatment are often suggested which cannot be taken because the community lacks the required resources. Many times tragic situations occur because an agency is not staffed to perform a needed service; foster homes are not available; no residential treatment center exists; an institution lacks personnel to do therapy; volunteers to bring a seriously disturbed young child to group therapy three times a week are unavailable.

Let us assume for a moment that a community is ready to put into effect a program to lessen emotional suffering, unrest, tension, and delinquency. What steps should be taken? Since the family is accepted as the basic unit of our society, many important functions are assigned to it. A family which is economically sound, whose members are physically and emotionally healthy, which provides an opportunity for satisfaction to all its members, and which has an atmosphere free from marked emotional tension, is the most valuable unit in any program for preventing emotional conflict in children.

Everything possible should be done to strengthen a family that is weak. Family social agencies are staffed with social workers trained to deal with all aspects of behavior which create emotional problems. The more disorganized the family, the more intensive must be the casework services to make the family a functioning unit. Public welfare agencies usually are familiar with the most disorganized families in any community. Many of these agencies, however, have from seventy-five to two hundred families on the case load of each worker, when experience has shown repeatedly that one caseworker can rarely give adequate casework service to more than thirty families. Recent experiments conducted by the New York City Youth Board (contained in a report by Overton [3]), indicate that twenty families with serious problems are a maximum

[3] Overton, Alice, Serving Families Who Don't Want Help, paper presented at the Eightieth Annual Meeting of the National Conference of Social Work, 1953. *Social Case Work*, vol. XXXIV, no. 7, July, 1953, p. 304.

case load for any one worker. Studies by the Gluecks [4] demonstrate that the most serious problems of juvenile delinquency appear in their largest numbers in these disorganized families. A pilot study now in progress in St. Paul, which provides intensive casework services for families with multiple problems, has established twenty as the maximum number of families one worker can serve. Studies at the Wilder Child Guidance Clinic show that children from families with chronic social pathology tend to be the most embittered and the hardest to reach.

The process of reconstructing a disorganized family takes time. Social-agency staffs already know the value of intensive casework with families in conflict. What they need now is an immediate reduction in the number of families assigned to each caseworker, so that she can use as much time as she needs to carry on her work and reach her objective.

A family caseworker must know the physical and emotional condition of each child in her case load. She should know where he is in school, how he is doing in all his subjects, and how he relates to other children and to the teacher. If his work is not up to capacity she should know why. She must not only do for him what his mother is unable to do, she must do more, because he has been traumatized by his mother's incapacity. The caseworker must be prepared to work with an alcoholic dependent father to help him regain status within his family, to reestablish a positive relationship with his wife, to find employment. As much or more time and effort may need to be spent on the mother. If the caseworker is not welcomed in such a home, she must have the time to overcome the family's resistance and distrust.

The demands on the worker's time made by disorganized families have not been exaggerated. Disorganization in these families occurs because these families have been neglected or they have refused help and have been considered unreachable. Frequently these families have been antagonized by emergency relief measures.

[4] Glueck, Sheldon and Eleanor, "Unraveling Juvenile Delinquency," New York, The Commonwealth Fund, 1950.

Children removed from their homes against their parents' wishes and placed in foster homes, financial aid withdrawn because intermittent earnings were not reported, psychotic parents placed in institutions against the families' wishes—such steps must be taken hurriedly when a worker is rushed. She cannot thoroughly discuss with the family the reasons for her actions, particularly when she has prematurely concluded that the parents are incapable of thinking and planning for themselves.

Many children must be removed from their own homes. Whenever it is clear that a home cannot possibly provide the required affection and security which a child needs, whenever it is evident that he will be neglected and unsupervised and unsocialized, another home or setting must be provided for him as a step in prevention. Removal from his own home, however, should be the last resort in the treatment plan. Casework services often result in a child's remaining in a home previously considered unfit for him. To help a child remain in his own home is in itself an important step in prevention, since children placed in foster homes against their wishes and the wishes of their parents tend to fight placement and act out their resentment.

Social-agency personnel are less enthusiastic than formerly about the use of foster homes for emotionally disturbed children. Residential treatment centers and small institutions have replaced them to some extent, but the dissatisfaction is due largely to failures in placement which require frequent changes and increase the child's feeling of rejection. Sometimes changes are unavoidable, due to the nature of the child's problems; more often the fault lies in the selection of foster homes. To be of use to a child, a foster home must meet his particular needs. The size of the family, the neighborhood, the school, the age of the foster parents, their interest in activities the child enjoys, their freedom from intolerance of his emotional or physical problems, their ability to accept his parents regardless of behavior are some of the factors which determine the success of the foster-home placement. To find such a home for a child means that the agency must have a list of homes available from which to choose. Only a well-trained caseworker, capable of recognizing weaknesses as well as strengths in foster parents, can adequately match the child to the foster home, and she must have plenty of time to do her work thoroughly. The agency must be prepared to pay a fee that will motivate families to open their homes to children with emotional problems. A fee of twenty-five to thirty-five dollars a week will not appear to be exorbitant when the only recourse in the event of failure with foster-home placement may be treatment in a residential treatment center, costing three to five times as much. The staff of the child-placement agency must be well trained and prepared to do casework therapy with the child, the foster parents, and the child's own parents.

Ample proof appears in the case records of every child-placing agency that seriously deprived rejected children, deeply conflicted and headed for serious delinquency, can be turned away from a criminal career through careful placement in foster homes.

Early recognition and treatment of a disorganized family is a practical means of saving the children of that family from emotional conflict. Since the parents in these troubled families usually do not refer their children for study, other methods must be used to discover when families need help. The juvenile police provide one such means of early detection. Large numbers of children from underprivileged families come to the attention of the juvenile police, and in recent years more policemen are trained to recognize social problems and prepared to make referrals to social agencies and to work cooperatively with them. They may work directly with a child, attempting to recognize his problems instead of simply dismissing him with a warning.

Evidences of physical and emotional neglect in a child may appear during examinations at the general hospitals. An observant doctor or nurse will sense a child's trouble when he wants to stay in the hospital after his recovery, suggesting that he dreads returning home. A child who is frightened or depressed, who seems excessively cruel or displays severe temper tantrums during his hospital stay, is in emotional conflict which warrants further investigation. A mother's overanxiety and overprotection are easy to recognize. Evidence that the parents lack interest or concern in their child, or that he feels abandoned, demands an investigation of the child's home life. The medical social worker at the hospital can arrange with social agencies in the community to investigate the sources of any social and emotional pathology revealed during the hospital stay.

Infant-welfare stations are a very valuable resource for detecting emotional problems early. An alert welfare nurse or pediatrician may recognize a mother who rejects her child, is in serious depression, or is suffering from beginning psychosis. They will recognize when a mother is inadequate to care for her child because of feeblemindedness or marked immaturity. Any of these facts, when recognized early in the life of the child, may make treatment possible long before the pathogenic conditions in the mother can influence the development of her child.

Other kinds of parental behavior which can harm a child's development, excessive anxiety, indulgence, rigidity in training, when recognized and prevented early, may save a child from later emotional maladjustment. Evidence of unhappiness and incompatibility between husband and wife may appear during a history-taking at an infant-welfare station, and the family may be referred to an agency for help before their problems become well established.

Many public health nurses in recent years have taken graduate work in the mental hygiene aspects of public health to prepare them for supervising in infant-welfare clinics and inservice training programs. Some of them will work in prenatal clinics where they can help ease the fear and anxiety of expectant mothers.

The United States Children's Bureau has published several helpful pamphlets on the care of the infant and young child. Dr. Spock's popular book on child care [5] provides the new parent with

[5] Spock, Benjamin, "The Common Sense Book of Baby and Child Care," New York, Duell, Sloan & Pearce, Inc., 1945.

important information without fostering anxiety, and lessens any anxiety already present. Any information a worker can give which lessens tension in an insecure, frightened mother helps improve the mother-child relationship.

The best place for detecting emotional problems in the growing child, however, is the school. The teacher usually sees the child for several hours each day and is in an excellent position to recognize unusual behavior habits and attitudes. She can detect differences from one day to another, and if these changes are extreme, she can try to learn the reasons for them. The school social worker contacts the home, and if her visit discloses a problem, she can formulate plans to deal with it. The teacher, to be alert to disturbances of the children in her room, cannot be burdened with classes of forty to fifty pupils. Brownell [6] advises a reduction in the number of pupils to twenty-five so that the teacher can know her pupils and teach them as individuals. To be able to recognize subtle problems in children, the teacher should have some training in mental hygiene and the emotional development of children. She will benefit from courses in these subjects throughout her teaching career. All persons whose work brings them in direct contact with children, recreation directors, workers in character-building agencies, clergymen, camp counselors, should have the opportunity to attend seminars in the recognition of emotional problems in children.

Every well-trained, well-adjusted, mature teacher makes a significant contribution to the mental health of her pupils. Every physically or emotionally sick teacher may have a destructive effect on the children she teaches. Emotional disturbance in a teacher may not affect the stronger, more secure children in her classes, but it can harm the insecure, conflicted ones. Often physically and emotionally sick teachers remain at their work longer than is good for them or their pupils. To avoid this, the security of

[6] Brownell, Samuel Miller, The Unique Position of the Schools in the Prevention and Control of Delinquency, *Federal Probation*, vol. XIX, no. 1, March, 1955, p. 14.

the teacher must be ensured, and every effort must be made to reinstate her as soon as she can resume her work.

Few better methods exist for ensuring a good emotional adjustment in children than by allowing every child who attends school some feeling of achievement. School curricula at present are woefully lacking in this respect. Children with special learning disabilities remain in classes with children who learn well and are subjected to continuous feelings of inadequacy. Some schools have special classes for the poor readers, but most do not. Few supply special tutors, though this one step would be tremendously valuable for the large number of children who need the special help. Children who suffer from chronic feelings of inferiority often choose undesirable methods to relieve emotional tension. In being unable to provide the means for helping such children, the schools lose a valuable opportunity for preventing emotional maladjustment.

Tutoring need not be confined to the subject matter in which the child is deficient to be valuable as therapy. The close relationship which develops between the teacher and the child may motivate the child to study, since children deprived of love often have little interest in their school subjects and may fail to do well in spite of their ability.

Some children fail to learn because of an emotional block. They unfortunately equate learning about the subject matter with sexual curiosity of which they are afraid. In an experiment in prevention in a small community,[7] Lindemann and Dawes found that learning problems could be cleared up by giving both the child and his parents factual information to take the place of forbidden fantasies or superstitions. This program, in which the school child, parents, and therapists cooperated, lessened many problems which, if untreated, would have become fixed neurotic patterns.

Schools lack facilities for training children of prepubertal and

[7] Lindemann, Erich, and Lydia Dawes, The Use of Psychoanalytic Constructs in Preventive Psychiatry, in "The Psychoanalytic Study of the Child," vol. VII, New York, International Universities Press, Inc., 1952, p. 429.

pubertal age who are not proficient in academic subjects. Many of these children hate school, and the aggressive ones become truant. They dislike the work, defy the teachers, disturb other pupils who want to work, and learn little or nothing. Every large school should include in the curriculum some subjects requiring the use of the hands. Manual training, sewing, cooking, electrical work, and even simple auto mechanics could be taught in the sixth, seventh, and eighth grades. All the students could take these courses, and those without ability in academic subjects could spend most of their time in the manual courses. Such an innovation would not eliminate delinquency, but it would give some encouragement to the aggressive youngsters who are under average in achievement or intelligence and find school a source of frustration and failure.

The school social workers, advisers, and counselors could do more direct treatment work with children with minor emotional problems, if they had more time. One school social worker for every school is not an exorbitant number, especially in underprivileged sections of the city where one school social worker may not even suffice. Because of the many problems in behavior and learning which she must be prepared to recognize, the school social worker should hold seminars in behavior problems during the course of her work.

School principals and supervisors usually are happy to cooperate with outside service agencies which contribute to the emotional welfare of the children in their schools. At the White House Conference for Children in a Democracy, in 1950, the discussion by teachers and principals and other school staff members indicated that they incorporated modern theories of psychology, social work, and psychiatry into their philosophy.

The probation officer is in a strategic position to do preventive work in juvenile delinquency. Most of his active case load are active aggressive youngsters, often members of gangs, for whom delinquency has become a way of life. To modify the attitudes of such youngsters is difficult and calls for special talents. The probation

officer must have time to know the family of each of his probationers, since most of them will have other children living under
the same delinquency-producing conditions. The usual case loads
of seventy-five to one hundred are far too high for a probation officer to do his work effectively.

Usually parents wait longer before referring girls to the probation office, and by the time the probation officer hears of them their
problems have been fairly well established. Sexual problems in
adolescent girls are difficult to solve, since the girls have found a
pleasurable outlet for reducing tension. Many of them, rejected
and unloved by their parents, have never felt loved or wanted by
anyone until, reaching adolescence, they found they were in demand by boys. Many of them are dull, have failed in their schoolwork, and felt inadequate until they found a place for themselves
through their sexual behavior. They feel little guilt since they
have never been socialized, and frequently identify with their sexually promiscuous parents.

The probation officer has a serious problem in trying to find acceptable satisfactions in life to replace those the adolescent delinquent girl has found. Nothing but the strongest positive relationship gained through frequent contacts with the girl will compel her
interest. Through continuous and patient help the probation officer
may eventually win the girl's acceptance and become the mother
figure the adolescent has always looked for. Again the only solution
to such a problem is sufficient time.

Institutions for delinquent adolescents fail miserably to "re-
form." Despite all we now know about the treatment of delinquents, many if not most of these institutions are understaffed,
and few demand that their staffs be professionally trained. The
youngsters often remain in the institution for one to two years and
could work through many of their emotional problems if skilled
therapists were available to spend time with them. However, because of the lack of skilled therapy, these youngsters return to the
community more embittered and hostile than when they left. Dur-

ing their stay at the institution they have acquired greater skill in delinquency. Their stay in the institution may be their last opportunity for socialization.

Gisela Konopka [8] and Redl [9] strongly advocate the use of group therapy for delinquent adolescents in institutions. Aichhorn [10] found that when he could group together youngsters with similar emotional make-ups and interests under the supervision of a counselor or therapist he had greater success in socializing them. Harris Peck and Virginia Bellsmith [11] have made a careful study of the use of group therapy with delinquent adolescents in an outpatient setting and are encouraged by their results.

The present system of combining mild and serious delinquents in the same institution subjects the less disturbed youngsters to an atmosphere encouraging delinquency. The more seriously disturbed adolescents should live in a separate institution where they can receive special forms of therapy for the more resistant character disorders. In the meantime the less disturbed youngsters could be allowed more privileges in a cottage setting, where trained cottage parents could help them through casework methods. A system of institutions which allowed the delinquents to move from a more severe to a less severe setting, finally reaching one from which week-end visits could be made home or to special foster homes set aside for this purpose, would be helpful. These homes could accept the youngster after his release from the institution, unless his own home setting had changed materially through casework treatment during his residence in the institution.

Such a program, while not presented as ideal, would prevent a

[8] Konopka, Gisela, "Therapeutic Group Work with Children," Minneapolis, University of Minnesota Press, 1949.

[9] Redl, Fritz, Adolescent Changes as a Factor in Delinquency, in "Probation and Parole Progress Yearbook," (edited by Marjorie Bell) New York, National Probation Association, 1941.

[10] Aichhorn, August, seminar, Vienna, August, 1930.

[11] Peck, Harris B., and Virginia Bellsmith, "Treatment of the Delinquent Adolescents," New York, Family Service Association of America, 1954.

waste of time, effort, and money in maintaining institutions as they are at present. Little of value comes from our present program except a temporary protection of the community from the destructive acting out of the young delinquents. Undoubtedly some youngsters are helped by being removed from vicious homes to a place where they are fed regularly and treated humanely. Some improve through a close relationship to a chaplain or house parent. The large majority, however, pass through the institution untouched.

The cost of the program of prevention outlined in this chapter is great. The cost to the community in suffering, loss of life, destruction of property, and treatment of chronic recidivism which is the alternative is infinitely greater. Whether such a program would prevent neurosis and delinquency we do not know, but it is reasonable to assume that it would help materially. We do know that similar recommendations, made by the psychiatric team of the clinic in conference with staff members of social agencies, have eased the patients' suffering, curbed their acting out, and prevented major catastrophes.

These suggestions regarding prevention are practical and within reach. They are based on cases thoroughly studied and treated at our clinic and on the experience of agency workers who have devoted the major part of their lives to improving the emotional welfare of the children in their communities.

During the past quarter of a century many constructive steps have already been taken to meet children's emotional needs. Educational programs for children have improved greatly; in many places schools have tried as much as possible to meet the individual needs of children. Forward steps have been made in probation services, in juvenile-court procedures, and in many institutions for young delinquents. The medical schools now offer courses dealing with emotional conflict in physical illness; physicians have introduced psychiatric concepts in their treatment of children. The rapidly growing number of child-guidance clinics throughout the country reflects the interest of communities in the emotional welfare of their children, and the current research in methods of gaining the cooperation of disorganized families in a welfare program are indications that attempts are being made to safeguard the emotional well-being of families.

These improvements are a beginning, but they must be enlarged and extended if we are to secure and protect the emotional well-being of our children.

Section 9

SOME PRINCIPLES
OF THERAPY

Some Principles of Therapy

A child whose emotional conflict produces distress or disturbing symptoms needs therapy. The sooner he obtains it, the sooner will his emotional development proceed along a normal course. The energy he is using to handle his conflict will become available for relating himself to others, for learning, and for play.

Basic to all therapeutic work with conflicted children is a strong, positive, warm relationship between the child and therapist, which assures the child that he is accepted and respected as an individual, that the therapist believes he can help him, and that he can help himself.

The therapist must enjoy his work with children and be fond of them. Zulliger [1] calls this relationship pedagogic love, which demands nothing from the child except the satisfaction of accomplishment in therapy. This affection is objective, not personal.

The therapy of a child in a child-guidance clinic is essentially ego therapy, and the goal may be anything from a quick relief of a symptom, so that the ego can react more efficiently, to intensive insight therapy of unconscious factors. In the main the treatment deals with conscious and preconscious material, with only occasional cases in which the therapist interprets unconscious material.

The ego is strengthened through suggestion or support which

[1] Zulliger, Hans, "Schwierige Kinder," Bern, H. Huber, 1951.

helps to break down resistance and develop self-confidence; through abreaction which releases dammed-up tension; through manipulation which exposes the child to new experiences that reveal the mistakes in his present adjustment; and through clarification which provides insight into his conscious and preconscious behavior and attitudes. These methods differ from interpretation which involves unconscious repressed material.[2]

The treatment to be used in a given case depends on the clinic's evaluation of the total situation, particularly on the strength of the child's ego, and the treatment which the staff can provide. The therapist tries to strengthen the child's ego defenses by re-establishing the defense system that existed before the breakdown of the child's adjustment.[3] At no time is a defense removed without being replaced by a better one. As Gill points out, some defenses are combined with a symptom, which may be adaptive or maladaptive. When the defense in the symptom offers an adaptive gratification such as compulsive hard work, it may be encouraged; when it is one that creates a destructive adaptation such as stealing, it must be discouraged.

Treatment of the emotionally conflicted child is best accomplished through the use of the "psychiatric team," consisting of the caseworker, the clinical psychologist, the child psychiatrist, and, recently, the group therapist. Others may also be involved in the therapy, depending on the needs of the child and his parents. The child-guidance clinic is a medically oriented clinic, and all direct therapy with children is under the psychiatrist's supervision; but the total therapy requires the combined services of the members of the team. It is rarely possible to single out any one member as "the one" who made the significant contribution.

Group work with children in a child-guidance clinic offers a valuable aid in diagnosing emotional conflict and for providing

[2] Bibring, Edward, talk on Basic Principles of Therapy at meeting of American Psychoanalytic Association in 1953.

[3] Gill, Morton, Ego Psychology and Psychotherapy, *Psychoanalyt. Quart.*, vol. XX, no. 1, 1951, p. 62.

therapy. The diagnostic group often provides data that cannot be secured through the clinical history or the study by the psychiatrist and psychologist. It is natural for a child of latency years to communicate through his peers and through the medium of play. Group therapy may supplement the work of the individual therapist or may be the preferred method for providing therapy.

Few set rules apply in therapy with a child in a child-guidance clinic. Most children, for example, are threatened when asked early in treatment about the immediate problem which brought them to the clinic, but many children are willing to begin with their problem at once and speak unhesitatingly about a subject, even though it may embarrass them to do so. Psychiatrists are often opposed to using reassurance in treatment. In the clinic, reassurance is frequently given to children and parents who are insecure or dependent, as a step in lessening resistance and providing needed courage. Reassurance can be costly when the therapist is largely limited to this measure and disregards the reality problems which must be met.[4]

The therapist welcomes a child's dependence on him during the early part of therapy; he will discourage this dependence as the therapy continues, however, especially toward the end of treatment. When dependence persists, the therapist must evaluate the effect it has produced on the child. If dependency enables the child to rid himself of other pathologic defenses, the therapist allows it to persist. When dependency results in the child's inability to relate himself to others, however, or a parasitic relationship to the therapist develops, more intensive and perhaps analytic therapy will be required. In most instances the child, through his dependence, becomes stronger as the therapist provides him with the security denied him in early life.

Any child in emotional conflict and both his parents need fre-

---

[4] Levine believes that guidance and support are often necessary when the parent is weak and dependent, especially early in treatment: Levine, Maurice, "Psychotherapy in Medical Practice," New York, The Macmillan Company, 1942.

quent interviews. To formulate a diagnosis the staff must see the varying attitudes in the child and parents toward each other and toward the emotionally laden situations to which they are exposed. Treatment depends on this diagnostic evaluation, which is still tentative after several interviews, and may be changed if the interviews fail to substantiate previous findings. Every person who has had contacts with the child and his parents can give valuable information for the diagnostic evaluation and treatment plan. The more known about the child, the less need there is for speculation.

Anxiety is the basic underlying factor in a child's emotional conflict. The lessening of anxiety is the surest indication that the conflict has diminished. It does not indicate, however, that the conflict is being resolved, since any positive transference can lessen anxiety. Only when the therapist has evidence that the child's ego is dealing with the anxiety or that the child understands the nature of the conflict well enough to overcome his anxiety can he say that therapy has been effective. When the important sources of anxiety have been dealt with, a child is no longer vulnerable.

Anxiety based on unconscious conflict can be decreased when the therapist recognizes the unconscious source of the anxiety and indirectly lessens its effect on the child. Thus a child whose anxiety results from unconscious rejection by his mother will lose his anxiety when the mother learns to recognize her own unconscious feelings and can modify her behavior and even her attitude toward her child. Under favorable conditions recently repressed anxiety which has been based on sibling rivalry can be reduced by allowing the child to displace the hostility onto a substitute play object.[5]

Children's dreams are an invaluable aid for recognizing unconscious conflicts. Often a current conflict may be revealed in several dreams, permitting the therapist to inject the theme into the interviews. The result may be a free discussion of the conflict, an

[5] Levy, David, Release Therapy, *Amer. Journ. Orthopsychiat.*, vol. 9, 1939, pp. 713–736.

explanation of the anxiety, and the disappearance of symptoms.

Scolding is useful occasionally to motivate a child for therapy. Unhappy rejected children often cannot accept the therapist's attempts to help as sincere. Their refusal to cooperate is based on their need to attack adults whom they distrust, thus denying them the satisfaction of being helpful. The therapist who scolds such a child may take him by surprise and shock him into recognizing that this adult is really concerned that the child is not being helped. An evacuated, twelve-year-old British boy in World War II, when asked what he missed most about home, replied that he missed the beatings from his father which meant to him that his father really worried about whether he did the right thing or not.

The therapist must concentrate on current reality situations which produce problems. Not until these are thoroughly discussed will the child concern himself with events of the past which have led to his present distorted ways of feeling and behaving.

The fact that a child has not previously responded to therapy does not mean that his next therapist will fail. The clinical approach, the age, appearance, gestures, the kinds of subjects chosen help or hinder the therapist in conditioning to the child. When the child does not respond in due time to the therapist, a change to another member of the staff is often helpful.

How long the therapist waits until he feels he will not effect a positive tie to the child depends on his clinical experience in making such an evaluation and the time the staff can devote to resistive children. Most narcissistic children can develop a positive emotional tie if enough time and skill is available. Whether a very busy clinic can devote time in this manner while many families are waiting for service is a matter that must be weighed by the clinic staff.

Clinic staffs are research-minded, but rarely can devote time to involved research, because of demands for services to children. Their research is usually clinical, based on careful studies of individual cases.

The emotional conflicts of adolescent youngsters respond to

therapy. We are not justified in refusing therapy to disturbed adolescents because they often do not respond to psychoanalysis. Many of the most troubled adolescents at the clinic responded well to therapy.

The services of a psychiatric team should be available for children with emotional problems which cannot be treated by the social-service agencies in the community. These agencies have on their staffs caseworkers and supervisors trained to provide therapy for emotional problems. The psychiatric team should be reserved for the more seriously conflicted children who need the combined services of highly trained persons.

The child who is reticent or seems blocked is often keeping conscious material from disclosure. The material may be an act or wish or thought that embarrasses him, especially when it is related to a loved person; it may be due to a warning from his parents to keep a certain family scandal a secret. A child who holds back any important incident may have to withhold related material and in the end may be entirely blocked. Calling his attention to what he is doing may be all that is required, after a positive relationship has developed. Occasionally the parents may be helpful in locating the subject of concern.

When therapy should progress well according to available data but does not, something is blocking treatment. When the difficulty is not due to the child's resistance, there may be veiled resistance in the parents. When an impasse is reached, it is often worthwhile to inform the parents that some important information has been withheld and is interfering with the therapy. Aichhorn suggested in his seminar that the parents be asked to give the history all over again.

The use of any one technic of therapy with a child may prove disappointing. Play alone, drawings alone, or interviews without play material may prove uninteresting or boring to the child. An element of lightness and humor helps to make morbid, depressing matters easier to tolerate.

It is important to recognize early a child's difficulty in, or inhibition to, learning, especially difficulty in learning to read. The reason for the learning problem should be determined and treatment provided. A child's inability to learn may condition him early against learning, usually causing him to feel inadequate and insecure, and may leave him with a feeling that he will never be able to learn.

The therapist frequently may experience countertransference attitudes. These do not disturb treatment when the therapist recognizes them and does not permit them to affect deeply his feelings for the child. The therapist who frequently responds to children or their parents with hostility or anxiety is not adequately prepared to perform therapy.

The child rarely is motivated for therapy by his own emotional conflicts. He accepts therapy to please his parents, or because therapy has been ordered for him. Even when he has anxiety, unless it is acute enough to produce panic, he is not impressed, as is the adult, by the need for therapy. It remains for the therapist to develop this motivation in the child.

Any child treated for emotional conflict must be considered as a unit in a family. This does not only refer to the parent-child relationship. The therapist must keep in mind how the treatment of one child is affecting all the other members of his family. Therapy that lessens the conflicts of one child but creates problems in the other children offers little of value.

Much serious delinquency in children is due to neurotic conflict. Special technics are required to help a delinquent youngster accept therapy. Most delinquents are satisfied with their adjustment, which provides emotional gratification plus an opportunity to punish their parents and society. The delinquents who are deeply established in their patterns of acting out often are convinced that society rejects them and has no interest in them, that all treatment methods are motivated by society's interest in protecting itself from them. The most seriously delinquent youngsters *can* respond to therapy by eventually identifying with the therapist, accepting his ego ideal for themselves, and later his superego.

The statement frequently made that the superego is established by the time the child has reached a certain age and cannot later react to change is not borne out by clinical experience. Waelder [6] refers to many components of the superego which weld together, following the development of the Oedipus complex. This is followed by a long period when the superego is unstable and can be modified by new identifications. The child and even the adolescent is not fully established in his character make-up. This period of superego instability may last till the twenties.

Parents are often blamed unjustifiably for the emotional conflicts of their children. Many conflicts develop through characteristics in the child which are totally independent of his relationship to his parents. And those conflicts in the child which do result from conflicts in the parents are not there because the parents wanted them. The conflicts occur in spite of the parents' conscious attempts to raise a happy, physically and emotionally healthy child. To blame a mother for the neurotic conflict of her child is the same as blaming her for his diabetes or feeblemindedness. The material which parents read, with some notable exceptions, fails to emphasize sufficiently the unconscious features of the child-rearing problem. Parents often feel guilty and ashamed when faced with a problem of emotional conflict in their child.

It is doubly unfortunate if the therapist cannot resist blaming the parents of the emotionally conflicted child he is treating. Hilde Bruch [7] states, "One cannot treat a child successfully if one does not respect his parents. . . . He (the child) needs to gain from treatment the conviction that his parents, in spite of their shortcomings and errors, are fundamentally good people." She mentions exceptions but correctly emphasizes the importance to the child of the therapist's not condemning his parents.

Preventing the development of conflict in children is of great-

[6] Waelder, Robert, The Problem of the Genesis of Psychical Conflict in Earliest Infancy, *Int. Journ. Psychoanal.*, vol. XVIII, 1937, p. 406.

[7] Bruch, Hilde, The Role of the Parent in Psychotherapy with Children, *Psychiatry*, vol. XI, no. 2, May, 1948, p. 169.

est importance. Prevention as prescribed in this book involves putting into operation practices which clinical experience has proved to be effective. The most practical method of preventing emotional maladjustment is through eliminating early in life those factors which are known to produce later maladjustment.

Many children who are emotionally conflicted cannot respond to methods of therapy available in the child-guidance clinic. Their disturbances are based on conflict repressed in their unconscious. Nothing short of child analysis will cure these children.

Some children cannot be helped at all; this may be due to factors within the child, within the parents, within the community, or within the culture. The child who steadfastly refuses to accept treatment cannot be helped. Parents who have an unconscious need to interfere with therapy prevent the child's responding unless they learn to recognize their unconscious sabotage. Collaborative therapy involving psychoanalytic treatment of the child and the parents may be the only effective method with some acting-out problems of children.

Effective treatment of an emotionally conflicted child should lessen anxiety, insecurity, and inhibition, help him to deal with reality problems and relate himself to other children and members of his family, provide him with energy to enjoy work and play, and help him to accept himself as a capable and love-worthy child. Therapy should reduce the problems that have made life less pleasant for him and his parents.

Therapy rarely continues until all this is accomplished. When the findings indicate that development is in the direction of emotional growth and lessening of conflict, one may assume that the necessary strengths have been provided and the child and parents can manage through their own efforts.

Index

361